The AIDS Miasm

Contemporary Disease

&

The New Remedies

Peter Fraser

Printed by Biddles, Guildford, England

ISBN 1 874581 231

Front cover reproduced from Night Birds.by Alasdair Wallace
Reprodution facilitated by Rebecca Hossack Gallery, London

Winter Press, 16 Stambourne Way, West Wickham, Kent, BR4 9NF
e-mail: winterpress@hotmail.com

About the Author

Peter Fraser was a bookseller and publisher before discovering homœopathy. He has been involved in many recent provings and has collated and edited more than a dozen of them. He has practices in Bristol and London.

Abstract

Technological advances, particularly advances in communication technology, create stresses in the vital balance of human beings. These stresses are countered by symptoms, diseases that match the original stresses.

In some circumstances the new technology is so significant that it brings about a major shift in our understanding of the world. These major shifts are answered by a myriad different diseases but one, often venereal, disease encompasses the spirit of them all. These are the main miasmatic diseases. Psora was the response to speech and tools; Sycosis was the response to writing and the wheel; and Syphilis was the response to printing and industrialization. In our own time AIDS has been the response to the stresses induce by electronic media.

Miasmatic remedies are ones that directly correspond to some part of the diseases that arise from the dynamic stresses, not just ones that are used to treat the miasmatic disease itself.

When we have acclimatized to technological change and found a new balance, the stresses involved in maintaining that balance are different and a new set of semi-miasmatic diseases arise. The Hydrophobic or Acute Miasm corresponds to settled Psora; the Tubercular to settled Sycosis; and the Cancer to settled Syphilis. It is too early to be sure about what settled AIDS will look like but there are indications that it may correspond to a CJD/Alzheimer's Miasm.

As each individual replays the evolution of both his species and his culture; so it follows that the individual may be particularly affected by the stresses of a particular point in his or her development. This may be a very specific point or it may be more general and miasmatic.

By looking at the combined pattern of the stresses, the nosode and the remedies that appear to belong to the miasm, it is possible to form a picture of the miasm as a whole. Using proving symptoms to describe that picture ensures that they are described in the language of the remedies and allows some understanding of the slight differences between remedies when dealing with very similar issues.

Contents

A note on terminology and use of fonts

Anything printed in this serif typeface is the author's comment.
Quotations from provings and materia medica are in this sans serif.
Cross references are in italics
Subject is used to denote a person experiencing a symptom this can be a prover and a proving symptom or a patient and a disease symptom.

Abbreviations

Remedy abbreviations are as found in the Remedy Catalogue of Synthesis (8th edition). Works are referred to by the abbreviations as found in the Author Catalogue of Synthesis (8th edition) These are listed in Appendix 1.

Preface

In considering the new Electronic World we find that the understanding of the technologies of that new world are insufficiently developed to provide a medium for discussion and exposition. It is therefore necessary to use the media of the old world which are woefully inadequate to the task. Like the inhabitants of Abbott's *Flatland*, we simply cannot describe a 3-dimensional world in the language of only 2-dimensions. Marshall McLuhan, whose insights during the sixties illuminated this new world has been invaluable to me in understanding how technology has changed mankind. He experimented with trying to find new ways of expression that would allow understanding of the new world. Ultimately McLuhan's 'mosaic' writing was not entirely successful. His works are difficult to read and most people, trained in reason and sequential thought, are unable to jump and dip in the way that the thought of Electronic Man requires. Hypertext, that moves from one place or thought to another instantly and without acknowledgment of anything in between, is ideally suited to electronic thought and will inevitably become an important medium for this type of expression. However, writing about the Electronic World in the form of a sequential history and in the format of a printed book inevitably leads to the dissonance of repetition and non sequitors.

In the second part of this book the features of the Contemporary Miasm, which I have chosen to call the AIDS Miasm, are examined in terms of remedies, proving symptoms and rubrics. This way of finding the patterns (that are reiterated through many different manifestations) is one that homœopaths have used for two hundred years. To comprehend our provings, to understand our remedies and our patients and then to match them together, is ideally suited to the thought of the Electronic Age. Details are important, but only in so much as they enlighten these patterns.

We live in an infinitely complex universe, one that's comprised of many patterns or threads. Here follows just one of the threads of both the history of modern media and of the AIDS Miasm. There are many different possible iterations of both these stories, and they tie into many different versions of reality. This is one that may be useful in understanding both our patients and the remedies we have available to us. However, there are many other patterns and they are no less or more correct. The more patterns that we see and learn to know, the better we will be able to see them in both patients and remedies, and so to match them.

One of the most interesting comments that I have had from people who have read early drafts of this book is the question, "Who is it for?". Perhaps the most important feature of electronic media is the quality of instantaneity and simultaneity and their consequences, which are the end of sequential thought and of the principle of cause and effect. Just as this leads to the demise of Weber's Protestant Work Ethic, it also means the end of any objective oriented activity; so it is no longer sensible, or perhaps even possible, to do something for a reason or for a particular audience. We can only do things for their intrinsic value and meaning and for what they offer us in their doing; perhaps they will have a value or meaning for someone else though it may never be the same as ours. This is the spirit in which I have compiled this study. It has been of value to me and I offer it in the hope that it may be of some, perhaps unpredictable value to others.

Acknowledgements

This book was only possible because a number of often anonymous people gave of themselves in the proving experience. I was only able to write it because of my many teachers, especially my father, my brother Michael and Bob Miller; and all the homœopaths who have taught me, especially Misha Norland, Janet Snowdon and David Mundy.

Part I

An Understanding of the AIDS Miasm

Introduction

The last dozen years have seen the proving of new remedies on a scale not known since the pre-war period. The best of these provings have been carefully conducted by experienced homœopaths using a sufficiently large number of provers to provide a clear, recognizable picture of the remedy.

In spite of the clarity of these pictures they contain a large number of common elements which are not so common in the pictures of remedies proved in former times. This can lead to a confusion that makes these remedies difficult to use. Some homœopaths find them confusing and ignore them all together. Others know the pictures of a few of these remedies and tend to see features of those few remedies in too many cases. It is therefore important that we, as homœopaths, are able to distinguish between those symptoms that are common to these remedies and indicate that one of them is called for; and those symptoms that are characteristic of the individual remedies.

It is not entirely surprising that the symptoms appearing in current provings should share a certain degree of homogeneity. The provers are generally homœopaths, homœopathic students or people with experience of homœopathic treatment. They tend to come from a similar socio-economic background and will often have spiritual and philosophic common ground. The remedies chosen for proving are chosen because they reflect issues important to the proving coordinators but they are often also chosen for their relationship to issues important in our society in general.

This situation is not a new one and modern provers and provings reflect our society in the same way that the work of Hahnemann's Provers' Union reflected his.

Critics of modern provings have taken the commonalities found in these provings as evidence of their inadequacies. They take them as evidence that they have brought out the symptoms of the provers rather than of the remedies. On the whole these critics have not participated in the proving process and so do not have first hand experience of understanding a proving from within. Those homœopaths with experience of well run provings are able to discern the picture of a remedy when it has emerged from a proving. They are also able to tell when the nature of the remedy has not emerged from the proving and they then conduct a further proving. Several modern provings, including the AIDS Nosode, have required second or third provings to produce a definite picture; unfortunately many more have been published in an unsatisfactory state.

Many of the provings have been conducted by some of our most experienced and perceptive homœopaths, and they tend to choose remedies that might address the problems that they see in their consulting rooms. They see little need for the proving of remedies that are likely to be very similar to the ones that we already have and know well.

Modern Society is Different

Many of the pictures of illness that homœopaths see in their patients are not that different from those seen by Hahnemann or Kent in theirs, and they respond to the same, well understood remedies. However, there are many features of the modern world and of modern disease that are significantly different.

Iatrogenic illness was as important then as it is now, indeed it was one of the motivations that led Hahnemann to look for radical new forms of medicine. However, the agents that caused it were different. Mercury, Sulphur and blood letting have been replaced by thousands of different drugs, radiation, and amazingly complex surgery. The pill, HRT, hysterectomies and changes in family structure have radically altered women's health. When Kent and Clarke talk of vaccination they are referring almost exclusively to smallpox vaccination; yet children today will often have had vaccinations for up to a dozen different diseases.

There are many diseases around today, including AIDS and new variant CJD, that were completely unknown a generation ago, and many others, such as the autoimmune diseases, chronic fatigue and forms of dementia, appear to be much more common.

Even the physical world we live in has changed. Some forms of pollution have diminished but others have increased. Heavy smogs and filthy waterways may be things of the past, but pesticides and hormones have permeated earth and water; while nuclear activity, civilian and military, has even changed the make up and balance of the elements in the air.

These changes in disease have required changes in the way we look at illness and at the remedies we use. It is hardly surprising that there are large gaps in our homœopathic armamentarium that need to be filled. We are fortunate that leading homœopaths, including Misha Norland, Jeremy Sherr, Nancy Herrick, Rajan Sankaran and many more, have chosen a considerable number of substances to prove which are helping to fill these gaps. It is now necessary that we make sure we have the ability to differentiate them and to use them properly.

Miasmatic Theory

In many ways we find ourselves in a position that echoes that in which Hahnemann found himself after the publication of *The Organon* and *Materia Medica Pura,* and which led to the writing of *Chronic Diseases*. He found that he and his most devout students had great success in treating many of the most virulent epidemic diseases. However, though they were also apparently successful in treating non-epidemic diseases, they found that they tended to recur and that the recurrences became both more frequent and more serious.

Hahnemann concluded that there were diseases that deeply infected the entire organism, and which the vital force reacts to by externalizing in skin symptoms. The suppression of these skin symptoms through applications of allopathic medicine and even homœopathic treatment of only the superficial disease, results in the central disease having to find deeper and more serious expressions. This process results in illnesses that affect the internal organs and tissues rather than just the skin.

The suppression of external, and therefore more obvious, expressions of the disease had also meant that the disease was less apparent and thus could spread more easily. Psora, The Itch Disease, which Hahnemann considered to be the same as the Leprosy found in *The Bible* and in medieval times, had been carefully controlled. In Biblical times the disease and contact with it was proscribed by the rules carefully laid out in Leviticus XIII and a major role of the priests was to prevent the spread of the disease. In classical and medieval times the disease was abominated and sufferers were outcasts or confined in the lazar-houses and prevented from contact with the uninfected. By the Nineteenth Century the obvious symptoms of the Itch were much less apparent, and today full blown Norwegian Scabies is very rarely seen. Those infected with the now suppressed disease have been in free contact with the rest of society resulting in almost universal infection. Similarly, treated Syphilis and Gonorrhoea no longer caused obvious and horrible symptoms; but as the figwarts and chancres were cauterized and medicated the likelihood of widespread infection was greatly increased.

Hahnemann's method of treating chronic disease was based on his very effective way of dealing with epidemic diseases. In epidemic diseases he took the symptoms of a large number of people affected by the epidemic and thus drew up a picture of the common symptoms of the epidemic as a whole, the *genus epidemicus*. The remedies that covered this picture were the ones to be used and were differentiated by their own characteristic differences.

In treating chronic disease Hahnemann used these principles in two ways. He took the symptoms of the many different expressions of the chronic diseases to find what might be called the genus of the chronic disease and so to find the remedies that covered the chronic diseases. This process led him to believe that there was one great, almost omnipresent, chronic disease: Psora, and two lesser ones: Sycosis and Syphilis, which he termed miasms.

The same principles used in epidemic diseases could be used to group the different expressions of a chronic disease within a person. Thus the many different acute diseases experienced by a patient needed to be analysed and divided between those diseases imposed by epidemics or other outside influences, and those that were an expression of the internal chronic disease. The totality of those symptoms that express the internal disease would give a picture of the internal disease itself, and those symptoms that were unusual and characteristic could be used to choose which of the remedies that cover the genus of the miasm was indicated in each particular case.

Most modern homœopaths do not prescribe in this way. Some, especially the 'practical' homœopaths and the allopathically trained, practise in much the same way that Hahnemann and his followers did before the discovery of chronic disease. They prescribe in a straightforward way on the obvious presenting symptoms. Their short term results are impressive but they are almost certainly suppressive in many cases.

Classical homœopaths, although they no longer necessarily follow the method used by Hahnemann, are in effect doing the same thing. The pictures of the major remedies have been considerably developed, particularly by Farrington and Kent and more recently by Vithoulkas, and the method of taking and interpreting cases has changed to such a degree that classical homœopaths look, almost without thinking, to the inner chronic disease and match it to the distinctive essence of the remedy.

Although some decry it, there is not the necessity to use miasmatic theory that there was for Hahnemann. However, these essential pictures have not been developed for most of the lesser remedies. This means that there is a growing tendency to use the polychrests and thus the other remedies are used less and become even less well known.

Miasmatic theory today is mainly used as a way of classifying important remedies and disease pictures, and it is often used to trace disease complexes that may go back many generations; it no longer seems to be a vital prescriptive tool.

The Three Classic Miasms

Hahnemann proposed that there were three miasmatic diseases. Psora or The Itch which is caused through infestation by the scabies mite. The fully developed form of this disease, which is now known as Norwegian Scabies, is very rarely seen except in the severely immuno-suppressed. It is seen more often in animals where it takes the form of Mange, but it was common in ancient times where it was known as Leprosy (it is distinct from Hansen's disease, the modern leprosy caused by *Mycobacterium leprae*). For Hahnemann, Psora was the most important of the chronic miasmatic diseases. Its primary expression was in an itching eruption, but even in Hahnemann's day this had been effectively suppressed and become the thousand headed hydra, expressing itself through a long roll-call of secondary symptoms.

Hahnemann believed that Psora accounted for seven-eighths of chronic disease, the other eighth he attributed to Sycosis and Syphilis. Just as the suppression of the psoric eruption led to internal miasmatic disease, so the suppression of the sycotic figwart and the syphilitic chancre had the same result. With the more effective suppression of outward symptoms it is likely that the incidence of the Sycotic and Syphilitic Miasms is much higher today than it was two hundred years ago, an observation borne out in homœopathic practice.

Miasmatic Qualities

The miasmatic diseases have several common qualities. The most important of these is that they have a metaphoric importance that appears to transcend the physical reality of the disease. It is as if there is a spiritual essence to these diseases of which the disease itself is merely a physical and secondary manifestation. These diseases have received attention that goes far beyond their physical importance and those affected by them have often received opprobrium and been reviled and outcast in a manner that vastly exceeds practical considerations.

They are all diseases in which the immune system plays a role.

They are much more expressive and virulent in those whose immune systems are compromised and they tend to cause a diminution of the immune response, allowing secondary infections to thrive.

These three diseases are also, primarily, venereal diseases. They are transmitted through sexual activity and they are inextricably linked to promiscuity and immorality. They have often been seen as the wages of sin and as divine retribution meted out on those whose personal standards of morality has been found wanting.

The diseases have long incubation periods or have the ability to lie dormant for a long time and then to come to life again.

There are a number of other diseases that have been variously classified as miasmatic. The most important of these are Cancer and Tuberculosis, though some commentators have added several more. These diseases definitely do have miasmatic qualities. They are metaphoric diseases and come with meanings that go beyond the purely physical. However, the most important difference is that they are not true venereal diseases, and though they carry some of the idea of fault and divine judgement it is not as clear cut as it is in the more directly sinful venereal diseases. These diseases are also less directly connected with the immune system. There is almost the sense that these diseases are imposed on the body by an outside force while the true miasmatic diseases are in some way invited in.

AIDS

There is a disease, AIDS, that has appeared in the last quarter century that has all the qualities of a true miasmatic disease.

It is a venereal disease, it involves a breakdown of the immune system, it has a long incubation period and it very quickly acquired enormously significant metaphoric importance.

AIDS follows the pattern of the other original miasmatic diseases in that it takes disease to a new, deeper level. Psora is a parasite whose primary action is confined to the skin. Sycosis is a bacterium whose primary action moves from the skin through the blood and begins to destroy the soft tissues. Syphilis is also a bacterium and again moves through the skin and the blood but eventually attacks the nervous system, which it destroys along with the bones and hard tissues.

HIV is a virus, the next finer type of morbific agent, it moves from the skin to the blood and results in the destruction of both soft and hard tissues and especially the nerves. However, HIV is a retrovirus and in its action it moves to a deeper and more fundamental level. It subverts the organism's own genetic material and processes and uses them to its own ends at the expense of the host.

AIDS, both in its material manifestation and in the potentized form of the proving, has shown itself to contain and exemplify many of the most important features of that set of symptoms that have appeared, or become much more apparent, in the diseases of patients, in society and in the new provings.

Just as the theory of miasms allowed Hahnemann to analyse and understand chronic disease and the remedies that could be used to treat it; so the concept of a Contemporary or AIDS Miasm can be used to understand new diseases and the remedies, both new and old, that might be used to treat them. Not everyone will agree that AIDS is a miasm at all, but even if time does not show it to be absolutely central to the Contemporary Miasm; it is the best candidate we have and is quite central enough to the issues to act as a hook on which we can hang and inspect those features of diseases and remedies that are unfamiliar and warrant investigation and clarification.

Miasmatic Disease as a Reaction to Human Development

Platonic Ideals

That which is below is like unto that which is above and that which is above is like unto that which is below.

This is the primary statement of *The Emerald Tablet of Hermes* which is the first and most important text of alchemy. The concept that there is a correspondence between different worlds was central to alchemy and to alchemical medicine, and as such it passed through Paracelsus, Hahnemann and Kent to be central to homœopathic philosophy.

The most important expression of this concept is a spiritual one that was first, and perhaps most clearly, to be seen in the philosophy of Plato. The Platonic Forms exist in another place but they are the model that is imperfectly echoed on Earth in everything that we can sense. The same principle is found in Kabbalistic thought, where the perfect forms that are the thought of God become increasingly manifest as they come closer to the material world. In the Swedenborgian philosophy that was so important to Kent and Farrington, the Angels of Heaven represent the various forms, and they become manifest in the physical world. A modern version is Sheldrake's morphic fields, where an unmeasurable energy field guides material growth and creation.

In all these philosophies this concept implies the important corollary that though the material world is a poor manifestation of a divine perfection, careful study of these poor manifestations can allow the perceptive mind to cut away the many divergent imperfections of the material world and come to an enlightened understanding of the divine image.

This concept is extremely important in homœopathy, not so much because so many of our forefathers were immersed in it; but rather it is because they had an understanding of this principle that they were able to understand homœopathy. The remedy has a perfect image that we can come to some understanding of through study of its manifestation in provings, the remedy picture; and equally then recognize in its many manifestations in patients, the disease picture. If we do not have this understanding we are unable to practise real homœopathy.

Another form of this concept is found in the theory of the Microcosm and the Macrocosm, that the smaller world reflects the same pattern to be found in the greater one. The principle version of this is that the Body of Man and the Body of Mankind, the body politic, are reflections of each other. Thus a society behaves as a being in the same way that a person does, and a person in the same way that a community does. Just as a society is made up of smaller communities and each is a reflection of the other; so the body is made up of smaller bodies, the tissues and organs, and they in turn of cells. Each cell has processes that are, in essence, the same processes of whole communities: absorption, growth, reproduction, elimination and death. Even our view of the atom is a scaled down view of the solar system which in turn can be scaled up to a picture of galaxies.

The implication of the theory of the Microcosm and the Macrocosm is that things appearing in one will correspondingly appear in the other. Thus the ailments of society brought about through the stresses of technological developments and changing world views will both reflect, and be reflected in, the ailments of the individual. By studying society we can enlarge our understanding of the individual and through knowing the individual we also know the society.

Microcosm

In the Microcosm, the individual human, the vital spirit reacts to disease by expressing that disease through physical symptoms and the physical symptoms that it chooses are those that will do least harm to the function and well being of the organism. These are tenets that are basic to the understanding and practice of homœopathy. The body produces symptoms in a number of ways. It does so directly by disrupting function and even making structural changes. This type of symptom is referred to by allopaths as idiopathic, as it has no obvious external cause. The body can utilize an external force to provide the necessary physical symptom. This may be through the action of what Hahnemann calls a *zufall*, an accident, an occurrence or perhaps even a coincidence. If the body is not in a position to physically manifest symptoms it can create the illusion of the symptom through a delusion or a dream. However, the most common means of manifesting symptoms, and the one that is central to allopathic understanding of disease and poses many difficulties for homœopaths, is through the action of external morbific agents.

Those symptoms brought about through parasites, bacteria and viruses pose difficulties because they might be epidemic diseases afflicting the whole community in which the individual finds himself caught up, they might reflect a susceptibility on the part of the patient, or they might be something that the vital force needs and has actively acquired. The distinction is important, as it is an understanding of it that allows us to judge what is to be cured in a case, one of the three requirements for a practitioner of the medical art.

Macrocosm

In the Macrocosm, the wider world or society, the same thing can be expected to happen. There are stresses that are beyond the power of a society's vital spirit to deal with. That society must then find symptoms that will allow it to continue operating. Some of these will be symptoms of the society itself, others will affect a number of individuals. These individuals become the scapegoats of society; just as some organs and tissues are sacrificed for the good of the whole individual. The four principal miasmatic diseases (including AIDS) can be studied in relation to the history of culture and society. By understanding the stresses to which they were, and are, a response, we can better understand them and better differentiate the remedies that might be used to treat them.

Extensions of Man

During the 1960s Marshall McLuhan, a professor of English Literature at the University of Toronto, proposed a radical rethink of the way that we view media and the effect that it has on us. Although he became something of a guru at the time, his theories were little understood and soon faded from the mainstream. In spite of his current obscurity most of his observations have been confirmed by subsequent events and much of the material in *Understanding Media*, his seminal work of 1964, can now be seen as prophetic of the way in which the media, the internet and the corporate world have developed.

McLuhan's basic observation was that all media, which he used in a broad sense to mean any invention or discovery, effectively extended one of man's faculties. The wheel is an extension of the feet, clothing an extension of the skin and writing an extension of the eye.

Any extension results in an unbalancing of the organism by increasing the importance of the faculty that has been extended in relationship to the other faculties. There follows a dynamic reaction to return harmony. This reaction takes the form of a numbing of the extended faculty and an enhancement of all the other faculties. The unfortunate consequence of this pattern is that we tend to be relatively unaware of the extended but benumbed faculty and so are unaware of the effect that it is having on us and on our society.

Each medium contains within itself another, simpler medium: the book contains the story, the film contains the book and the television contains the film. It is the newest, highest level medium that has the greatest effect on us; yet, through the numbing effect we do not feel or perceive this clearly. The new, extended medium becomes invisible and so we tend to look at only the content: the older medium that it carries. People talk about and study the content of television, the effect that programmes might have on viewers. In truth the effect of the content dwindles into complete insignificance when compared to the effect that television has in and of itself. McLuhan's best known aphorism "the medium is the message" refers to the fact that by its very existence a medium has changed our world, and the message that is that change is far more important than the content, which is the only message that we tend to see.

Though there has been a continuous history of new media and of extending man's faculties; there have been four points in the history of Western Society that have seen such powerful changes that man's entire world view has altered. These points have involved the simultaneous development of several aspects of life. It is hard to tell if one change led to another, if steady development led to a state in which there was potential for sudden change in many areas, or if it was simply synchronicity, but whatever the case there are four points in the story of mankind that appear to have outstanding importance. What is of most interest to homœopaths is that these significant changes bear a strong relationship to the appearance and nature of the four miasmatic diseases.

Only two of these points are historical, one is prehistorical and the other perihistorical, and so some of what follows involves many assumptions and much speculation, but it does seem to have enough consistency to make it worth looking at.

Language, Tools, Awareness and Psora

The first extension that caused a complete shift in the way mankind thought, felt and behaved was the invention of language. The same change in behaviour, bipedalism, that allowed the physiological changes to the larynx and so complex speech; also left the arms free to develop the use of tools. The extension of the hands through tools allowed a greater diversity of activity and made mankind more adaptable. However, it was the adoption of speech, and especially of language, that caused the most important changes in the way we are.

In primate societies without speech, almost all the interaction within the society, the things that bind the group together and structure the relationships between its members, is tactile. This usually involves fighting or playing and especially mutual grooming, though with the Bonobo chimp it consists substantially of recreational sex. Verbal signals can play a part in establishing a hierarchy but they are more important in keeping the outsider away.

In human society, speech plays much of the role that is borne by touch in other primate cultures. This allows for a much larger group size. You can gossip with more people than you could possibly interact with through picking nits from each other's fur, and you can gossip with a substantial number of people at once, while you can really only groom, wrestle or have sex with one other person at a time. An alpha male can give instruction or leadership to a greater number of followers through speech than is possible through physical interaction. He may still need to maintain his status through physical prowess, but his influence extends further through speech. Not only does speech allow a larger group, and the tribe to replace the family as the basic unit, but it allows interaction between groups. Tactile contact is all or nothing, but speech allows a much wider range of interactions that do not commit participants to total embrace or total war. Tribes can live in proximity without quite as much need for aggression and can even form alliances.

However much speech changed the way early humans lived, it was nothing compared to the way language changed the way people thought. The content of speech was the old threats, comforts and endearments which had previously been tactile, but the message of speech itself allows conceptual thought which contains within it reason, education and forethought.

This change in humans took place so long ago and was so comprehensive that it is very difficult to study. However, a similar change can be observed in primates that have been taught language skills. One of the clearest examples of how language frees the mind involves an experiment with chimps who have been taught numbers and basic arithmetic. Sheba is offered two piles of sweets. She knows and understands that the pile she chooses will be given to another chimp and she will get the remaining pile. When she is offered the sweets she always chooses the bigger pile even though she knows that it will got to her friend Bobby; you can sense her frustration every time as she knows that she is choosing the wrong one but just cannot help herself. When the piles of sweets are replaced by cards with numbers on, Sheba's abilities are miraculously transformed. Every time she immediately chooses the lower number and so gets the larger number of sweets.

By transforming reality into abstract language it is also freed from the bounds of time and space. An object only exists where and when it is, but the word for that object can be anywhere and anywhen.

The use of language, a medium whose content is thought, causes a numbness that allows thoughts to be handled in a different, more abstract manner. This more dispassionate approach to thought changes once and for all the way we see and deal with the world. Nothing can be taken at face value any longer, but is understood in how it relates to other things, and most particularly to ourselves. This process also extends through time and things now have roots and have consequences. The invention of language created awareness of ourselves, of others and of time.

The development of awareness allowed for immense change. Art and culture, society and the very concept of development and progress are now not only possible but unavoidable.

However, there is an obverse side to this. Change causes stress and the changes caused by speech were so fundamental that they caused great unease in individuals and in society. Illness, disease and distress were themselves also irrevocably changed. For the pre-aware primate they are matters only of the moment. Without awareness there can be no real memory of disease and certainly no apprehension, but for the aware animal, difficulty and disease become constant companions. Apprehension and anxiety become unavoidable and are just as much part of the new world as are creativity and ideas.

In order for the individual vital spirit and for the society as a whole to externalize and express their dis-content and dis-ease, chronic illness developed. The first and most basic form of chronic illness is Psora, for it expresses the feelings of anxiety and struggle that awareness brings.

For some commentators the story of Adam and Eve and the fall from grace is the story of the origins of Psora. Eating of the tree of knowledge brings about awareness, and from it arise the struggle and chronic disease that are man's irrevocable lot.

Writing, Travel, Empire and Sycosis

The next technological development with major implications for mankind was the invention of writing. As one of the consequences of writing was the invention of history, we do know a little more about what happened than we can possibly know about the discovery of language.

Speech and language freed man from the instant of time and place, and extended his awareness, but that awareness was still bounded to the experience of one person, and to some extent his or her direct contacts. Writing changes this and frees awareness from the experience of a single person. Awareness for literate man extends across the frontiers of his lifetime and across the frontiers of his experience.

He has an awareness of distant lands and of the past.

The development of literate (or conscious) man from the simply aware man of primitive cultures is well documented by Jaynes in *The Origns of Consciousness in the Breakdown of the Bicameral Mind.* Jaynes attributes the changing mind set to the breakdown in the separation of the two sides of the brain, which results in consciousness and allows an ability to reason, to consider and to meditate. The bicameral man did not reason as to what he should do but completely obeyed the instinctive side of his brain, which came to him as a voice, one that it was impossible to disobey, just as happens in some forms of mental illness today. The conscious man has an interplay between his instinctive brain and his active one and this interplay allows him to consider what to do. He has choice in how he lives his life.

Jaynes acknowledges the tremendous importance of writing in the breakdown of the bicameral mind, as he does the role of metaphor; which is only fully possible in a literate culture where the extension of language results in a numbness that distances a person from what is being said.

The process of transformation can be clearly seen in two events: the siege and fall of Troy; and Moses's meeting with God and return with the written tablets of law that constituted the Covenant.

The written law that Moses brought from God, and the law and history that he created through the *Pentateuch,* marked the end of the visual, iconic and primitive society embodied in the golden calf. Semitic society was changed as evidenced by the role of the prophets and priests who were no longer messengers of the Word of God but became interpreters of the written law. This change facilitated the move from slavery and exile to the establishment of a large and successful city based society.

The fall of Troy likewise marked a change in culture and society, a shift that can be seen in the very different styles, assumptions and narratives of *The Iliad* and *The Odyssey*. The hero of *The Iliad* is Achilles, fleet of foot, and almost invincible. His life is plotted for him by fate and the gods and he follows his appointed path straight to his death, never questioning it. In contrast Odysseus is "the man of wiles", he pits his wits against fate and the gods to plot his own life and though it is never easy he succeeds. It is trickery not bravery that brings the ten years of war to an end, and it is only through the use of his wits that Odysseus gets home, none of his companions can manage it. In the same way it is by her wits that Penelope defies the path decreed by society, and remains faithful to her absent husband for twenty years.

There are many things that contribute to a major shift in mind set and it is not always possible to be sure about how they interact. The physiological changes resulting from bipedalism allowed the development of both speech and tools, and speech led to language. The change from aware man to literate man comprises many more elements than just writing; and some may have come fairly closely together, because the underlying development of mankind and culture was fertile ground for both, some may have led directly to others and some may have come along by chance.

Whatever the case, there were many interrelated developments taking place during the second millennium that preceded the Christian era. Just as tools are the physical extensions that mirror the mental extension of language, so the wheel is the physical extension of literate man. It extends the scope of his awareness in the physical world in the same way that writing extends it in the mental and psychological world. Trade, money and banking are all direct consequences of writing and of the wheel. They, with the surpluses generated by settled agriculture, in turn lead to the city and other institutions, which can only thrive in a literate society ordered by the rule of law. Jaynes makes clear that the bicameral mind broke down under the influence of writing and trade, and from necessity in an increasingly complex world where the primitive structures simply could not cope. His insistence that the development was a breakdown of the old order rather than a growth into a new one is the common, pessimistic perception of change.

The structure of society in a primitive culture is tribal. It is set and certain, the pattern does not change and there is little scope for change. Tribal Man is born to his place. Physical prowess or accident may lead one person rather than another to take a particular role, but the structure between the chief and all the other members of the tribe are set and unchanging. What behaviour is taboo and what permitted is known by the whole tribe, it is never questioned and appears to be unchanging. The structure of the societies of literate man are very different. They are basically feudal or imperial. They begin to reflect the importance of trade in the world. Feudal society is built on an interchange of obligations but it is always a two way exchange. The weaker partner offers service and in return is given protection. This arrangement cascades from the centre, king or emperor; to edge, the youngest daughter of a serf. Unlike Tribal Society which involves direct, personal contact between every member, Feudal, and especially Imperial Societies operate a chain of contact that is not limited by distance. However, this chain is dependent on a written law and on written instruction from the centre to the periphery, with corresponding reports from the edge to the centre. The wheel, especially the spoked wheel, is physically part of this but it also becomes the predominant image and metaphor. McLuhan convincingly traces the gradual break up of the Roman Empire not to the central corruption or to the threat of barbarians at the edge; but to the loss of Egypt and with it of the steady supply of papyrus on which was written the instructions and the reports that fuelled the law and the chain of command.

Though the invention of writing was the prime mover in much of the change from Primitive to Feudal Man, there were two things that it permitted whose effect on the way man thinks was profound. The first of these is metaphor. Although metaphor is possible in spoken language, it is not as comfortable with the spoken word as it is with the written word. Writing causes further numbing and so brings about another step away from reality. It thus allows certain aspects of things to be seen and compared in isolation from the whole. A metaphoric attribute seems justified in a written setting; in a spoken setting it is less acceptable and in a purely visual culture it seems absurd. This distancing effect and movement away from a visual culture is furthered by the invention of a phonetic alphabet. The letters used to write a word have no direct connection to the thing to which they refer. The connection is purely an intellectual one and is therefore subject to intellectual modification and processing. This is not true of all types of writing. Hieroglyphics and the pictographic writing of the Oriental cultures do not have the same power to separate the object from the written word. This partly explains why the culture of ancient Egypt did not have the same effect on Western development that Judaic, Greek and Latin culture did. It may also explain why Oriental cultures have not found it as easy to move from the feudal to the industrial way of life as have those of the Occident that use a phonetic alphabet. On the other hand this pictorial view has allowed Oriental medicine and science to maintain an holistic view of things.

The consequence of these developments is that literate man is aware not only of his own culture but also of others distant in time and space. He is also locked in a hierarchical structure in which he owes allegiance to those above him and is responsible for the welfare of those below him.

The most important thing for him is to portray himself as superior to other cultures and to maintain, and preferably improve, his status within the hierarchical structure. The impulse is towards expansion, excess and unregulated growth, to make himself appear bigger and more powerful. There is always physical growth but also a need to expand and display possessions and power. Sexuality, food and drink, clothing and many other features of life are subverted from their natural purpose and become evidence of power and wealth and as such are used to excess. The complement to this is the feeling that the person feels inferior and will be forced lower in the hierarchy. The feeling that he or she is a sinner, fraud or criminal, and especially that he or she will be found out, are of major importance for literate, Feudal Man. They result in secrecy and deception and also in religiousness, and particularly repentance. These patterns apply as much to the political and social body as they do to the individual. They can be seen in the propensity of empires and feudal kingdoms to expansion and growth, to the subjugation of weaker neighbours and the submission to stronger ones. These patterns are well known to homœopaths as the Sycotic Miasm.

Printing, Mechanization, Nationalism and Syphilis

The next stage of human development, and its consequences, fall clearly within the historical record. The disease syphilis appeared in Barcelona in 1493, the same year that Columbus returned to the city from his first journey to the Americas. In less than 5 years the disease had spread virtually throughout Europe. It has been assumed that syphilis was brought from the Caribbean by members of Columbus's crew, though there is mounting archaeological evidence that it was present in Europe long before then. However, it is indisputable that the supposed discovery that the world was a globe was an important part of a shift in mind set that shook Western man during the second half of the 15th Century and the beginning of the 16th, and that the appearance of a new and terrible disease was part of that shift.

The new world had its roots as much in the printing of the Gutenburg 42 line bible of 1455 as it did in the discovery of a physical New World. Printing was the first industrial process and it changed mankind suddenly and completely. There are two related aspects of printing, and of industrial production generally, that made the world different from that which had preceded it: reproducibility and specialization. In producing a manuscript in a monastery scriptorium one monk might work on the same book, often for years, though another might illuminate it. Yet in printing many different people work on different parts of the book at the same times, and each has a specific and limited role. The books that they produced were identical, and any mistakes were to be found in every copy. They were no longer individual items but were completely interchangeable with each other. These changes were not gentle and premeditated, they were an absolute consequence of the new technology and they appeared immediately, with the printing of the very first page.

The manufactured product is a commodity, and as each one is the same as the next it must have the same value. No longer were merchants trading in individual items, rather they were dealing in commodities and the distancing of trade from that which is traded changed the principles of commerce and money.

Just as printing separates the worker from the fruit of his toil, it also continues the distancing of the reader from what he reads, intensifying the process of isolation that was begun by language and deepened by writing and the phonetic alphabet. Many of the other products of industry have had a similar distancing and isolating effect. The cannon and the gun distance their users from their victims. The car distances the driver from the road, and the toilet distances the user from his or her excreta.

The low cost and availability of books gave an immediate boost to knowledge and scholarship, a boost that fed further discoveries at an exponential rate. The idea of the Renaissance Man, the man who knew everything that there was to know in every subject, almost immediately became an impossibility. The new scientist or philosopher had to specialize, and the more he specialized the better he could master his field. The ideal feudal prince was well versed in all the arts and sciences and had the knowledge to make decisions on his own. The leader in the industrial nation state knows little himself, and uses the knowledge of specialist advisors and counsellors to make his decisions. Eventually the prince himself became irrelevant and he was either replaced by a structured government or became a figurehead for one.

The obligation of the individual in an industrial state is no longer as a link in a feudal chain, but becomes a direct obligation to the state, one that is spelled out in the printed law and regulated by the judicial machinery of the state. For Industrial Man the political system that is adapted to the way that he is, is nationalism and the nation state.

Martin Luther was nine years old when Columbus discovered the New World and it was just twenty five years later that he posted his 95 theses in Wittenburg. Protestant theology is a religious reflection of the Industrial World. The individual has a direct obligation to God and it is one that is laid out in the printed Bible, written in his own language. The church regulates only in the same way that the judiciary does, it does not interpret or mediate in the way that the Catholic Church did.

The occurrence of a major innovation, such as printing, changes the community and its members immediately and completely. The degree to which a society adapts to the new situation varies as does the speed of such adaptation. However, the society that adapts quickly and reasonably completely to the new mind set is almost always more successful. This effect can be seen in the way in which many of the states of Northern Europe adapted quickly and relatively painlessly to the new situation. They accepted Protestantism and the concept of Nationhood, and they were ultimately the powerful industrial and nationalist states which passed on their systems and abilities to North America.

However, the old systems do not simply disappear. In many of the countries of Southern Europe there was an unwillingness to give up the feudal principles of the Catholic Church and the Holy Roman Empire. These societies fought inevitable change through the Counter-Reformation, the Inquisition and the Thirty Years War. Ultimately they either faded in importance or, like France, were forced to change through bloody revolution. The British established a nationalist state and were ready for the industrial revolution at home. Abroad they created an empire of feudally based client states. Initially this was a successful strategy but it was not one that could be maintained, as literacy and industrialization were introduced into the client states, and nationalistic pressures were created. Within Europe there were many wars of conquest over the next 500 years, but none could overcome for long the power of nationalism and ultimately nationalism has invariably triumphed.

The philosophy and science of Industrial Man, like the industrial process, are reductionist. They break things down into constituent parts, examine and test those parts before breaking them down further. This is a a blinkered process that tends to ignore the consequences of an action, and it is basically destructive. The keynote of the reaction to the relentless industrial condition is destruction.

The specialization of Industrial Society requires an immense amount of cooperation. Feudal Man is dependent in some way with those directly above and below him in the hierarchy, but the importance of everyone else is limited. Industrial man interacts with everyone in his society and is dependent in some way on them all. This, when combined with the basic competitiveness of the industrial ethos, results in the feeling that everyone may be against him, and a suspicion of conspiracies and plots that will bring about his downfall.

For Industrial Man situations tend to be all or nothing. His relationship both with the State and with his God are direct and clearly defined. If the Feudal Man fails he drops a level or two in the hierarchy. However, for Industrial Man failure represents complete and irreparable disaster and eternal damnation. Purgatory is not a concept found in Protestant theology. Despair is the usual outcome of this situation.

These three elements: destruction, suspicion and despair are the central themes of the Syphilitic Miasm.

Radio, Television, Electronics, Globalization and AIDS

Exactly which invention ushered in the Electronic Age is less clear cut than the birth of the Industrial Age and the invention of printing. Telegraphy developed slowly through the first half of the Nineteenth Century, and was established by 1850. Marconi invented radio transmission in 1895, and broadcasting began after the First World War. The first television broadcast occurred in 1936 but it only became widespread after the end of the Second World War. The invention of the transistor in 1948 and its improvement in

1952 were probably the key inventions, as they allowed the development of computers and digital electronics.

The defining moment of the shift in mind set that electronics brought about is also not quite as clear as Columbus's discovery was for the industrial age. McLuhan takes it to be the launch of Sputnik in 1957, which circumscribed our world and defined the stage on which life is enacted. The landing on the Moon and Armstrong's first steps in July 1969 is another strong contender. The picture of "Earthrise" over the Moon, brought back by Apollo 8 in 1969, is perhaps the most powerful, for it encompasses the similar feelings of the other two. Yet it is an image and so has an iconic power which is particularly important, as one of the major shifts for Electronic Man is a return to the visual image from the written word. The discovery of the New World, and the realization that the world is a sphere, shifted understanding from the concept of an endless creation moving at the whim of God, to that of a limited creation bound by the laws of mechanics. The view of the Earth from space caused a similar shift in understanding and a feeling for the smallness and fragility of the planet, a feeling that is central to the AIDS Miasm.

Though many of the discoveries that were to become important in the creation of Electronic Man have their roots in the Second World War (atomic energy, antibiotics, rocketry, DDT and pesticides, aeronautical technology, computer theory and communications), the full force of them was suppressed by the war itself and then by the Cold War stretching through the fifties. However, during the sixties the power of their meaning could no longer be contained and widespread changes burst out all over the world.

The contraceptive pill, though more a symptom than a cause, signalled a shift in power from society to the individual and allowed women to separate sexuality from procreation. The changes in attitudes and the law with respect to homosexuality and abortion brought sexuality into the open. These changes in turn allowed for the disentanglement of sex and gender, and clarified feminist issues.

The release of *Sgt. Pepper's Lonely Hearts Club Band* in 1967 was an important marker in several ways. It was the first album that was conceived as a single work rather than a collection of individual songs. The album as a whole became the work of art. It was also a work, undoubtedly partly inspired by LSD, that saw a melting of the boundaries between sound and vision. The album cover was designed by one of the leading contemporary artists and the visual effect was entwined within the musical one. The summer of 1967, the so called Summer of Love, the hippie enclave at Haight Ashbury, the apparent birth of free love and sexual freedom, and the anti-war protests were all expressions of the concepts of beauty, nature, peace and love that became the objectives of youth in a way that the generation raised in the age of the Nation State (and often the Nation State at war) could not comprehend. These events also stressed the importance of drugs in the Electronic Age. The body creates its own internal defences against the overwhelming nature of the unbounded modern world in the form of detachment, numbness and isolation. It also seeks out external forces that will help create these states and recreational drugs are undoubtedly the most powerful way of doing this.

1967 also saw the first heart transplant. The heart, the very centre and in some ways the soul of a person, could be exchanged. This ties in with a confusion of identity that is also important in the Electronic Age.

The Vietnam War with its television coverage, increasing technological basis, and ultimate ineffectuality were the first clear signs that warfare was changing. The protests against the war were also the first important evidence that the will of the people and that of the Nation State were not one and the same thing, as they had been throughout the Industrial Age.

1969 saw many of the important events that defined aspects of the Electronic Age. The Moon landings were undoubtedly important but they were part of a wider revolution. The first flight of Concorde, which meant that you could get to New York earlier that you left London or Paris, indicated a new understanding of time; but the Anglo-French cooperation which transcended the priority of the nation state, and the pride taken in it was just as revolutionary. Woodstock was the last great expression of the hippie ethos. However, 1969 also saw many of the first signs that the sixties were never to fulfill their promise. Altamont and the Chicago riots showed how close violence and bloodshed were to peace and love. Nixon was now president, and promised a return to the ethos of the fifties and his vice presidency.

Although the changes wrought by technology are complete and permanent, they are not universally accepted, and the fight against such change, however futile it might be, is bitter and protracted. McLuhan tends to ignore this in his work. This is partly because, as a devout Catholic, he did not fully see the Counter-Reformation and the Spanish Inquisition as the powerful reaction to the Industrial Age that it was. A reaction that was to condemn the countries of Southern Europe to a gradual waning of power and a susceptibility to corruption. He also died just a few weeks before Ronald Reagan was inaugurated as president and so missed much of the greed, nationalism and superficiality that marked the eighties of Thatcher and Reagan, and which constitute a counter-reformation to the world of Electronic Man.

The Consequences of the Electronic Age

The Dissolution of Boundaries

The particular effect of man's extension by electronics, which McLuhan called the extension of the nervous system of man, is to bring about an almost complete destruction of the concept of distance in both space and time. Electronic communication moves at the speed of light. Electronic communication is instantaneous. Sender, receiver and all the people and places in between become a single unified point in space and time. Even outside the virtual world, the aeroplane rolls up the road as it leaves the runway, and airports half way around the world become connected directly to each other, all the countries, towns and peoples in between simply vanish. Boundaries disappear, they are of absolutely no consequence to electronic communication or to aeroplanes.

The result of this is that the world becomes the Global Village. The scope of an individual's interaction with others has moved from family, to tribe and village, to town, to state and now encompasses the whole world. Our actions can affect others wherever they might be and we cannot but be affected by the actions of others. Censorship becomes impossible as information available anywhere becomes available everywhere.

The implications for economics and finance are enormous. The lack of boundaries means that it is almost impossible to protect intellectual property. Music on the internet, and eventually books and films, make it difficult to see how artists will be recompensed for their work. Even trade in physical goods is affected. One of the basic principles of trade economics is that profit is made through moving goods from one place where they are of lesser value, to a place where they command greater value. This can be from one country to another, or from the farm or factory to wholesaler, then to retailer and finally to the consumer. In a world without boundaries it is much more difficult to distinguish between two places, and in time value will equalize, making such trade unprofitable. The consumer will buy directly as if from the factory, and will be able to compare factories to such a degree that prices will have no opportunity for markup. In Tribal Society trade is by barter and value is intrinsic to the goods themselves. In Imperial Society money is used but value is still a real equivalent of goods. In Industrial Society value becomes to a degree notional and represents a means of state control. In the Electronic Age money has become almost completely virtual, the concept of value is difficult to define and so far these concepts have not found a new role.

In politics the Nation State is given an emotional charge and its boundaries are defended at all costs, particularly by those with a stake in it. However, in spite of the distrust and dislike with which they are viewed the larger, basically federal, organizations such as the European Community and the North American Free Trade Area grow inexorably wider and more powerful.

Ecology and Our View of the Planet

The lack of boundaries has resulted in local activities having global effects. This is most apparent in our understanding of ecology and the environment. In the Industrial Age nature was acknowledged as an all powerful force. Nature could be viewed with an almost religious awe as it was by the Romantic Movement or it could be seen, as through the myth of the Pioneer Spirit, as a malevolent force against which a continual war must be waged, a war that was noble even if it would never be won. In the early sixties this view was completely shattered by an understanding of the effects of pesticides, particularly the organochlorines, on the natural world. DDT was developed with great urgency and widely used through the Second World War to kill the mosquitoes that made malaria such a threat to the troops in tropical theatres of war. In the years immediately following the war stockpiles were turned to domestic and horticultural use, and before 1950 its agricultural use was widespread. In 1961 the British government commissioned Derek Ratcliffe to study the population of Peregrine Falcons in Britain, following demands from farmers, gamekeepers and pigeon fanciers for action to be taken on their growing numbers. The result of the study was shocking. The population rather than rising was in free fall; the Peregrine had virtually disappeared from Southern England and there was an immediate danger of extinction. It was discovered that DDE, a metabolite of DDT, was causing a softening of the eggshells and that almost none of the young were hatching. Use of DDT was restricted in 1962, and further restrictions followed leading to an EC ban in 1980. By 1990 the population had recovered to well above historical levels and it continues to grow. In the US the effect of pesticides was as great, and in 1962 Rachel Carson published *Silent Spring,* which brought to the attention of the public the effect that pesticides were having. She described how the birds and insects had vanished and gave voice to the ominous silence that now hung over most of America, a change that had occurred in just fifteen years. Although some restrictions were introduced in the US, the lack of boundaries means that actions in one country cannot be enough. Peregrines are migratory in the New World, and the continued heavy use of crude pesticides from Mexico southwards means that there are still virtually no Peregrines in Canada and the US east of the Rockies.

Since the sixties a deeper understanding of the holistic nature of the environment has come about. Much of this understanding can be seen expressed in the concept of Gaia as developed by Lovelock in his book of the same name. This view of the world as a single organism, which is emphasized by the pictures of Earth from space, has brought some recognition of the delicate balance involved and issues such as global warming, the destruction of the ozone layer and the depletion of fish stocks are making more people aware that they are the custodians of nature not its subjects. This recognition involves a level of responsibility and a sense of doom that is a constant note in modern society, and has been since the threat of nuclear destruction, though now it seems to be even less under our control. This engenders a painful degree of vulnerability and uncertainty, but even more disturbingly the Gaia model can cast humanity as a disease that afflicts the Earth, which like any other disease will have to be excised. This tends to lead to nihilism and feelings of self-disgust and hatred that are turned on society and on the self.

The Changing Role of Women

The way in which the move from Industrial to Electronic Society and the consequent dissolution of boundaries has changed the world can perhaps be most clearly seen in the changing role of women. In Feudal Society sexual relationships are contained quite neatly within the feudal hierarchy. They are as much part of the exchange process as any other, and ideally they take place between husband and wife or man and mistress or whore, that is between adjacent members of the hierarchy. In the industrial framework in which the individual is accountable to the State, to God or to the industrial complex the sexual relationship has no easy valid place and continuously threatens to undermine the structure. This danger was contained partly by commercializing sex and bringing it under the control of the market, but more importantly by making the family a microcosm of the state in which all authority was vested in the paterfamilias and all relationships, including sexual ones, were directed through him. Thus in the Victorian household the only acceptable sexual relationship was between the head of the household and his wife and even that was not fully approved of.

In the Electronic Age a reversed situation occurs. Sexual interaction reflects many of the issues of the times. It is about the diffusion of the boundaries between participants, the ideal being a melting into oneness. It encompasses the themes of love, beauty, youth, novelty and nakedness. Most importantly it is an activity that is between individuals and needs no structure, just two bodies.

The dissolution of boundaries has weakened many of the restrictions on sexuality. Marriage and the politics and economics of family connections cemented through marriage are far less relevant. The bounds of class, religion, race and gender that had controlled sexual relations and marriage are also no longer relevant. The result is that the individual relationship, however, transitory is of more importance than the relationship to the state or even to the family. This puts tremendous pressure on the relationship and brings about a tremendous sense of loss when a relationship fails, and a sense of worthlessness and failure for anyone that is not in a perfect sexual relationship.

The views of sexuality predicated in Feudal and Industrial Societies lead to the suppression of women's sexuality and of women's position in general. This no longer applies in the Electronic Age. In a world without boundaries the arbitrary differences between individuals can no longer be supported. This leads to the concept of rights for the individual and opposition to all forms of prejudicial discrimination. The change in the status of women demands that they are empowered to behave and aspire in the same way that men do. This in turn requires the changes that have occurred in contraception, abortion, divorce and in the workplace, and not, as is often postulated, that these changes have led to the changes in women's status. The feminism that grew through the sixties and whose most important expression was Germaine Greer's *The Female Eunuch* of 1970, was as much a verbalization and description of what was happening as it was a call to arms and a demand for change.

Like so many of the effects of man's extensions, the new situation is not one of absolute positives. The status of women today gives them rights and opportunities that were unthinkable just forty years ago; it also makes many aspects of life very difficult. The mechanisms that have allowed women to start assuming an equal place in society have involved a severe suppression of many natural functions. Fertility is the most obvious suppression, but there is also a suppression of passivity, of the yin function. There is a corresponding suppression of aggression and the yang function in the male. However, the power of yang energy makes it much more difficult to maintain such suppression and it tends to break out in sudden and violent destructive rage at regular intervals; whereas suppressed passivity tends more to a slow and festering self-destructiveness.

The conceptual dissolution between the genders can be seen in a multitude of ways, from dress to opportunity, but it is also becoming physically apparent. Pollution from pharmaceutical oestrogens, stemming from widespread use of HRT and the contraceptive pill, phyto-oestrogens from increased consumption of soya and similar crops, and oestrogen-mimics, found in chemicals such as pesticides and plasticizers, are creating a physical feminization of the entire animal kingdom.

Children and Childhood

The same process that has resulted in equal rights for all individuals of whatever race, creed, gender or class, at least theoretically and in western, developed cultures, has resulted in a change in the way that children are viewed. They are regarded as individuals and are given a voice in a way in which they have not been in the past. We have a much stronger sense of them as individuals and feel a duty to protect them. The upside of this is that children are listened to and abuse is much less likely to be tolerated. Before the sixties it was considered perfectly acceptable to beat children quite severely for the least misdemeanour and sexual abuse was very rarely discovered because it was taboo. The downside of the dissolution of the boundaries between children and adults is that children have much less of a childhood and become subject to the woes and excitement of adult life at a much earlier age.

Even the boundaries between ourselves and animals have become much less defined. Genetics has informed us that the difference between ourselves and the great apes is a matter of a few percent of our DNA, and we identify with the great apes and with the cetaceans in a way that no developed society has before. Genetic engineering has meant that the DNA of one creature can be inserted into that of another without regard to species, or even natural kingdom. Transgenic animals, particularly pigs, are being created which produce human secretions or with whom we can exchange organs. We are also open to transgenic disease, AIDS and new variant CJD have probably come from animals, as have the Hanta and Ebola haemorrhagic fevers.

The Concept of Place

Not only does the concept of distance have very little meaning for Electronic Man but even our sense of place is no longer fixed. The universally irritating thing about the use of mobile phones is the way in which so many conversations begin with a statement like "I'm on the train". Yet this fixing of our position or place is vitally important to us when we use a mobile phone, as without it we do not have any bearing on where we are but seem just to be floating about in the ether. This lack of fixity is expressed in many other ways in a general feeling of being lost.

The Loss of Time Boundaries

Even more important than the loss of boundaries in space and the vanishing of distance and of a fixed place in the universe, is the end of a separation in time that electronic technology causes. The media of electronic communication are electronic current and electromagnetic radiation. These travel at the speed of light, which is in turn the speed of Einsteinian time. This means that everything happens instantaneously.

The first consequence of this is that we live only in the present, the past and the future break away. Instead of the smooth rolling out of time along which we used to move at a steady pace; time is now a series of disjunct instants and we jump from one to the next.

However, the most important ramification is that cause and effect no longer follow in a steady chain. Cause and effect come to be perceived simultaneously. An example of this can be seen in television news where the news of an earthquake and the devastating effect will be shown at the same time. This means that the predictive possibilities of cause and effect come to no longer apply. Cause can no longer be used to postulate an effect, because the effect is known at the same time that the cause is. In quantum physics this process becomes manifest in that cause cannot be observed separately from effect: cause, effect and observation cannot be separated from each other and become a single, indivisible entity.

Cause and effect and the certainty that one would follow the other are central tenets of industrial/nationalist thought. They result in the concept of a goal or objective. Industrial Man can reasonably expect certain consequences to result from an action and judges his actions on that expectation. Electronic Man can no longer be sure of the results that will come from an action, and so must learn to judge his actions on the qualities of the actions themselves, not on their possible consequences. The Protestant Work Ethic, central to the Industrial State, where current discomfort is tolerated for future gain can no longer be sustained. Only current conditions can be considered in evaluating a course of action. This results in what appears to be, and often becomes, selfishness. It also makes conventional religious morality, where present courses of behaviour are chosen for their future consequences in paradise or in hell, no longer a meaningful concept.

Another example of the impact of a world without cause and effect is in the concept of justice. In Tribal Society justice is a means of maintaining the balance between the individuals in the tribe. It is there to make sure that members can live together and any solution that allows this is acceptable. In Feudal Society justice maintains the chain of obligation within the hierarchy, and it is imposed by any member of the chain on those immediately below him. In Industrial Society justice is used to impose the will of the Nation State on the individuals that are its subjects. The law is written, it applies equally to everyone, and it is administered by the appointed instruments of the state. In this law an action has an effect and that in turn has consequences. This cannot be sustained in the Electronic Age. For one thing interactions are between individuals and not mediated through the state, justice must therefore meet individual circumstances and cannot be universal. Furthermore as there is no longer a connection between cause and effect, motivation can no longer be used to decide what is criminal and what is not. This can be seen clearly in the concept of sexual harassment. Actions which are offensive to one person might not be to another and it is the perception of the recipient of these actions which decide whether they or criminal or not, not the motivations of the person who enacted them. This means that the justice system in Electronic Society must deal more and more with aiding the victim than with punishing the criminal. This is reinforced by the fact that the criminal is often the victim of something or someone else, and that the concept of deterrence has no meaning in a world without cause and effect.

Complexity

The lack of boundaries also means that every event, however trivial, may influence every other one. This results in complexity on an unimaginable scale. In classical mechanics the interaction of two gravitational bodies is easy to predict and has been since Newton. Merely introducing a third body does not just make prediction more difficult, it actually makes it inherently impossible, the long term interaction of the three bodies is too complex to be described mathematically. In the world of the Electronic Age nothing can be predicted because it might be affected by too many other things. Minute changes in seemingly unrelated systems are communicated instantly and might have enormous ramifications for each other. It is impossible to predict what changes might or might not have ramifications, let alone what those ramifications might be.

Not only is modern society unbounded and incredibly complex but many of the innovations of the Electronic Age conspire to keep it on the very edge of chaos and so prey to sudden, complete and unpredictable changes. A simple example of this is stock control and logistics. Computerization and communication have allowed the principle of "just in time" to become the norm in all forms of stock control. This means that new stock arrives just in time to satisfy demand. This is extremely important for increased profitability as it cuts down on the costs of keeping unnecessary stock and reduces the risk of wastage through exceeding sell-by dates and allows for immediate responses to the demands of fashion. However, it also means that the system is inherently unstable, any delay or problem in any of the links of the supply chain can cause a complete breakdown and the effects of that breakdown will be felt far beyond the actual chain itself. Thus a minor protest about fuel prices in one place spreads nationally and internationally almost immediately, brings instant shortages and within a few days threatens to bring the whole of society to a standstill.

This aspect of being on the edge of chaos and sudden unpredictable change is particularly observable in politics. The fall of the Berlin Wall and the various revolutions in the former Soviet satellites are striking examples. Changes of whatever kind no longer happen quietly and at a measured pace, rather they are sudden, unpredictable and complete. It is the completeness that is perhaps the most remarkable feature. In previous revolutions there followed long civil wars and periods of reprisal and power struggle. In recent revolutions a few figureheads, such as the Ceausecus, have received summary retribution; but most changes have occurred without the need for a protracted bloodletting.

The Impossibility of Specialization

Specialization is the key to the industrial way of thinking. It appeared with the printing of the very first printed book which was produced on six different presses working simultaneously, each one manned by teams of specialists: typographers, typecutters, typesetters, inkers, pressmen, etc. The coming of the book caused such an explosion of knowledge that it was no longer possible for one person to know everything. However, it was possible for a person to know everything about a particular subject. In the Electronic Age there has been a further explosion of knowledge which makes it hard for a person to know everything, even about a very restricted subject. More important than this is that, without boundaries between subjects, it has become impossible to define a single subject and circumscribe it. Everything is affected by everything else and any subject involves many other subjects which interact with it and each of those interact with others. Although the specialist is still the accepted model in almost every field it is one that is not sustainable in the Electronic Age.

New Ways of Thinking

The merging of cause and effect and the complexity of all systems that makes them inherently unpredictable mean rational, sequential thought is no longer capable of dealing with our world. Thought in the Electronic Age has to be very different from earlier ways of thinking if it is to be effective. In the Tribal World the most useful form of thinking is historical. If someone knows and understands what has happened in history they are better prepared when it starts to repeat itself. This knowledge was experiential and lay within the scope of a person's life or that of those with whom he had direct contact. Language allows the passing on of history, either as such or in the form of myths and legends. In the Feudal World the possession of knowledge becomes the most effective way of understanding the world and of dealing with it. This knowledge extends beyond personal experience but still lies within the compass of one person. The personal experience of many different people can become the knowledge of one. The person with access to the widest knowledge is in a position to interpret events and so to take advantage of them. In the Industrial World knowledge is too complex to be available to one philosopher. It is the ability to use reason and to follow a train of sequential thought that allows understanding of what happens and to deduce the inevitable consequences of the happening. This ability allows for the integration of the knowledge of several different people into the logical interpretation of one.

In the Electronic World consequences are no longer inevitable or predictable and we need a new way of looking at things if we are not to get completely lost in the complexity of possibility. We need to follow the progression that has taken place to the next highest level. We need a system that will allow one person to combine the logical conclusions of many people in many different and often unrelated fields.

Chaos mathematics has revealed some of the important aspects of a world in which reason is not an effective interpreter. In a complex and chaotic problem it is not possible to predict what will happen. The individual result is unpredictable, however, there is a pattern in chaotic behaviour and that pattern is not only unchanging but applies over different scales and across different manifestations of the problem. In complex worlds even different, unrelated questions can have the same pattern. This can be seen in fractals, which are visual representations of mathematical equations that have chaotic properties. Although it is impossible to predict how specific solutions to the equation will behave, it is possible to see an overall pattern and to understand that the same pattern will apply in all possible solutions.

The type of thought that does fulfill the needs of the modern world can best be described as pattern thinking. It requires an ability to stand back from any particular expression of a thing and see it as a complete pattern. The beginning and end of a chain cannot be separated and it is the overall way that a chain lies rather than the details of each link that is its most important feature. It is also important to see the pattern iterated in many different ways. The pattern viewed from only one angle can be deceptive but the understanding of the pattern gained from looking at it again and again from many different angles will be much clearer. An analogy, or perhaps an example, is the hologram. A hologram is an interference pattern that holds a three dimensional image. Every part of the hologram contains the whole image and if the plate containing the hologram is cut into pieces, each piece contains the whole image, though the smaller the piece the less clear the image is. Each pattern on each piece is complete, but it is by using many of these patterns that the clearest image can be seen. The hardest part of this to understand, especially for someone trained in the world of reason by our outmoded educational system, is that the concepts of premise and conclusion simply do not apply. The path to a conclusion cannot be derived from the premise. Indeed both premise and conclusion do not exist other than as points on the path, and the path itself is the rightful object of our investigation.

Using pattern thinking requires the ability not only to see a pattern but to match it to other patterns that embody the same qualities, even if they are in completely different areas of life and study. A pattern found in mythology, biology and developmental psychology can inform and explain a pattern in politics or particle physics. It is by understanding the pattern itself that we can more clearly see its particular manifestation in a particular problem.

The successful thinker in the Electronic Age looks at patterns and not details, and she must be a polymath and be able to look for those patterns in many different places. Dyslexia is regarded as a disability in an educational system that is still predicated on the principles of the Industrial Age, but most able pattern thinkers are in some way dyslexic. Dyslexia often arises from a view of things that examines the whole and ignores the details. A dyslexic can appreciate a whole concept but cannot see the details. He or she can often learn to read by seeing the whole sentence but, being unaware of the individual letters and punctuation marks, is unable to create sentences with the correct orthography. A quick and easy measure of an education system that is designed to be effective in the modern world will be one in which dyslexics have a distinct advantage over their fellow students.

Echoes of Earlier States

Each extension to man creates a new way of thinking, indeed of being, that permeates the whole of the relevant society, which in the case of the electronic extension is the entire world, and changes everything for ever. However, the new way includes within itself all the ways that preceded it. The spoken tale is included within the manuscript which is in turn the content of the book which in time becomes enfolded in the film or TV show.

McLuhan felt that because the Electronic Age filled an auditory, uncentralized space rather than the fixed, visual space of Industrial Man it would be easier for non literate societies to adapt to it. In fact the reverse is true: Electronic Man contains within himself Industrial Man and he in turn contains Feudal and Tribal ways of thinking. Feudal societies are now doubly out of their depth as they have neither Industrial nor Electronic understanding.

The new way may also have superficial similarities that can be extremely misleading. An example of this is the tribal nature of the Electronic Age. Electronic Man behaves in ways that are very similar to Tribal patterns of behaviour. The most obvious way is through clearly marking himself to show his allegiances. This has manifested itself in the increased popularity of tattoos, but the wearing of designer labels on clothing is an equally valid assertion of tribal identity. However, the nature of Electronic tribalism is very different to that of the original tribal cultures. Modern tribes are chosen, their members are not born into them. As with everything Electronic they are of the present only, they do not have a history and members are not bound to them in the future; though this does not make them any less powerful in the moment. One of the most important features of the Electronic Age is the way in which complete absorption or devotion at one moment in time does not affect what happens at another moment. This is often seen as fickleness and as implying that involvement in the Electronic Age is always superficial. In fact the reverse is true: because everything is contained within the present, devotion or absorption can be absolute within that moment and at another time another, different allegiance will be just as complete.

The Macrocosm of Disease in Society

When a culture with one way of thinking is suddenly faced with a change to a new way for which it is not yet adapted a disease state is almost inevitable. An example might be a developing country with a basically feudal society. The country is probably ruled by a military leader for the military structure is a strongly hierarchical one and so adapts very well to a feudal society. The country might be rich in natural resources and does a deal with international multinationals. These companies are part of the Industrial Age and their actions are mediated through an industrial understanding of money. They are object driven and subject to the written law and the rules of trade. In the feudal society the checks and balances are built into the structure of obligations which run both ways in the hierarchy. When Industrial Age money replaces obligation in a still feudal framework, neither work properly. Money does not have the Protestant Work Ethic, or the control of an independent law and judiciary to make sure that it remains productive. At the same time the system loses the obligations and counter-obligations that keep the hierarchy in balance, as they have been replaced by money. The immediate result is that corruption, bribery and nepotism become the norm. Productivity never develops along industrial lines, and the old feudal productivity collapses. Decay follows and is accompanied by mistrust and growing paranoia and cruelty. These are the symptoms associated with the Syphilitic Miasm. This is a pattern that has been seen throughout the developing world, and also in large countries such as Russia, when there is a mismatch between the structure of society and the prevalent social paradigm.

Semimiasmatic Responses

The true miasmatic diseases are a reaction to the situation that a person or a society finds itself in as a result of the transition from one state or way of thinking to another. The extensions of man bring about the new state suddenly and completely, and this leaves no time for individuals or for the culture as a whole to adapt. The result is an immune type of reaction, a sudden and extreme disease that spreads suddenly and very quickly. This was the pattern of syphilis in the 1490s as much as it was of AIDS in the 1980s. As a society begins to adapt to the new state the disease becomes less immediately threatening and adapts to a more chronic form. This certainly happened with syphilis, which in its early years was an almost immediately fatal disease, but within less than a quarter of a century began changing its nature to the slow, deep disease we recognize today. It is likely that a similar path is being followed by HIV infection. The early cases were invariably fatal and tended to become apparent within a few years. There were also a fairly limited number of specific secondary infections that were connected with HIV: Karposi's, PCP and a few others. Today the incubation period of HIV is much longer and the secondary infections are much more diverse. These changes are usually attributed to developing medical treatment and it is almost impossible to get a clear overview of what is happening. However, the pattern matches that of earlier diseases and it is quite likely that the pharmaceutical companies are to some degree claiming credit for what is the natural path of the disease.

There is another type of disease that has miasmatic qualities but which has a different pattern to it. It is not so much a reaction to mismatched states, rather the long term effect of the imbalances that are inherent in that state.

When man moved from a state of unawareness, through speech to awareness, he reacted with the Psoric Miasm, and a deep steady struggle to deal with what the world throws at him. As he becomes adjusted to the state he reacts in a slightly different way, rather than struggling with everything and keeping it at bay (especially through the slow expressive itch eruption), he now takes on the attacks he faces with strong, sudden and dramatic fevers and illnesses. This state is often known as the Acute Miasm, but the disease that it most closely resembles is rabies, and I refer to it as the Hydrophobic Miasm.

With writing and literacy we move into a new situation. An understanding of a larger world in which we need to preserve our place causes a feeling of inadequacy, and the reaction to this is the Sycotic one of growth, inflation, cover up and secrecy. When the society and its members become acclimatized to the Sycotic State a slightly different feeling pervades. The fixity and lack of natural movement imposed on Feudal Society become suffocative and oppressive. This feeling of suffocation and the reaction to it which is a desire to escape and explore are keynotes of the Tubercular Miasm.

With printing and industrialization the feeling of being a small part of the bigger machine is met with Syphilis, a destructive reaction in which suspicion and fear are important elements. In time the society becomes used to the Industrial World and is forced to accept its role, to conform and to dispense with individuality, though at the same time to rage against the system. This is the Cancer State.

It can be seen that the true miasms are reactive and to a large degree passive, whereas the assimilated states and their miasms are more aggressive, in that they are both part of the new condition and at the same time fighting it. In the Hydrophobic and Tubercular Miasms this element of rage and fighting back is fairly obvious. In the Cancer Miasm the acceptance is stronger and the fighting more subtle. However, Carcinosin does have a strong element of rage, and one of the features associated both with the remedy and with cancer in our society is a propensity to war and fighting metaphors.

In the Electronic Age the AIDS Miasm reacts to a world that is too big and too complex by throwing itself open and by taking excessive responsibility.

The Electronic Age is still too young to be able to be certain what the corresponding secondary miasm will be. One contender is likely to be spongiform encephalopathy (BSE/CJD) and its non infective relative, Alzheimer's disease. (*See Appendix 1*)

Epidemic Disease

Although epidemic diseases appear suddenly, disappear as quickly and would appear to be without meaning, this seems to be an anomaly and in theory these diseases should have meaning.

One instance where this meaning is fairly obvious is the situation in the Americas that complemented the arrival of syphilis in Europe.

The effect of moving from one world view to another is traumatic and causes a powerful disease reaction; but it is as nothing when compared to the effect of moving through several at once. Syphilis was a serious and destructive force as it swept through Europe but the counter effect in the New World was on a completely different scale. The population in the Americas in 1490 was about 100 million, perhaps a fifth of the total human population. Within the next fifty years most of that population was to be wiped out by waves of disease that accompanied the explorers and invaders.

The indigenous population of the Americas had developed cultures and societies that were incredibly advanced. The building skills of the Incas and the political sophistication of the Iroquois have never been matched. However, they had no draught animals, the horse having become extinct and the large ruminants being too wild to domesticate, so the wheel, about which they knew, was of no use to them.

They had also never developed a phonetic alphabet. They had some beautiful and sophisticated methods of record keeping: the Iroquois and Cherokee used wampum, patterns of different coloured beads made from shells; the Incas used quipu, fringes of fine threads whose colour, position and knotting all have meaning. The Aztecs had a sophisticated written language but it used hieroglyphics and they had no alphabet.

These two factors meant that the indigenous American societies were basically still Tribal. They had developed awareness and had continued to develop it to a higher degree than the Europeans, but without the wheel and the alphabet they had not translated into the world of feudalism and literacy.

The shock of the European contact was a double one, introducing them not only to the new Industrial World but at the same time to the Feudal World, which the Europeans had become acclimatized to over two thousand years. The disease reaction to this shock was terrible, as smallpox, measles and similar diseases spread quickly with devastating results.

A similar effect can be seen in Africa where AIDS has been so devastating. The colonial powers tended to impose a feudal, imperial pattern on their colonies. These societies moved from Tribal awareness to Feudal literacy, but their imperial conquerors did not want them to develop dangerous nationalism and industrial power, as they wanted consumers not competing producers. Their transition was cushioned and Africa remained basically feudal. The Electronic Age cannot be introduced gently, as its overwhelming feature is its unbounded influence. It came suddenly and completely to the whole world. Industrial societies coped poorly enough, but the effect on tribal and feudal societies in developing countries has been devastating. The AIDS epidemics in Africa are killing the same proportion of the population that smallpox killed in the Americas. There should also be considerable concern about what will happen in other societies that have not made a full transition to Industrial society. In the Orient the phonetic alphabet has not fully replaced the hieroglyphic pictograms, and the mind set of the population is often more feudal than industrial. Even in Russia and India the fundamental spirit of the society is more feudal than industrial, and the likelihood of AIDS becoming a devastating epidemic is high.

The epidemics of bubonic plague between the fourteenth and seventeenth centuries were so massive that they too must surely have meaning. It is possible that they were a reaction to the effects of continuing urbanization. Likewise the 1918-19 flu epidemic may have been a reaction to the effects of the Great War. This is speculation.

The Microcosm of Disease in the Individual

The microcosm of an individual's life reflects the pattern found in the macrocosm of society. The newborn baby is unaware, but soon learns speech and self awareness. At this time he might be prey to the first signs of the Psoric skin diseases. As he grows into this state he faces the Hydrophobic Miasm illnesses, which are often called "the childhood diseases". As he goes to school and learns to write we might expect to see the Sycotic affections: snotty nose, glue ear and warts. Tubercular asthma and lung trouble might follow.

The teenager enters the bigger world. learns to deal with sexuality and relationships, and takes on a Syphilitic interaction with authority. In time there are powerful pressures on them to conform, to pass exams and to get a job; these are Cancerous traits. As adults today they enter a world that puts them under tremendous pressure to succeed, but a world that does not have any rules or certainties and one in which the future is not a predestined path. This is the AIDS Miasm state.

This is of course not to say that every child undergoes all these miasms and is afflicted by all these diseases. Rather the pattern is there as children grow up. Circumstances, whether they be genetic, racial, historic susceptibility or just the accidents of birth and life, will cause people to stick in one or more of the stages and transitions and it is in these places and in these miasms that their disease will manifest.

This is not the only way to look at the stages of life in relation to the miasms. In many ways the AIDS Miasm corresponds to the state of the teenager. This has come out in many of the modern provings where provers state that they feel like teenagers and are interested in many of the things that interested them when they were teenagers, particularly music. The teenage years lie at the boundary between childhood and adulthood. They represent the removal of many of the restrictions of childhood yet the corresponding restricting mechanisms of adulthood are not yet properly formed. Teenagers push against the boundaries set by families and societies in the same way that toddlers do, but they often find that those boundaries are not actually there. This results in a tendency to excess and to overindulgence. At the same time many of the protective forces that keep children safe are beginning to dissolve. Teenagers find that they are extremely vulnerable but have no way of expressing or mitigating that vulnerability. Youth is, with beauty, peace and love, one of the quadrumvirate of ideals that express the spirit of the AIDS Miasm.

Using Miasmatic Theory

There are a number of ways in which miasmatic theory can lead to a better understanding of symptoms, disease and remedies and so help us to make a better prescription.

When we look at an object it has many features and qualities. Shape and size and colour are immediately obvious, but there are others such as texture, temperature, odour, etc.

A disease picture or an individual symptom has a number of different qualities. What might be called the overall shape of a symptom, that which is repertorized, is fairly obvious. It certainly narrows the choice of remedies but, unless it is a very strong SRP (strange, rare and peculiar symptom), it will still leave a large and diverse selection of suggested remedies. The qualities, what might be described as the flavour, of a symptom and more generally of a case, help to make clearer the overall picture.

Much of the development of homœopathy over the last 30 years has been involved in clarifying the qualities of remedies, and in finding clear ways of seeing those qualities in patients. The Essences articulated by Vithoulkas, Reeves' Circle, Sankaran's Central Delusions, Rosenthal's Kingdoms, Herscu's Cycles and Scholten's Periodic Table and Families of Remedies, are all examples of this development, and they have allowed major advances in our understanding of patients and of remedies.

However, the first of these and still the most important is miasmatic theory. It allowed Hahnemann to develop and use a theory of chronic disease, and has been developed by many homœopaths since. The Bombay School has now brought it to a new level but there are many older versions that are also useful. The other systems are powerful tools and, in the hands of those that really understand them, produce amazing results, yet all too often in the hands of those that do not understand them they become simplified to the point where they produce very little understanding. The advantage of miasmatic theory is that it doesn't refer to things that are outside the closed world of the homœopathic philosophy of disease. This makes it much harder to use it superficially. A miasmatic system is rigorous, and can only be useful if you have an understanding of what animates and motivates a symptom, and so an entire disease picture. Unlike the other systems, it can only be used if it is understood.

In the following pages there are descriptions of the AIDS Miasm and some individual differentiations between the expression of symptoms in it and in other miasms. The miasms can be described in very basic terms. The Psoric Miasm is about struggle, the Sycotic is about covering up, the Syphylitic is about destruction and the AIDS Miasm is about losing boundaries. In the same way the keynote of the Hydrophobic Miasm is overreaction, the keynote of the Tubercular is oversensitivity, while in Cancer compliance is the most important feature and in CJD it is confusion. Although there is a simplicity in this description, it is the complex way in which these principles are expressed that makes them useful, and it is often not easy to work back from expression to origin.

As is found in homœopathy more generally, it is not the result that really matters but the path that is taken to that result. Finding out which miasm informs a case requires a meaningful understanding of that case, and it is this understanding that is important and helpful in choosing a remedy.

This understanding is also useful in deciding which symptoms are features of a case – are part of the disease picture, that which is to be cured – and which might not be. A disease picture should have a consistency and integrity that covers every individual part. If one symptom does not have the features of the same miasm as the overall picture, it needs to be examined very closely and this anomaly needs to be resolved. Either our understanding of the picture or of the symptom is incorrect, or this particular symptom may not be part of the current disease but something that is external or presently non-pathological.

Miasmatic theory can, however, be misleading and it is always dangerous to rely on it without support from other ways of looking at a case. This is particularly so with the AIDS Miasm, which is a powerful feature of contemporary society as a whole, and will appear quite strongly in a patient's life without necessarily being part of their disease picture. The AIDS Miasmatic picture is also a relatively recent one, having only been around for the last thirty or so years. Features of it therefore tend to stand out much more clearly than those of the other miasms, of which we have a two hundred year history, and which have become much more deeply assimilated into our understanding.

It is common for patients to present with concerns around the issues of the AIDS Miasm. Thus they will often talk about things like appetite, isolation, sexuality and confusion; however, it is when their response to these issues is characteristic of the AIDS Miasm that we need to look for an AIDS Miasm remedy. The healthy vital spirit is able to respond to pressures and toxins in an appropriate manner. It is an inappropriate response that constitutes a state of ill health, and it is the nature of that response that should match the chosen remedy.

Thus a feeling of isolation, which is practically universal in the modern world and is a definite marker of the AIDS Miasm, can cause a reaction with a profound sense of isolation, and of separation from the world. The remedy called for in this case is likely to be one found in the rubric: "MIND – FORSAKEN feeling – isolation; sensation of", which contains primarily AIDS Miasm remedies. However, in a great many cases although the sensation might have been inspired by the contemporary situation, the reaction might be of another quality. In this case the more general rubric: "MIND – FORSAKEN feeling" is likely to contain the indicated remedy. The three remedies listed in bold in this rubric give examples of how each of the older miasms might react. Psorinum has the sensation that they have been left to struggle through the trials of life alone and that it is only their constant efforts that will carry them through. Pulsatilla has the Sycotic sensation that they have not managed to get enough support and friendship to help them when things are difficult, they also have a need to cover up this failing. In the Syphilitic remedy Aurum, the sensation is that they have failed in their responsibilities and so their friends have all turned against them. The thought that they will have to carry on, not only alone but surrounded by former friends who have now become foes, fills them with suicidal despair.

There is another danger in relying on miasmatic theory to find a remedy. The only sure way of correctly selecting a remedy is to find a matching pattern in the disease picture and in the picture of a remedy. The many tools we have are merely ways of finding remedies to look at and compare. This is deeply unsatisfactory to many homœopaths. We are a print based and logical discipline and many of our number have a scientific training. We always seem to be looking for a formula that will reliably lead us to the correct remedy. At its worst this has resulted in an undifferentiated use of disease specific remedies, but it has also lead to the misuse of systems that can be applied to cases. In the past the main one of these was the repertory. Rubrics were chosen until they indicated a remedy and that remedy must be the correct one. In recent years, the increase in the number of ways of looking at a case has allowed us to rely on these systems, rather than on an understanding of the remedy and the patient. Although this is less easy to do with

Miasmatic theories than some of the others, they still represent a temptation to take short cuts.

The theory of miasms that is outlined in this book is slightly different from that which is being used to great effect by Sankaran and the Bombay School of homœopaths. Their understanding of the standard miasms and of several that they have added, including typhoid, ringworm and leprosy, allows the choice of remedy to be narrowed, and also helps in differentiating between remedies that are related in other ways, especially the families of plants and animals. The theory I outline here can be used to decide which miasm is important, and therefore which miasmatic group of remedies is likely to be called for. The symptoms of the miasm then need to be discounted in the choice of remedy, as they are common to the whole group, and it is either major symptoms that are not especially of the miasm or the particular and characteristic flavour of the symptoms that matter.

Using the Remedies of the AIDS Miasm

Treating HIV

The remedies of the AIDS Miasm should be the remedies that can be used in the treatment of HIV. However, there are aspects of the disease that raise important questions about how HIV should be treated homœopathically. The first of these revolves around the fact that the disease expresses itself not directly but through secondary, opportunistic infections. Many of these would not constitute a threat to the healthy individual, but for those who are HIV positive they are serious and can be life threatening. Often these infections must be addressed immediately because if they are not, there will be no patient to treat in any other way.

The fact that HIV causes an infectious, epidemic disease that is currently pandemic in Sub-Saharan Africa, suggests that it may have to be treated as an epidemic disease rather than an expression of a constitutional disorder. This is possibly more important in the developing world, where the disease manifests more acutely, and clearly has more of the nature of an epidemic. In the developed world, through better hygiene and living conditions and through treatment of opportunistic infections and of the disease itself, HIV infection has somewhat more of the nature of a chronic disease. The population of the Western World is also more attuned to the AIDS Miasm in its social manifestation and so there is likely to be a better match between the constitutional and the epidemic states.

The life cycle of the disease also makes the approach to treatment an important consideration. The virus commandeers certain cells of the immune system and uses them as factories dedicated to the production of more viruses. This removes the cells from their proper functioning place in the immune system and eventually destroys them thus opening the body to opportunistic infections. The damage to the immune system is an unfortunate byproduct of the virus's need to reproduce. If a constitutional prescription enhances the immune system without tackling the underlying viral infection, there must be a danger that the increased availability of "virus factories" will speed up rather than delay the disease process.

In treating an underlying HIV infection, the concept of the

AIDS Miasm is a useful tool for distinguishing the features and symptoms that are part of the case of HIV infection, and those that are part of the patient's underlying or constitutional picture.

This leads to the assumption that it will usually be a remedy of the AIDS Miasm that will be needed to treat HIV positive patients, at least while they are asymptomatic. Though as this survey is by no means comprehensive, it should not be assumed that all, or even most of the AIDS Miasm remedies will be included in this book.

Using AIDS Miasm Remedies with Diseases Not Related to HIV

The miasmatic conditions that affect us find personal or individual expression in diseases that reflect the nature of contemporary society. This happens in two ways. It can be the diseases themselves that are a general expression of the miasmatic stresses and concerns. These are the diseases that are particularly of our time: ME, Anorexia and Bulimia, Gulf War Syndrome, and of course HIV/AIDS itself. It can also be expressed in more common and general diseases, but in a particularly AIDS Miasm version of them. Thus something like depression is a common illness and it can be found in the pictures of virtually any chronic disease and so of any Miasm. However, there is a particular version of depression that centres around issues of isolation and vulnerability which is a part of the AIDS Miasm. In this case it is not the disease itself that matters but the flavour of its expression.

Understanding the Miasm allows the homœopath to recognize the symptoms that are of it and, what is more difficult but also more important, to recognize symptoms that are flavoured with aspects of the AIDS Miasm.

When the homœopath is convinced that a case is informed by the picture of the AIDS Miasm, he or she can be fairly confident that the remedy needed will be one of those that is also informed by the picture of the Miasm.. However, these symptoms now become of very little use as they are common symptoms within the group of possible remedies and offer very little differentiation.

To differentiate other strategies are then needed. Physical symptoms are now much more important, as different remedies within the Miasm can have very different affinities for parts of the body, and they often express themselves physically in a particular pathological pattern.

There are often connections that can be made to other remedies that express a similar theme in a different way. This is where the families of plants and the periodic table can be most helpful in finding a useful remedy. The use of myths, fairy tales and legends in understanding remedies is also a means of making them stand out from each other, and of finding connections to the patient's disease picture. This is perhaps most important in the very complex pictures that are coming out of the mammal and bird remedies, and the more complicated substances now being proved.

However, the most important differentiation is through the particular themes, issues and imagery of the remedy. This feature which is perhaps most characteristic and so most useful, is also the hardest to define. It is the flavour of the remedy, the small things that consistently differ from remedy to remedy and give each their individuality. In the older remedies the most experienced homœopaths have been able to catch something of this flavour and to put it across in their Materia Medicas. Yet even the work of our greatest teachers only catches a part of the full flavour. In the case of the new remedies no one yet has the clinical experience of them to be able to describe their flavours.

The only way to truly taste a remedy and get its flavour is to study the provings, and this applies as much to the older well known remedies as it does to the new ones about which there is so much to discover.

I certainly do not have enough experience of them to even consider interpreting the remedies of the AIDS Miasm, and I have chosen to illustrate the themes of the Miasm with proving symptoms in their purest form.

Speculating on Coming Disease States

There are a number of disease states that are emerging, both from the diseases themselves and from groups of proving symptoms, that indicate new miasmatic or semimiasmatic disease pictures may be ahead of us.

Creutzfeldt-Jakob and Alzheimer's Diseases

There are a number of diseases involving the destruction of brain tissue that are already important and seem destined to be even more so in the coming years. The contagious form of these diseases are the spongiform encephalopathies of which the bovine form, mad cow disease, is the best known and Creutzfeldt-Jakob disease is the human form. Alzheimer's disease has quite a similar pathology with plaques forming in the brain that destroy the tissue and result in dementia that gradually worsens.

There is a strong case to be made that these diseases represent the Miasm that comes about when a society becomes acclimatized to the AIDS Miasm state. Like the Hydrophobic, Tubercular and Cancer Miasms, it contains elements of both acquiescence and of violent rage. Like them it is also less fixed, and what is in Cancer and Tubercular states a desire for travel, in CJD and Alzjheimer's is often a tendency to wander, both mentally and physically. The primary feeling of these diseases is of being lost in an unbounded world, without support and without anything to hold onto. This would seem to match the settled state of AIDS in much the same way that Cancer's need to conform and make the world a nicer place fits the settled state of Syphilis.

There is also some support for this supposition in the pattern of disease in HIV positive people. Neuropathological disease was a feature of AIDS from its earliest manifestations. A number of the opportunistic infections particularly associated with AIDS, including Toxoplasmosis, Cryptococcosis, Cytomagalovirus, Progressive multifocal leukoencephalopathy, and a range of inflammatory neuropathies can cause damage to the central nervous system or to more peripheral nerves resulting in the expression of neuropathological symptoms.

However, the evidence is mounting that AIDS dementia, which is the most prevalent of neurological manifestations linked to HIV, is not a result of opportunistic infections but is a direct result of the Virus. Thus AIDS dementia is beginning to appear in HIV positive patients even where the infection has been held in check, or suppressed, by antiretroviral drug treatments. It is quite possible that the same pattern will occur in society as the AIDS Miasm is suppressed and as we become adapted to it, a Miasm that is similar to AIDS dementia and to spongiform encephalopothies will become dominant.

While the major miasmatic nosodes, including AIDS all have a clear picture arising out of provings; the pictures of both Tuberculinum and Carcinosin have come from clinical experience rather than provings. It is my belief that this has, quite surprisingly, resulted in over rather than under use of these remedies. Where we have a proving to help bring out detail, it is much easier to see the miasmatic picture in other remedies. However, as our pictures of Tuberculinum and Carcinosin are a bit fuzzy we find it harder to see the other related remedies and so tend to stick with the nosodes. It is to be hoped that there will be a good proving of CJD that will help to bring out a clear picture.

Ebola, Hanta and Marburg viruses

The haemorrhagic fevers have certain qualities of the AIDS Miasm: a similar origin to AIDS, transgenic features, a terrifying infectivity and especially a quality of breaking down barriers. However, their action rather than leaving the organism open to infection, results in a syphilitic destruction of the body, rapidly and fatally liquifying the inner organs. This dissolving of boundaries accompanied by destruction and corruption would appear to be a combination of the AIDS and Syphilitic Miasms. Crotallus horridus is the most important of the remedies for this type of condition but there are several other remedies made from toxins that contain this serious destructiveness.

The haemorrhagic fevers are rare in Africa and virtually unknown in the developed world. However, there is a similar condition that is becoming a serious health issue around the world. E. coli 157 is a mutation of a common intestinal bacterium that produces Shiga toxins. In food poisoning caused by E.coli 157 these poisons cause serious damage to the gut resulting in bloody diarrhoea. However, if the toxins enter the bloodstream they cause hemolytic uremic syndrome, which can destroy the blood, nerves and other tissues. HUS causes seizures, nerve damage , kidney failure and anemia. In serious cases, particularly in children, the toxins cause the fatal liquifaction of internal organs, including the brain.

E coli 157 is widely distributed in cattle and other livestock. Modern industrial food processing spreads it widely and antibiotic prophylaxis in farm animals is causing other varieties of bacteria to start producing Shiga toxins. More than 25 people a year die from this disease in the US and this count is likely to rise dramatically.

A Future Miasm?

There is an interesting trio of remedies: Plutonium, Antimatter and the Rat which have some very clear similarities. They have many AIDS Miasm features but they have differences.

They connect very strongly with history while the AIDS Miasm is very in the present. I have a vision of faces and profiles of alternating warriors and peacemakers. Also the face of a Stone Age man. [plut-n][srj7] I have a delusion that I am elbowing my way through an enormous crowd of past generations. [plut-n][srj7] I feel that the proving is dissolving the "Sins of the Fathers". [plut-n][srj7] There are dreams about the neolithic era and about Neanderthal people. It is all about primitive instincts, male aggression and sex. [plut-n][vml3] It has been suggested that at the beginning of time the universe was largely, though momentarily composed of positrons and electrons, of positronium. [positr][nl2] I felt very moved, as if I had been there. A sense of my own history going back over the millennia – all I've seen, lived and witnessed – all my actions – unaware and violent, loving and kind – all these stick to me light a kind of glittering snow – they are enriching and building me. Sculpting me into this moment of present time. So, the feeling of my own ancestry and history linking strongly with my own bloodline and the connection with all those people who have walked this earth. [positr][nl2] I had been talking about what seemed to be the importance of the family to the proving. One of the first lines of the movie was "The family is your own personal antimatter. The place you come from and the place you go to." [positr][nl2]

There is a feeling of great heaviness. Feeling of extreme heaviness. [plut-n][vml3] "Feeling as if having put on 20 kilos over night." [plut-n][vml3] Body seems to be like lead. [plut-n][vml3] Head very heavy, like an enormous weight; difficult to keep head up. [plut-n][vml3] Feels the pull of gravity. [plut-n][vml3] A sense of solidity. [positr][nl2] Woke feeling as if I had been turned to stone. [positr][nl2] Alternation between a crushing state and a state of I don't care. In a tomb, by myself, under a mountain, and I don't care. [positr][nl2] Heavy, enlarged, relaxed, ponderous. Body feels thick and heavy. Liking the way I look; flushed and rosy. [sanguis-s][hrn2] Heavy and ponderous like an old dinosaur missing his mate. [sanguis-s][hrn2] There is a strong and direct connection to evil. Image of falling head first, the fall from grace, Paradise Lost. [plut-n][srj7] I see the dark side of men. [plut-n][srj7] I have the feeling of battling against something evil out there that is actually inside me but not quite part of me. [plut-n][srj7] I'm wholly evil and I don't care. [positr][nl2] Feel I've got the devil inside me. [positr][nl2] This is a little different from the feeling in Anacardium where the subject does care. As Kent points out. His external voluntary will is continuously excited by external influences, but his real will, in which is his conscience, restrains that and keeps him from carrying the impulses into effect. This can only be observed when its action is on a really good man. [anac][k2]

These remedies also interact with the subject's environment, disrupting the physical world, particularly electronics. I keep getting electric shocks from touching metal objects. [plut-n][srj7] Car wouldn't start, had electrical fault which disappeared later. [plut-n][srj7] The burglar alarm went off with a mysterious fault in the middle of the night twice running. [plut-n][srj7] I broke a glass while washing up. I did not hit it on anything, it just seemed to come apart in my hands. [plut-n][srj7] Broken glass is a recurrent theme. Like the breaking of glass in the night of crystals. [plut-n][vml3] I played back the recording, finding that as the tape progressed the images began to break up. As a latter prover delved into her sensations of contraction, as if squeezed into impossible denseness accompanied by a sense of having touched pure evil, the video tape image blanked out entirely. [positr][nl2] Everything going wrong tonight, fuses blowing, things breaking, but I didn't worry about it and it all turned out alright in the end. This continued right through the proving with things, especially electrical and mechanical things, going wrong at an exceptional rate, but I was unfazed by it. [positr][nl2] The computer wouldn't turn on, the printer wouldn't print, and so on. Most amazing of all, when we finally got everything typed and printed, we discovered significant gaps in the typed pages. What was missing? The section of the transcript from beginning to end containing the dreams about the Goddess was simply gone. [sanguis-s][hrn2]

My guess would be that in the coming years there will be the development of first purely verbal computer inputs and then connections to machines and through the machines, between people, that are direct from the brain and not mediated by keyboards or even microphones. These developments are already well under way. This would cause a new miasmatic state and these remedies might be the ones that are called for.

Some of the Remedies of the AIDS Miasm

The remedies that I have used to illustrate the AIDS Miasm are ones which I have observed contain important elements of AIDS as a disease and as a nosode, modern disease, modern issues or modern terminology.

This strategy suffers from the shortcomings of lifting itself up by its own bootstraps, in that the remedies are included because they match the miasmatic picture and the miasmatic picture is mainly defined by the remedies in it.

However, it also illustrates the value and power of pattern thinking. The pattern of the miasm can be developed from the fairly general picture generated by the disease and the contemporary world. As remedies are absorbed into this picture it becomes much clearer and those elements that do not match the pattern become fairly obvious and can be removed. As more remedies are added the picture becomes more refined.

In mentioning the remedies I am merely making suggestions towards compiling the list of AIDS Miasm remedies. I have only looked at a selection of those that might be included. There are now many new provings that have not yet been published or are not easily accessible, and there are many more that are completely unproved or for which there is very little reliable information.

There are many remedies and groups of remedies that I have not included because I don't understand how they fit in. An example of this is the Spider family, which have many features of the Miasm but about which I am not confident, and so have left them out.

This is only a listing of the remedies. I have not tried to interpret or to describe them in any way. Until we as a profession have much more clinical experience the only safe way to study a remedy is to consult the original proving data.

The starting point for investigating a miasm must be by looking at the corresponding nosode. The proving of the AIDS Nosode was conducted by Norland and the School of Homœopathy, and in Holland. It is available from The Schoolof Homœopathy's Website. The methodology of the proving left a lot to be desired and it took a tortuous path to publication through many hands, during which information was lost. However, the picture that has emerged is a very clear one. The nosodes have invariably produced very clear and definite pictures. Even those, like Carcinosin, that have never been satisfactorily proved, have unmistakable pictures and there is no need nor reason to prescribe them on anything but that picture.

The AIDS Miasm represents a response to the higher development of society. In a kabbalistic understanding of the kingdoms of creation this higher level is represented by the human form. The human sarcodes are therefore likely to be important. The two major sarcodes that have been added to the materia medica in recent years also encompass the theme of motherhood which is so important in the miasm. The proving of Placenta humanum was conducted and published by the Welsh School of Homœopathy, and was edited by Biggs and Gwillam.

Lac humanum is a remedy that is central to the Miasm and which has been adopted by many homœopaths as a favoured remedy. Published provings include those by Sankaran, in *Provings*, by Houghton & Halahan, and by Assilem, in *The Madhatter's Tea Party.*

Mammals generally form a major part of the miasmatic group of remedies. As in the human case most modern provers have taken milks as the substances used to represent the animals. Bitch's milk, Lac caninum, cat's milk, Lac felinum, and various cow's milks, Lac vaccinum; flos; coagulatum and defloratum have classical provings and usage. Herrick in *Animal Mind, Human Voices*, includes the provings of the milks of the wolf, Lac lupinum, the lioness, Lac leoninum, the mare, Lac equinum, the dolphin, Lac delphinum and the elephant, Lac loxdonta africanus. Sankaran in *Provings* has another proving of lioness's milk and one of goat's milk, Lac caprinum.

Traditionally mammals were more often represented by sarcodes other than milk and especially by secretions from anal and preputial glands. Thus the musk deer, Moschus, the beaver, Castoreum canadensis, the skunk, Mephitis putorius, and the sperm whale, Ambra grisea, all have a considerable history of homœopathic usage.

Of the recent proving only that of the koala bear, Phascolarctus cinereus, by Robbins follows this pattern.

The proving of rat, Sanguis soricis, in Herrick's *Animal Mind, Human Voices,* used the blood of the animal as milk was not obtainable. Some of the bird remedies also used the blood and the AIDS nosode was made from a blood sample.

The other particularly developed form of life is the bird. As birds are creatures of the Air and live their lives unbound by the restrictions of the Earth, they have a particularly strong connection to the AIDS Miasm. Additional to the themes of floating and flying and observing from above, the birds generally have issues around spirituality (rather than religion), vulnerability, appetite and responsibility. Shore has done a lot of work on the bird remedies and has conducted provings on the dove, Columba palumbus, the macaw, Ara macao, and the hawk, Buteo jamaicensis. Unfortunately little of this information has been published but quite a bit of it has come out in his seminars.

Norland has conducted an extensive proving of a trained peregrine falcon, Falco peregrinus disciplinatus, which is available from the School of Homœopathy's website. Sherr's proving of the bald eagle, Haliaeetus leucocephalus, is included in *Dynamic Provings, vol 1*. Bedayn has conducted a thorough proving of the American raven, Corvus corax. Rowe has conducted and published a proving of the turkey vulture, Cathartes aura, and Fink has done likewise with the seagull, Larus argentatus. There have been two recent provings of swans: Cygnus cygnus by Sherr and Cygnus bewickii by Stirling.

Another important group of remedies are the drugs. Substance abuse has become a major issue in the modern world. It is so important and has become such an intractable problem precisely because it so closely meets the overpowering needs of so many individuals. The themes of isolation and disconnection, and particularly of disconnecting from the pain of modern existence, are found throughout the drug remedies, as are feelings around the need for spiritual meaning. The most important of all the drug remedies has always been Opium, but it is its more powerful derivatives, Morphine and especially heroin, Diamorphine, that come even closer to capturing the spirit of the AIDS Miasm. Snowdon has conducted a proving of heroin which is available from the School of Homœopathy website.

The other traditional drug remedies: marijuana, Cannabis Indica, mescaline, Anhalonium lewinii, Coca, kava kava, Piper methysticum, are all well documented as are fly agaric, Agaricus muscarius, and nutmeg, Nux moschata, which have powerful drug effects. Coca cola, which is included in Sankaran's *Provings*, has some relationship to cocaine and can be looked at in that context.

Among the most important of the modern drug remedies are acid, LSD-25, proved by Norland (on The School of Homœopathy website), and ecstasy, MDMA, proved by Hammond and by the Travelling Homœopaths Collective. For many of the drug remedies there is extensive literature that details the experience of taking drugs, which form a valuable group of provings. Saunders' *E is for*

Ecstasy, is an example of a non homœopathic book that is a good proving text. Much of this drug related information is available on the internet.

Another very important modern remedy that should be grouped with the drugs is Chocolatum. It was proved by Sherr's Dynamis School and has been published.

The importance of the air and the unbound gaseous state to the Miasm is reflected not only in the bird remedies, but also in the importance of gases. Sherr has proved and published Hydrogen, the simplest not only of the gases but of all substances. He has also proved most of the Noble Gases, which are important for their nobility as well as for their gaseous state, though only Neon, which is in *Dynamic Provings vol 1*, has so far been published. Oxygen has some traditional usage, but it is the triple molecule Ozone with its connections to barriers and ecology that more closely ties into the Miasm. It is available in a published proving by Schadde. Carbon dioxide has been proved by Klein, and the proving is available on the Homœopathic Master Clinician website.

Just as the birds represent the air in the Miasm, the sea creatures, and particularly the more evolved forms, represent water in the Miasm. The sea mammals, the dolphin and the sperm whale, have already been mentioned. The fish remedies have been grossly under represented in the materia medica, only cod liver oil, Oleum jecoris aselli, having much information. The cod itself, Gadus morrhua, the weever fish, Trachinus draco, and the red mullet, Erythrinus, are also mentioned. The provings of stingray, Urolophus halleri, by Rowe and of tiger shark liver, Galeocerdo cuvier hepar, by Grimes have been published. There is also an unpublished proving of the salmon, Oncorynchus tsawytscha, by Sherr.

Reptiles also seem to be important but are underrepresented. The green lizard, Lacerta agilis, the gila monster, Heloderma horridum, and Amphisbaena vermicularis, are the classical reptile remedies. Rowe has added Heloderma suspectum and Norland has proved Amphisbaena alba. The proving of dinosaur fossil, Maiasaura lapidea, by Herrick is included in *Animal Mind, Human Voice*.

The insects form an interesting group of remedies. Many of the well known one's such as the wasp and the bee seem to bear little relationship to the Miasm, though bee glue, Propolis, does seem to be more closely connected. Like the birds, the butterflies and moths are creatures of the air with a special relationship to the soul. One species, Lepidoptera saturniidae, has been proved by Rossetti, while another, Limentitis bredowii californica, is included in Herrick's

Animal Mind, Human Voice.

The scorpion, Androctanus amoureuxii hebraeus, is one of the most extreme of all the remedies, and it has a powerful correspondence to the isolating elements of the Miasm. Sherr published the proving and included a revised edition in *Dynamic Provings vol 1.*

The house fly, Musca domestica, combines elements of air and flying with the theme of dirt and disgust, which came out in the proving by Stewart & Sonz. Many other insects have similar themes. Klein has proved the earthworm, Helodrilus caliginosus, and the result is available on the internet. The leech, Hirudo medicinalis, has some information, though the cockroach, Blatta orientalis, has not yet had a proper proving.

There are a number of mineral remedies that have features of the AIDS Miasm. They tend to be found in groups scattered around the periodic table. The most important group are found around the border between the metals and the non metals. Germanium metallicum is the remedy that seems to have the strongest correlation both to HIV/AIDS and to the AIDS Miasm. It is the remedy that comes closest to being a specific for HIV. It is also the remedy that I tend to use when presented with a case that is definitely AIDS Miasm, but which has no characteristic symptoms that might point to a particular remedy. The remedy was well proved by Sherr and is included in *Dynamic Provings vol 1.* My only quibble would be that as we tend to use the oxides of its neighbours in the periodic table (arsenic and silica), it might be a good idea to use the more toxic germanium dioxide.

The other minerals in this part of the table that have AIDS Miasm features are the very well know remedies Arsenicum album and Phosphorous, and the less well know but classically proved Tellurium and Selenium.

The other important area of the table is that containing the noble metals, that is the part of the Gold series leading up to Platinum. Platina, Platinum metallicum, is a well proved remedy. Osmium metallicum is less well known but also has classical provings. Iridium metallicum, which lies between them has been proved by Sherr and is included in *Dynamic Provings, vol 1.* Tungsten, Wolfram, is also in this group and it had a proving by the North West College of Homœopathy which has been published by Bond.

Diamond, Adamas, is a particular form of carbon and its hardness, value and sparkle indicate its affinity for the AIDS Miasm remedy. It was proved by Sherr and is included in *Dynamic Provings, vol 1.*

Plutonium, Plutonium nitricum, was proved by Sherr and is

published in a separate edition. It has many AIDS Miasm features, but there is something more to it, and I suspect that it addresses something that is yet to be fully manifest in the world. This probably also applies to other radioactive minerals.

The Vegetable Kingdom is simply so vast that categorising and understanding the relationships within it is a mammoth task. Although Clarke made some tentative steps in this direction more than a century ago, it has only been in the last few years that Scholten, Sankaran and their colleagues have started to make significant progress with it.

The two families of plants that seem to have clear connections as a whole to the Miasm are the cactaceæ and the anacardiaceæ.

The established cactaceæ remedies include the major drug remedy anhalonium, and Cactus grandiflorus, Cereus bonplandii, Cereus serpentinus, and the prickly pear, Opuntia vulgaris. The major addition to this group in recent years is the saguaro cactus, Carnegia gigantea, which has been proved by Rowe.

The anacardiaceæ include a wide range of plants from the poison ivy to the pistachio, cashew and mango. The family also includes plants that are important in the commercial production of varnishes and lacquers. There are a number of species of rhus, but especially Rhus toxicodendron, that have a long history of homœopathic usage. They show many features of the AIDS Miasm, but this was more clearly revealed in the proving of Rhus glabra by Tumminello. Anacardium orientale, is a very well known remedy and many of its symptoms are clearly of the Miasm. Comocladia dentata has substantial information but not a very clear mental picture. There are many remedies in the family that might be very useful if they were properly proved. These include: the cashew, Anacardium occidentale, the mango, Mangifera indica, the pepper tree, Schinus molle, the pistachio, Pistacia vera, and many others.

Another part of the vegetable kingdom that appears to be important in the Miasm is the group of trees. This is difficult to quantify as this is not a family type grouping, trees are represented in many plant families and most of these families include a range from small plants to large trees. Many of the trees do not have substantial provings, or are not much used, but do have indications for usage in the AIDS Miasm. These include: the prickly ash, Xantoxylum fraxineum, the mountain ash, Pyrus americana, and the wafer ash, Ptelea trifoliata. Some of the trees do seem to have strong AIDS Miasm. The oak, Quercus robur, is undoubtedly important but it has resisted attempts to find a substantial picture. Oak galls, Galla quercina ruber, were proved by Norland but appear to be as much to do with the insect than the tree. The walnut, Juglans regia, has some information, as does the yew, Taxus baccata, another species, Taxus breviolia, was proved by Olsen and is in *Trees and Plants that Heal*.

The giant trees: the redwood, Sequioa sempivirens, and the kauri, Agathis australis, which was proved by Norland, have strong Miasm features. As does also the ancient and venerable Gingko biloba, which might be even more important in a Alzheimer's/CJD Miasm.

Stirling's proving of crack willow, Salix fragilis, showed it to have AIDS Miasm features; though, like many of the trees it is also a very sycotic remedy. Sherr is publishing a book of tree remedy provings in the near future and this should substantially increase our knowledge in the area.

Another tree remedy is Snowdon's Dreaming Potency, though the exact species has not been ascertained, the remedy has shown itself to be a powerful one in the treatment of HIV as well as of the AIDS Miasm.

There are several other plants that have come to my attention as being part of the group of AIDS Miasm remedies, but they must be only a tiny part of the whole. Vetiver, Anantherum muricatum, is a very important HIV remedy, especially as it is often expressed in the Western gay community. The chaste tree, Agnus castus, is another plant in which sexuality links it closely to the Miasm. Other interesting plant remedies are Curare; mistletoe, Viscum album; coriander, Coriandrum sativum; the various species of bindweeds and morning glory, Convolvulus arvenis, stans, duartinus, Ipomoea purpurea, Jalapa; and angastura bitters, Angastura vera.

There are a number of modern remedies that are to do with barriers and are important. The Berlin Wall has received sustained mockery and much opprobrium has attached to it, but as a remedy it is an important expression of a great deal of contemporary angst. Perhaps it would make more sense to look at it as the remedy concrete, the sample having been taken from an extreme expression of the substance. In the same way for the proving of rubber, Latex, Norland and Fraser used a sample of condom as it seemed to best express the nature of the substance, and connected it more directly to modern issues and to the AIDS Miasm. The proving of Polystyrenum, which is in Sankaran's *Provings*, is another example of these modern barriers.

Finally there are a number of imponderabilia that have been proved. This is not a new phenomenon in homœopathy, Hahnemann included magnetism remedies in *Materia Medica Pura*, and defended there the concept of imponderable remedies. However, centuries later they still attract criticism from those that Hahnemann called atomists.

Eising has proved and published both fire, Ignis alcoholis, and the very absence of substance, Vacuum, both of which have shown themselves to be very good AIDS Miasm remedies. Norland took this to a further extreme, proving the annihilation radiation of antimatter, Positronium. This like the other extreme of plutonium, has AIDS Miasm features, but seems also to describe something that is only starting to appear in our world. Mobile Phone Radiation, is another modern imponderable that must be important in the Miasm. It was proved by the South Downs School of Homœopathy and is available on the internet.

This is only a tiny selection of the remedies which must be useful in treating AIDS Miasm cases, and it represents a jumping off point to discover many more, and to find out more about all of them through careful clinical use.

A great number of these provings are now included in the Materia Medica software programs, especially Radar's *Encyclopedia Homeopathica*, MacRepertory's *Reference Works* and Cara's *Similia*.

Information on new provings is available on a database that is compiled by Sherr's Dynamis School website (www.dynamis.edu).

Many provings are now published on the internet including those coming out of The School of Homœopathy, The South Downs School of Homœopathy and The Homœopathic Master Clinician Course. These and many others are indexed and linked on the excellent Homœopathy Home Website (www.homeopathyhome.com) which is the best place to start for any homœopathic exploration on the internet.

Quite a few provings are published individually or in batches and are available from good homœopathic bookshops and pharmacies. Most of the many journals of homœopathy regularly carry outlines or even detailed articles on new provings.

The best source for the provings of the classical remedies is TF Allen's *Encyclopedia of Pure Materia Medica*.

Summation

The coming of a new and deeper miasm has, as have all things, both positive and negative implications. Disease is undoubtedly deeper and is more serious, and is also more difficult to treat and to cure. However, the potential for more serious disease arises from a much greater potential in everything that we do. Much of the enormous ill that we see in the world appears to be more terrible than it has been in the past, but this perception comes partly from a very recent feeling that suffering and ignorance are unacceptable. The rights and respect that were once only accorded to rich and powerful men are becoming the rights of every man, of women and of children, and that they might also belong to other creatures is now seriously considered. We are no longer in a position to disregard the welfare of others. In the Global Village every man, woman, child and sentient being is our immediate neighbour. The potential for disease is matched by a potential for creativity, knowledge and understanding that is unequalled in history. The potential for disaster is great, but the potential to move to a new level of spiritual and material enlightenment is even greater. The chaotic nature of the Electronic Age means that progress is non sequential and unpredictable, but it also means that the possibility for a quantum leap in who and what we are is there.

Undoubtedly the lack of a spiritual dimension in the modern world is cause for great concern and likely to lead to a future that is more likely to be negative than positive. However, this has arisen from the complete unsuitability to our age of both the Feudal form of religion, exemplified by Catholicism, or the Industrial form that Protestantism represents. There is no reason to believe that the Electronic Age will not generate a form of spirituality suited to it, and if it does that religion will be universal and will spread completely and instantaneously.

The potential for us as homœopaths in the Electronic Age is unimaginable. We are one of the few disciplines that has studied and begun to master the concept of pattern thinking. It is something that is intrinsic to the nature of homœopathy and to a few esoteric areas of mathematics and physics. No other significant group of thinkers has developed access to this invaluable tool, let alone to two hundred years of experience, study and exposition.

The irony is that just when homœopathy is coming into its own as a philosophy and way of thought, as well as a practical medical methodology, there are tremendous pressures to abandon what is most valuable in homœopathy. There are attempts to define homœopathy within the scientific, reductionist model; to find the reasonable, cause and effect explanation for what we do. There are attempts to systematize homœopathy; to find an objective and object oriented approach that explains and describes what we do. There are also attempts to bring our practice within the structures of the professionalism of the passing Industrial World.

It is not easy to be prophetic, to be ahead of your time. However, Hahnemann managed to understand our world two hundred years ago, and Kent did the same one hundred years ago; it should be possible for us to maintain our principles and integrity as the world finally catches up.

Part II

A Picture of the AIDS Miasm

Introduction

The modern world has created many new and different pressures on the personal economy of mankind, and these pressures have been answered by a variety of previously unknown diseases or new variations on old diseases. The homœopathic community has recently proved a large number of new remedies that have many symptoms that match the new diseases, and which also help us to better understand these symptoms in old remedies. Jan Scholten says: "An unknown disease picture requires an unknown remedy." In the same way a new disease may require a new remedy.

In his picture of Anhalonium, Vithoulkas describes one important part of the contemporary state: Anhalonium activates specific areas of the brain which seem to be concerned with the higher and highest functions of this organ; it appears to affect what could be called the spiritual aspect, or, even better, the transcendental aspect of our existence. I believe that these functions, or rather, this capacity of the brain to apprehend new dimensions in understanding and achieving higher consciousness are going to come into play increasingly in modern times, either through natural means, such as spiritual practices, or artificially through the action of powerful hallucinogenic drugs, such as Anhalonium. As members of this generation, and probably future generations, intensively pursue spiritual goals through consciousness-raising activities or the use of drugs, the sheer intensity of their focus and exertions in this regard, the impact of such fervent auto-stimulation will cause an unhealthy central nervous system reaction in more and more individuals. The drug culture, the sexual liberation movement, the decline in moral values, and the establishment of new codes of "ethics" propelled by greed and self-interest will put their seal on the diseases of the future. The tremendous increases in cancer, in mental diseases and AIDS are some of the warning signs of the wrongdoing not only of a few persons, but of an entire generation. This drug produces mental conditions that simulate what could be called false "spiritual" or "transcendental" or "mystic" states. Sometimes when dealing with the sick, you will be perplexed as to what is happening in Anhalonium cases. Is it a real spiritual experience the individual is going through, part of his spiritual evolution, or is it dangerous pathology which must be counteracted immediately? [anh][vh1]

Although Vithoulkas has a deep antipathy to much of what is happening in the development of new remedies; it is undoubtedly true that many of them offer positive treatments for the state he describes.

It is by no means necessary to identify the particularly contemporary aspects of disease with AIDS, or indeed with any miasm. This work can be used as a straightforward study of those unusual symptoms that are common in the world and diseases of the last 30 or 40 years. I have chosen to identify this particular overall picture with what I call the AIDS Miasm. As already outlined, AIDS fulfills the qualities of a miasmatic disease in a way that nothing else has since Syphilis in the final years of the Fifteenth Century.

The following list of observations about AIDS patients, taken from the proving of the AIDS Nosode, clearly reflects many of the general issues of contemporary disease and society and many of the important themes of recent provings.

- Patients often surrender to standard medical interventions or develop monomaniacal approaches to learning all about the disease (and then refuse treatment).
- Patients may feel that the health care giver is a partner – they must explain every move to the satisfaction of the patient or they will be dismissed.
- Fear of exposure and feeling unacceptable.
- A feeling of peace and calm, surrender to a higher power. (This is in contrast to the state of mind present when contracting the illness).
- Because the illness is almost always kept secret until some great force precipitates its revelation, the patient seemingly has within himself a very low self-esteem, oftentimes masked with a sometimes thick veneer of bravado and self-importance. Once 'out', a great relief is felt and another stage is set. This stage can then be a breakthrough into acceptance and forgiveness – also by loved ones and family.
- The worst aspect is that what they do touches on three fundamental taboos: sex, shit and homosexuality.
- Self destructive state, exemplified by numerous sexual partners, sexually transmitted diseases, recreational drugs and prescribed drugs for venereal and linked diseases, i.e. antibiotics, sulphanilamides, steroids and antifungals. [aids][nl2]

It is important to note that the Myth or Metaphor of AIDS that developed very quickly in the early 1980s, and which still permeates much of the discussion and understanding or misunderstanding of the disease, is only loosely connected to actuality of the disease today. Even the virulent disease that affected mostly gay men in the early days differed from the myth. The heterosexual disease that has devastated the populations of many African countries, and which shows no sign of lessening, is strongly related to poverty and a lack of resources. HIV positive status, at least in the developing world, is now a long term, often asymptomatic condition. Suppression with enormously powerful drugs has pushed the state into a much less violent but also less defined picture. The *genus* or spirit of the disease is, however, already defined. It is not out of a lack of thought or consideration that the Nosode and now the Miasm are referred to as AIDS, a term that is regarded as no longer accurate or suitable by most people working in the field of HIV.

Many of the remedies described here have also been used with some success in treating HIV+ patients. This applies both to older remedies such as Arsenicum and Phosphorous and to lesser known and new remedies. The picture of Agnus in its end pathology looks similar to the picture of AIDS, but to justify the prescription of this remedy, the peculiarities attributed to it should be present. [agn][vh1] The pathology of Anantherum reflects the effects of primary syphilis as well – chancre-like ulcers of the penis, sores and glandular swellings. Abcesses and Kaposi's sarcomata are met with this remedy as well, and it is a remedy which should be considered in AIDS patients when they exhibit behavior such as that described above. [anan][vh1] Germanium is an immune modulator and enhancer and has attributes of oxygen enrichment and antioxidant properties. It has been used to empower the immune system, and consequently to battle immune-type diseases such as cancer, AIDS, rheumatoid arthritis, and lupus erythematosa. [germ-met][srj5]

The HIV mechanism of T-cell destruction is also relevant to some of the remedies. Studies have shown that swimming with dolphins increases both the production of infection-fighting T cells as well as endorphins. [lac-del][hrn2]

AIDS is also an important icon in modern society and appeared in some remedies, particularly the Nosode itself and in Iridium. Dreamt that a friend told me a mutual ex-boyfriend had all along been having sex and therefore (sic) we were both at risk from HIV and AIDS. [aids][nl2] Dream: My child had AIDS. Met man in front of a marquee who was losing his hair and teeth although he was quite young. He was trying to talk about AIDS to me. I was thinking I knew I would outlive my child. [irid-met][srj5]

There are many valid ways of looking at miasms. This is one, and one that I have found useful, however, it does not deny the validity of others. In terms of pattern thinking there is a need to study as many different patterns as possible to clarify the overall, unseeable pattern.

Choosing the Remedies

The remedies and symptoms that are detailed here are those that I feel are part of an answer to contemporary disease states. They are often new remedies proven in the last decade. The reason for this is twofold. Good proving supervisors have chosen remedies that they have reason to believe might meet the needs of contemporary disease. At the same time contemporary provers are likely to be much more susceptible to aspects of the Contemporary Miasm, and so to bring these parts of the remedy out most strongly.

They may be remedies in which the issues of the past 40 years, such as communication, feminization and ecology are important. They may be members of groups that are in themselves relevant, these include the milks and animals, the birds and the drugs.

They may be remedies that are called for in diseases that have become important in recent years. These diseases include the obvious ones such as AIDS, CJD and Alzheimer's; but also less easily defined ones that have become more common especially among children: ADHD, chronic fatigue, dyslexia and autism.

The choice of symptoms and remedies cannot be based on rigid criteria, and so it to some degree a personal one, which means that it is liable to error. This work can only be a preliminary proposal, one that needs to be confirmed, challenged and amplified through further provings and the clinical experience of many homœopaths. One of the strengths of homœopathy is the value it places on tradition. Hahnemann's work of 200 years ago is still of great value to us today. However, the way that that tradition is passed from one generation to another, particularly through interpretive Materia Medica, can institutionalize error. If one author includes a mistake or a misinterpretation there is a serious risk that others will quote him, and the error will be repeated until it becomes accepted fact. It is partly for this reason that I have used original proving data whenever possible. It is also because of this danger that I have been cautious and not included some remedies which probably belong here.

The AIDS nosode is associated in a homœopath's mind with boundary issues. Keeping what is in, in; what is out, out. In health the vital force through the medium of the defence system reacts homeostatically to morbific influences, throwing them off. Keeping what is out, out. Acute manifestation are of this kind, such as fevers, discharges, diarrhoea, pus, and on an emotional level, such as shouting, hitting, moaning, tears. [aids][nl2]

The overriding pattern in the AIDS Nosode and in the AIDS

Miasm, as it is in the contemporary world, is the dissolution of boundaries and the stresses that are caused by that dissolution.

Boundaries are important to us and there has always been much stability to be gained from their permanence. When the Romans rebuilt the Capitol all the Gods acquiesced in the movement of their temples to make way for the new temple of great Jupiter. Only Terminus, the God of Boundaries, refused and his temple became part of the new one, which the mightiest of the gods was forced to share with him. No man would therefore challenge a legitimate boundary lest he seem to value himself above Jupiter. If Terminus, whose power out ranked even Jupiter, has been vanquished by the speed and pervasive power of electronics, it is not surprising that his fall has major ramifications for us. Many of the remedies looked at here are directly connected to boundaries. The most obvious example is Berlin Wall, which is made from a powerful physical and symbolic boundary which collapsed as a symbol and was then torn down.

Anacardium is made from the trituration of the layer of the nut between the shell and the kernel. [anac][a1] and Nux moschata often includes the membrane mace. (It would be well to make a tincture of the nut with the Mace, as some symptoms of Mace are included.) [nux-m][c1]

Many of the mineral remedies, especially Germanium and Arsenicum come from the area of the Perodic Table that lies around the boundary between metals and non metals. Others are among the Noble Gases which mark the boundary between one row and the next.

Propolis is used by bees to create a boundary between themselves and various dangers. The word 'propolis' stems from the Greek 'pro,' 'to protect,' and 'polis,' 'stronghold or community': to protect the community. Thanks to propolis, bee populations have been able to protect themselves against infection for millions of years. [propl][vml3]

A strong feature of trees is the boundary between inner and outer that is formed by their bark. This is particularly notable in Sequoia. They have such a thick bark (30 centimetres in large trees) that they are protected from forest fires. [seq-s][vml3]

There are also symbolic associations for many remedies. Not only do scorpions, like trees, have a strong outer barrier in their exoskeleton but they were probably the first animals to leave the sea and live on land. [androc][srj5] So crossing an important evolutionary boundary.

Many birds, especially those at the top of the food chain such as falcons and eagles, have come close to extinction through the weakening of their shells. DDE, a product of DDT breakdown, accumulated in the falcons and interfered with an enzyme that is important in the production of egg shells. The shells became so thin that they often broke under the weight of the brooding mother. [falco-pe][nl2] This effect was one of the wake up calls for the ecological movement.

Polystyrene is used both as a container and as an insulating material, the two roles being combined in the coffee cup which contains the coffee and prevents the heat from being lost or from burning the hand. The remedy is important for this insulating quality that puts a boundary between the patient and the horrors, or indeed the banalities, of the world we live in. Sankaran has said that he chose polystyrene as it was the most ubiquitous of plastics and he originally called the remedy Plasticum.

Latex (rubber) is one of the substances that is most often used to create a barrier between the individual and the world. This can be in the form of rubber tyres and buffers, that smooth out the roughness of the world so that it does not disturb us. Latex is particularly used as a barrier between the individual and a world that is dirty and infectious. Latex becomes a substitute for first the skin and then the immune system, which is destroyed by HIV infection, in preventing infectious agents for penetrating the person and causing infection. This aspect of rubber reaches its apotheosis in the condom (the source of the latex used to make the remedy), where it acts as a barrier against infection. It also acts to deny the natural urge to procreation, and like the contraceptive pill it liberates couples, but particularly women, from the restrictions of fertility and causes problems in the suppression of creativity and fecundity. In this situation it also acts as a barrier between people, separating and isolating at the point when connection should be strongest. Latex, particularly in the condom, embodies the contradiction between a barrier that must be strong and effective, but which ideally should be invisible and unfelt. This echoes the conflict in the Miasm, where unfettered connection and communication are the ideal, but the overwhelming feeling is of isolation and detachment. Rubber also has a powerful desensitizing effect, its use effectively numbs the most sensitive parts of the body, the fingers and the sexual organs, which echoes the overall numbing effect of modern technology. The condom has become a major icon of the world of HIV/AIDS. Over the last twenty-five years the old image of a symbol of immorality has been uncomfortably enfolded within a new image of safety and responsibility. Any connection between people that is not mediated by an artificial barrier is now considered innately "unsafe". The rapid growth of latex sensitivity and allergy shows just how toxic the substance is becoming. There are also interesting correspondences to other AIDS Miasm remedies. Other remedies made from plant latexes, including Opium and Hura, are important remedies of the Miasm. The word latex is cognate with Lac and there are connections between the two forms of milky secretion.

Ozone is another remedy that is intimately connected to barriers and boundaries. The ozone layer is a boundary between us and the dangers of spaces, and it is a boundary that is being breached and in danger of dissolving. At the same time Ozone is a dangerous pollutant and one that pays no respect to our boundaries. Ozone always attacks directly; even in the lungs there is no barrier to stop its penetration. [ozone][sde2]

Iridium is a remedy with a strong relationship to boundaries. It is an important component in precision tools required to do fine, precise and detailed work – surgical pins, aircraft spark plugs, pen-nibs and compass bearings. This is because of its resistance, hardness and capacity to maintain its relatively impervious boundaries. [irid-met][srj5] Even its presence on Earth is connected to a boundary. There is a theory that much Iridium may have arrived with a meteorite that collided with the earth at Mexico's Yucatan peninsula. This is the meteorite associated with the death of the dinosaurs. The collision vaporized most of the meteorite, causing a vast dust and vapor cloud, which eventually settled, depositing Iridium-rich sediments around the world in a layer that is called the KT boundary. [irid-met][srj5] It is also symbolically related to the rainbow, which in many mythologies is a bridge or messenger between Heaven and Earth.

Many of the remedies have issues relating to the breaching of boundaries. In Kauri there is the signature of the unhealing wound: the resinous gum which oozes (in the case of old wounds, for hundreds, even thousands of years) from damaged branches forming stalactites aloft and corresponding stalagmites upon the tree's mighty roots and the forest floor below. [agath-a][nl2] Mistletoe and Placenta also have pictures that includes the unhealing wound. Wounds slow to heal. [plac][Biggs+] Blood would not clot and wounds would not heal. [visc][ptk2]

A great number of the remedies are haemorrhagic. I had a nosebleed for the first time in my life. There was no reason that I was aware of at all. Bright red blood was pouring from my left nostril at 10:20 a.m. [maias-l][hrn2] Bleeds easily from all the orifices. [hir][jl1] Externally a gall ointment has been used to treat painful haemorrhoids and to arrest haemorrhage from the nose and gums. [galla-q-r][nl2] Sensation as if bleeding from vagina, nose and inner ear. [plut-n][srj7] Jug. r. is haemorrhagic. [jug-r][c1] Phosphorus seems to affect the blood, how is not exactly known. It decomposes the blood, rendering it more fluid, rendering it difficult to coagulate. [phos][fr1]

Many provers in describing their symptoms spoke in terms of boundaries. I feel an expansion of my boundaries; my mind feels expanded and taking on more work. [adam][srj5] A woman got into the bed with me and took up room. I felt crowded upon, and later on in the dream told a friend that the proving had something to do with boundaries. [coca-c][sk4] Feeling of great release – catharsis – my whole time scale has changed since taking the remedy. Even my work on Homœopathy has opened up – boundaries have disappeared. [hydrog][srj2]

An Outline of the Picture

There are a thousand ways of telling any story and each of them can be perfectly valid. I have chosen a particular story to use as the framework for discussing contemporary disease and the new remedies. It is a coherent story and one that has been of use to me in arranging themes and symptoms. However, it is just one of many possibilities. It goes something like this:

The primary effect of the dissolution of boundaries is that **connection** can be made without obstruction or interference.

However, without defining boundaries for ourselves and others we have no regulated way of interacting and become lost in an infinite space. Connection becomes **disconnection** and isolation. Without connection there is no reason to care and this leads to a feeling of **indifference**.

Without boundaries there is nothing to contain and define. This results in **dispersion,** and an emphasis on the elements of air and water which are those that will disperse if not contained.

Instability, a tendency to got to **extremes** and **confusion** are all consequences of dispersion, and of a world in which there are no boundaries.

Air and water are feminine elements and there is a tendency towards passivity and **feminization** to be seen in society and in symptoms.

One of the functions of boundaries is to act as a protective shell. The removal of that protective shell leads to a sense of **vulnerability**.

A sensitivity to **infection** and a **lack of confidence**, or even a sense of shame and self hatred, are natural consequences of feeling vulnerable and unprotected.

Finally issues around **boundaries** and the **portals** that penetrate them are of great importance.

There will always be issues and images that overlap. An example of this is the image of the child and childhood. The innocence and wonder of childhood are one manifestation of a sense of divine connection. The lack of knowledge and experience of children leads to confusion and a lack of stability that can be described as childishness. The child is a natural corollary of maternity which is in itself an important aspect of femininity. Children also epitomize the concepts of vulnerability and of lack of confidence. The image of the child is therefore common in almost every part of the story and any particular manifestation of the child or childishness is likely to carry several references.

To find a way of arranging things perfectly will never be feasible, however, too much repetition becomes confusing. I have therefore numbered each section and used cross reference to indicate how they might be linked.

The full arrangement of symptoms I have used is as follows:

Connection

Divine Connection; Grounding; Communication; Empathy & Clairvoyance; Clarity; Nature; Youth, Beauty, Peace & Love; Benevolence.

Disconnection

Not Belonging; In a Dream; Detachment; The Observer; Drugs; The Past; Isolation; Need To Be Alone.

Indifference

Apathy; Anaesthesia; Lack of Emotion; Selfishness; Cruelty; Despair.

Dispersion

Air & Water; Water; Waves, Circles & Cycles; Thirst & Dryness; Clouds, Balloons & Bubbles; Emptiness & Lack of Substance; Floating & Flying; Music; Space; Travel; Speed & Rushing

Instability

Oversensitivity; Childishness; Splitting; Chaos & Order; Structure.

Extremes

Tallness; Noblity; Strength & Hardness; Excess; Materialism; Appetite.

Confusion

Confusion of the Senses; Vanishing of Thoughts; Forgetfulness; Confusion of Identity; Transgenic Confusion; Confusion about Time; Confusion about Position; Confusion about Words.

Feminization

Left Sidedness; Motherhood & Pregnancy; Gender Confusion; Sexuality.

Vulnerability

Babies, Children & Animals; Danger & Violence; Rape, Child Abuse & Incest; Anxiety, Fear & Paranoia; Privacy & Secrecy; Trapped.

Infection

Flu & Non Specific Infections; Dirt; Shit & Toilets; Insects, Worms & Vermin.

Lack of Confidence

Old, Ugly & Fat; Shame & Humiliation; Self Hatred & Self Harm.

Boundaries & Obstruction

Obstruction of the Senses; Houses; Skin; Touch; Portals; Mouth, Anus & Vagina; Death.

I-1 Connection

The first and most obvious effect of the removal of boundaries is a sense of connection to everything and everyone. As with so many features of contemporary diseases, this is clearly expressed in the AIDS Nosode. A feeling of oneness with my fellow man and the whole of the universe. [aids][nl2]

It is similarly expressed in several other remedies. Harmony above and below. Outer and inner space. Oceans and skies. [adam][srj5] Felt really loving, on an almost global level. I have a feeling of heightened compassion and love in the world. I am receiving many compliments. I have smooth interactions with people that I usually "bump" into. [limen-b-c][hrn2] On receiving photos of a newborn niece, I had tears of joy to be a part of such an amazing family. The feeling of family went beyond my family to include the entire human race. My heart was overflowing with pure joy to be part of something so overwhelmingly beautiful. I felt so much emotion. My heart felt totally open. [neon][srj5] The feeling of absolute connectedness into oneness. [buteo-j][sej6] Felt a deeper sense of connection. [ara-mac][sej7] I feel my spiritual and physical being connected more. [rhus-g][tmo3] I awake consciously from a dream-space. I feel a connection to the universe and to eternity by living in this space. I feel that I want to care and look for this space again. [lars-arg][fkw1] Even Germanium, a remedy of disconnection, has this feeling. The last days I have had moments when I have felt I have been united to the world and people – to humanity. [germ-met][srj5]

This connection leads to an awareness and appreciation of that which is around us. More aware of people and environment. [helo-s][rwt2] On a high. Appreciate colours, the beauty of the surroundings, like I haven't since a child. [tung-met][bdx1] *(See I-6 Clarity)*

The lack of boundaries can mean that the subject and the environment become one. This is most noticeable in the powerful hallucinogens such as Mescaline and LSD. Identification of self with environment. [anh][sp1] I felt as if the universe had been passed into the neurons of my brain and engraved in my genetics. Preconscious cellular processes were now understood to me. [lsd][nl-lsd]

The seeing of the universe from within gives a sense of understanding, especially concerning space and time. This sensation was particularly strong in Eagle and in Diamond. Feel that I don't need a map to go anywhere, as if I know all routes from inside me. [adam][srj5] I know the time exactly without looking at the clock. I know my position in time and space. [haliae-lc][srj5] This view can also increase awareness of detail and individuality. Whilst looking at things, I can see the individuality in everything. [lsd][nl-lsd]

In Chocolate, which has major issues around truth, there is a tendency to express this feeling. I felt that I was making exceptionally profound statements about life. [choc][srj3]

Such a sense of connection is generally a positive thing and as homœopaths we are looking for those things that are poisonous and cause a morbid alteration in the state of health. A statement such as Feeling a sense of wealth of prosperity of a beneficent universe. [adam][srj5] is not obviously indicative of pathology. However, the feeling of connection is often linked to a sense of unease. On a high, synchronistic. Almost too overwhelming. I'm one with the universe. [haliae-lc][srj5] I feel whole and connected to everything, yet at the same time I feel I unreal, my boundaries don't feel the same. [irid-met][srj5]

The feeling can also be a false one, or more properly a superficial one. This can be seen in Coca Cola one of whose most successful advertising campaigns used a song whose most memorable line ran, "I'd like to teach the world to sing in perfect harmony". At the same time the corporation has been a leader in the multinational efforts to establish a worldwide hegemony. This feeling was echoed in the blissful proving statement: Feel my heart open to encompass all of humanity. [coca-c][sk4] However, the proving also brought out the deeper and perhaps more insightful: Expressed surprise that a colleague drank Pepsi-Cola, and then said, with a kind of serious and sleepy dismay, that Coca-Cola was what was wrong with the whole world, and that we had exported it all over the world. Then paused and asked my colleague if she understood this symbolic, rather drastic statement. [coca-c][sk4]

The idea of connection and particularly of merging into oneness, which are found strongly in Hydrogen and the Noble Gases, easily become a striving for an impossible goal and the ever thwarted desire becomes clearly pathological. The theme of Hydrogen is a desire to be one, to let all the loose parts come together into one large whole. In the 'alternative world' this is often described as 'holistic' thinking. In the scientific world we recognise this theme in the desire to bring all theories under one common law. In religion it is the one God. Forever, totally, completely, they are concepts that relate to this desire for unity. They are all expressions of a feeling of oneness. [hydrog][stj2]

The lack of boundaries can also result in connections, and so in relationships, that are not suitable and can be harmful. This is a particularly notable feature of the drug Ecstasy, Inappropriate bonding. [mdma][hmd1] But it is a general feature of the modern world and applies to a substantial number of our patients.

I-2 Divine Connection

The modern world has seen a rapid decline in the role of organized religion. Where it has remained of great importance it has often taken on a destructive syphilitc aspect with an emphasis on repression and religious warfare.

The religion of the electronic age can never be an organized one but must be an individual spirituality, a connection to the divine that is not fixed but fluid, changing and of the moment.

The need for this spiritual connection is important in contemporary disease, particularly as materialism and the modern idea of science leave little space for it. The need for spiritual wholeness is great. Synergy: through pursuing creative, enjoyable and relaxing spiritual pursuits together! [aids][nl2] Desire to connect to the planet and cosmos. [lsd][nl-lsd] I just long for some clear nights, so I can see my stars. If I could reconnect, then everything would be all right. [neon][srj5] Heart is full to overflowing with no boundaries. Tears of joy and gratitude. Great pleasure from and desire for far horizons. Before I just wanted enlightenment and now I am aware that there are higher states of consciousness. I have set my sights higher. [neon][srj5] I feel a great love for the world. [ignis-alc][es2]

Many of the new remedies have spiritual associations and implications. Some are the gifts of the divinity. The Aztec name for mescaline is Teonanacatl (meaning sacred mushroom, or God's flesh). [anh][sp1] Chocolate is produced form the beans of the cocoa tree, the Theobroma cocoa L.; Theobroma is Greek for 'food of the Gods'. The name was chosen due to the American Indian legend, which purports that the tree originates as a gift from the Gods. The man-god Quetzalcoatl had been led into the lost paradise, where the children of the sun god dwelt. Upon his return to the world of men, Quetzalcoatl brought the cacao seeds back with him. He began to grow cacao in his garden, nourished himself with its seeds and became inebriated with the liquor. Thus inspired he gathered disciples, taught them the civilised arts of agriculture, astronomy and medicine, and became the ruler of Mexico. [choc][srj3]

Some are sacred. Giant Kauri were used in the construction of ceremonial and war ships, yet prior to logging in the 19th and 20th century, the trees were regarded as sacred forest lords. [agath-a][nl2] The ginkgo is an ancient culture plant in the Far East, where the tree has been an object of veneration since time immemorial and is cultivated near residential areas and temples. Its cultivation as a temple tree spread from China to Japan, where the tree is sacred. [gink-b][vml3]

Others are traditional links to the divine, In the Old Testament [Genesis 9:13-17] the rainbow is said to be the symbol of the bond between God and humanity. [irid-met][vml3] or links to the primordial state, Being the first, it is a link with "the time which was before", to quote a phrase of the Kalahari Bushman, and oft-times quoted by Laurens van der Post. [hydrog][srj2] It has been postulated that in the big bang at the beginning of time, matter and anti-matter coemerged, each having opposite charge, opposite spin and moving in contrary motion, the one from time past to future, the other from time future to time past. [positr][nl2] or to stages on the personal spiritual journey. In his book, The Power of Myth, Joseph Campbell states: "In the first stage of this kind of adventure, the hero leaves the realm of the familiar, over which he has some measure of control and comes to a threshold, let us say the edge of a lake or sea, where a monster of the abyss comes to meet him. The hero, on encountering the power of the dark may overcome and kill it, as did Siegfried and St. George when they killed the dragon. But as Siegfried learned, he must then taste the dragon blood, in order to take to himself something of that dragon power. When Siegfried has killed the dragon and tasted the blood, he hears the song of nature. He has transcended his humanity and reassociated himself with the powers of nature, which are the powers of our life and from which our minds remove us". The lizard or dragon then represents a part of ourselves with which we must contact before we can proceed on our spiritual journey. [helo-s][rwt2]

Shore connects all the bird remedies to this particular type of spirituality, Spiritual, not religious – spirit – breath – air. [sej-birds] and it is particularly true of the Raven, the Eagle and the Falcon. Few creatures have been elevated to the status of Deity by the human race as has been Raven, whose profound and seemingly divine influence has encircled the globe since the beginnings of time. [corv-cor][bdg1] In Native American belief, the eagle is a spirit of great vision, wisdom and power, one who sees clearly and travels high, one who opens the magic door and can carry you to the place of vision and communication with Great Spirit. [haliae-lc][srj5] The Peregrine Falcon has been regarded as a mystic bird and often as a messenger from another world, a stranger in ours. The North American Indians believe it to be a messenger that brings us guidance from the spirit world. This idea partly comes from the fact that it is most active soon after dawn and in the evening twilight. Thus the Ancient Egyptians believed the Falcon brought the Sun in the morning and dragged it away in the evening. [falco-pe][nl2]

Many of these remedies inure a feeling of spirituality and a connection with the divine. This is particularly true of the drug remedies. Cosmic mysticism. [anh][sp1] Said he had been transported to heaven, and his language, usually commonplace, became quite enthusiastic. [cann-i][a1] Half of the participants mentioned changes in their spiritual outlook and values. [mdma][saunders] Through the power or mana of kava the presiding chief and other participants are brought into contact with the sacred, and temporarily incarnate the ancestral dieties, blurring the sacral and profane worlds. [pip-m][c1] I had traveled back to the primordial, undifferentiated oneness of being that preceded the big bang and the creation of the manifest universe. [lsd][nl-lsd] The ego-dissolution continued now, but peacefully. Whatever parts of me left were replaced by that Divinity. [lsd][nl-lsd] To fathom hell or soar angelic Just take a pinch of psychedelic. [lsd][nl-lsd] However, it is found in many others as well. A grateful feeling of dependence on a divine spirit was experienced. [cere-b][a1] An initial high and a kind of opening to the cosmos. [falco-pe][nl2] I felt in the presence of a totally pure energy, like meeting God and feeling totally unworthy or like meeting a lover and feeling unworthy – realizing all the mistakes of a lifetime. This pure energy was around for some time protecting me. I feel this unification cleared out lifetimes of symptomatology for me. [hydrog][srj2] Felt wonderful. Kept going outside during the night, between midnight and 3 am. At last the sky was clear, moon brilliant, stars familiar, air cold. I felt so much a part of everything again. [neon][srj5] There is a particular feeling that this connection is a gift of great value. Total trust in the Universe that all needs will be met. [adam][srj5] 'The best dream of my life'. In meditation with my Guru (a male) and other people. (First time in my dreams that I am there and others there also.) I started to go into shocks and moans – a kind of chorea – from the spiritual energy in my body. My guru leant over and uncovered his breast (a female breast) and fed me milk from it. I felt nurtured to my soul by God. [phasco-ci][rbp2] This is like being given more than you ever wanted, like wanting the sun and being given the Universe. [neon][srj5] It feels like I am being showered with gifts and abundance from a wonderfully fertile and nourishing universe. I know that I deserve this abundance. [positr][nl2] This benificence can aslo cause a recipricol obligation. The main theme of Cereus bonplandii is that the person is very much attached to God, to the extent that he feels that he is under the powerful influence of a God-like person and that he can thereby help to relief the suffering of mankind. [cere-b][Latha Iyer, I desire to be a useful remedy, Homoeopathic Links, 1/97] Helping someone in need, out of a sense of duty. [lac-h][sk4]

Although drugs have long been used by traditional societies as a tool to spiritual enlightenment they have been used there in the context of a whole culture and through complex rituals. Many modern users have taken them as a short cut to enlightenment. Recently Alexander Shulgin told the story of a Japanese poet who tried MDMA and said: 'It has taken twenty years of studying Zen for me to reach this clarity, but I'm glad I did it my way.' A Benedictine monk at a monastery in Big Sur, California, tried to see if MDMA could aid meditation, and concluded that the drug 'facilitated the search by providing a glimpse of the goal, but that it did not replace the hard work required.' [mdma][saunders] As Vithoulkas points out, it is a false mystical state that is the usual pathological version of divine connection. This drug produces mental conditions that simulate what could be called false "spiritual" or "transcendental" or "mystic" states. Sometimes when dealing with the sick, you will be perplexed as to what is happening in Anhalonium cases. Is it a real spiritual experience the individual is going through, part of his spiritual evolution, or is it dangerous pathology which must be counteracted immediately? [anh][vh1] The ecstatic state that Cannabis can produce is the reason that a whole generation of hashish users were misled into believing that 'grass' or 'dope' could provide them with a new dimension of understanding, more openness of the mind, an expanded awareness, and more spirituality. However, what it really created was a 'spaced-out' condition of the mind that could no longer discern the real from the unreal. [cann-i][vh1]

I-3 Grounding

There have appeared in the provings of many new remedies sensations of grounding and connection to the Earth. I felt so positive. I suddenly felt strength, and it was like somebody had plonked my feet into the ground. As if someone had put a strengthening thing around my spine and I felt stronger and more together. [aids][nl2] I feel like burying myself in grass and earth. I love touching and covering my hands with earth. I want to be enclosed and hidden in the earth. [adam][srj5] Feel my feet could root. [helodr-cal][knl2] Subjects also reported feeling more aware more "grounded" and feeling "blessed" and at peace. [mdma][saunders] A feeling that I am being pulled downwards. [hydrog][srj2] This remedy makes me feel settled in one place, planted. No desire to move. [irid-met][srj5] Felt rooted to the spot. Didn't want to do anything. Want to go and hibernate. [irid-met][srj5] I danced until very late. I felt very euphoric. Happy and young and lively. I am alive right now. This is something in my roots. [agath-a][nl2] My spirit feels light without being weightless. Prior to taking the remedy, I felt too far in the future, without realizing it. I feel as if I have taken a step back and am in the here and now. [neon][srj5] Feeling very grounded. [positr][nl2] I feel

I have both feet firmly on the ground. [ozone][sde2] A greater strength of my boundaries – feeling solid, contracted, unaffected by others' vibrations. Feel well emotionally, stable, Taurean, planted. [sanguis-s][hrn2] Realisation of being material – special. I do appreciate my life very much. Wonderment of the life forces to materialise. Wonder of being born into the material world. [tung-met][bdx1]

These experiences are on the whole in contrast to the main pattern of the remedies where lightness (*See Emptiness & Lack of Substance IV-7*), floating and flying, (*See Floating & Flying IV-8*) and a sense of disconnection (*Disconnection II-1*) are much stronger themes. The following description of milk gives some idea of the implications of this feeling of grounding. Milk is the most original and oldest food of humans. People drank it as heavenly food, when the earth's atmosphere was pervaded by a milky protein substance, of which the nitrogen in the air is the rudimentary remnant... Milk accompanied human beings during the long period of development... Milk strengthens our physical body as a vehicle for soul and spirit. Milk returns us to the earth and enables us to empathise with all humankind. Just as we breathe the air which is present for all human beings, we can imagine that in the collective unconscious there is an ancient memory of that common cosmic milk, which gives us a feeling of social solidarity. Milk makes human beings into citizens of the earth, brings us into contact with the earthly situation, without preventing us from being a citizen of the entire solar system at the same time. If we lacked milk, it would promote in us the tendency to love everything that comes from the earth. We would lose the ties that bind us with those things on earth that bring about the human condition. In order not to be fanatics and not to estrange themselves from human feeling and human activity on earth, it is good that as inhabitants of that earth we make ourselves heavier with the use of milk – also as adults." [Hauschka] [lac-h][vml3]

The symptoms above are on the whole fairly positive. The more pathological developments from it are to be found in an unhealthy materialism (*see Materialism VI-6*) and in a splitting of the physical and the mental or spiritual aspects of humanity. (*See Splitting V-4*).

I-4 Communication

The dissolution of boundaries leads to a sense of connection between people. Sensation of love and companionship for everyone. [aids][nl2] Relationships seem so good and smooth, interactions are full of love and mutual respect. [limen-b-c][hrn2] All the subjects felt closer and more intimate with all others present. [mdma][saunders] When outside and looking at people, thought to myself I know them. People were friendlier to me. Thought I could start a conversation with strangers. [germ-met][srj5] Had these feelings of being closer to people. [irid-met][srj5] Quite open to being with other people, normally have boundaries. [agath-a][nl2] Desire to touch people, be near them, feel their presence, feel connection, to have fun with them, to laugh with them. Normally I want time to myself. [lac-del][hrn2] Love contact even with strangers in bus, which I usually do not like and avoid. [polys][sk4] Very soft dreams last night. Feeling of images flowing into one another and a soft and sweet sense of contact between us all. [positr][nl2] Friendly feeling without judging people. [sanguis-s][hrn2]

Some of the remedies have a direct connection to communication that was reflected in the provings. These include Ozone, Oxygen combines with all other elements except the noble gases. [ozone][sde2] Iridium, The goddess Iris has her own highway. This female courier transports messages between earth to heaven via the iridescent highway of a rainbow. She can travel through air, water and the underworld, from the very fundaments of the earth to the zenith of the heavens. Her task is to be a joiner, uniter and conciliator. [irid-met][srj5] Felt I had been given the role of messenger. [irid-met][srj5] and Raven. The Kwakiutl offered the afterbirth of a male newborn to ravens to peck so that when the child was grown to manhood he would understand their cries. The interpreter could respond to nearly a dozen raven vocalizations that would tell him of a change in weather, the possibilities of attack from enemies, warriors, an imminent death, or what the hunting prospects would be (Boas 1913-14). [corv-cor][bdg1] She wants to interact with people. [corv-cor][bdg1]

In many remedies there is an increased ability to communicate. This is perhaps most apparent in Ecstasy, Increased ability to interact with or be open with others was reported by 85% of subjects. [Leister][mdma][saunders] Many subjects reported that they were more communicative and were more able to receive both compliments and criticism. [mdma][saunders] Emotional warmth; lack of emotional barriers; ease of heartfelt communication. [mdma][hmd1] Though it is evident in many others. Had a stronger level of communication on many levels and everyone could just receive it. [ara-mac][sej7] Dream of seeing a man I know and had tremendous regard for. I went up and hugged him with great spontaneity and affection and then stood talking to him, looking straight into his eyes. It was a very liberating feeling, as up till now, even in my dreams, I have behaved with great constraint with him. [androc][srj5] Increased clarity in expressing himself with words, communicating, and mental clarity in general. [germ-met][srj5] I am enjoying talking – a real energy for conversation. [lsd][nl-lsd] There is also a desire for contact and communication. Increased desire to communicate with people. [choc][srj3] Constant desire for company. Talking for hours. [polys][sk4] Dreams of communicating. [vacuum] [es-vac] Sensation of increased strength, optimism, loquacity, vivaciousness and activity, with the desire to communicate with others. [visc][vml3]

This can go further than just a connection and can include an element of looking after others, Felt protective, felt bonded to everyone I was with. [falco-pe][nl2] (*see also Babies, Children & Animals IX-2*) or of being looked after. She wants to interact with people and have them take care of her. [corv-cor][bdg1] Felt strongly I needed to be with someone. Went round to friend's house; felt immediately better in company. Blanket lifted a little. Felt detached but happy to be. [irid-met][srj5]

The need or desire for communication can lead to the opposite sensation that it is imperfect, unclear, difficult or obscured. Dream of talking to another long distance over the phone with a poor connection. [helo-s][rwt2] Inner vision, rows upon rows of letters. Thought, "This looks Greek to me." [irid-met][srj5] I looked at sun and there were words under the sun, don't know what. Feeling of messages out there, I needed to tune into, and hear and see things I hadn't seen before. [ara-maca][sej6] (*This is examined in more detail as Obstruction of the Senses XII-2 and in Confusion about Words VII-9*)

Dreams of food are quite common in the new remedies. Food, feeding and nurturing can be seen as substitute forms of communication, Dream: I am in Costa Rica where I used to live. Cooking a dinner for the people past, present and future, whom I have issues with. [carbn-dox][knl3] and, particularly in the case of Chocolate, for love. Chocolate is known to contain many substances that affect the heart. It has been reported to cause heart failure in animals. Blood and heart relate to love, sharing the function of supplying warmth and nourishment, thereby supporting the idea of chocolate as a 'love substitute'. [choc][srj3] This is one aspect of the modern confusion in our understanding and attitudes to food which is discussed later. (*See Appetite VI-7*)

Marriage is the most personal and deepest form of communication and it figures strongly in the proving of new remedies. Diamonds are the substance most closely associated with the concept of love and marriage. Diamonds, when worn constantly, were thought by the Romans to maintain marital constancy. [adam][srj5] Often referred to as, 'the stone or reconciliation,' diamond has, of course, from the very earliest times been a favorite stone for lovers. [adam][srj5] Dreams of weddings and marriage are not uncommon in these remedies. Dream: Two women are getting married. The feeling is of lots of beauty and abundance. [corian-s][knl6] Dream of marriage. [haliae-lc][srj5] Recurrent dreams of weddings. [polys][sk4]

Provers often found that the proving experience allowed close relationships to form and develop, This is a big deal for me – it feels as though barriers between me and other people can come down with this man. (Talking about new relationship.) [aids][nl2] Felt connected to romance and feeling of courtship. [lsd][nl-lsd] Within half a year of these proving experiences (having subsequently lost her fear of commitment) she married. [positr][nl2] For example, the nut was considered to stimulate sexual love, and walnuts used to be dispersed at weddings in Greece. Related to this use is the belief that a nut tree does not produce fruit without one of the same kind nearby. This is why nut trees are usually encountered in pairs. In Germany in the 17th century, a young farmer could not marry before he had planted and raised a few walnut trees. [jug-r][vml3] or to progress and deepen. Becoming more connected with husband, more in the present with him, not focusing on the past problems or future anxieties. Maybe I am more present in life. [haliae-lc][srj5] Afterwards one member of a couple "focused on how they were defensive with each other" while the other "saw love underneath" actions which they had thought implied that the other partner didn't care. [mdma][saunders] Worked hard to remain open with partner as it was his birthday, even bought make up to look better to please him. [falco-pe][nl2] My boyfriend and I discuss living together in the evening. (I do subsequently move in with him). [sal-fr][sle1]

The other side of this was a feeling, especially in dreams, of weddings going wrong. Woke from a dream about wedding, Patient said she was going to get married, I thought "big mistake." [irid-met][srj5] Dream I have married my childhood sweetheart, and am travelling with her to a distant place because my parents have driven me out of the house. [lac-h][sk4] Dream I found someone to marry; started final preparations for the wedding, make up etc; mother in law was there; turned out groom was never informed. [urol-h][rwt3] Dream: It's my wedding. I'm searching through my clothes for something decent to wear. I try on loads of things, panicking at the state of myself… It really was a total disaster. [vacuum][es-vac]

The most important aspect of this theme was a desire for marriage and a yearning for a partner and soulmate. Nervous debility in unmarried persons. [agn][c1] Felt lack of romance in my life. Desired romantic love, to be loved. [germ-met][srj5] Wanting a partner. Wanted to mate. Scary, wild. Hadn't thought about families and children before. Wanted responsibility, commitment and love. [lsd][nl-lsd] I have been living without a partner for 10 years, which I really enjoyed. Now I have an uncomfortable feeling of needing a partner. Usually I only want a partner because I have so much that I want to share it. This is a feeling of only being half and needing another. [neon][srj5] I fell in love with a man when I was eighteen. I felt he was my real soul mate but it didn't work out and we had to be separated. Although I'm married I've always thought back to him. [oncor-t][srj-case] Badly want close contact with someone of my own. [polys][sk4]

Similar, though perhaps less intense, feelings are aroused concerning the family, especially those of a heightened connection. I feel connected with my children, that a barrier I've erected due to the fear of losing them has gone. [adam][srj5] Felt incredible loving feelings towards my family, towards my kids and my husband. Really a delight, wonderful. Peaceful, happy, easygoing. [limen-b-c][hrn2] Feelings of missing family and wanting to connect with them. [corian-s][knl6] More genuine pleasantness than usual with little kids. [haliae-lc][srj5] Another important attraction of raving is the feeling of belonging to a family. [mdma][saunders] Family and family relationships are very important to birds. [sej-birds]

Many of the animals that have been recently proved by Herrick and others are herd animals and the extended family or group is very important. The dolphin, like the elephant, lives in a community with high levels of group cooperation. This is an important asset in the sea because it allows them to work together on tasks necessary for their survival. For example, they might herd a school of fish onto a rocky outcropping or trap them in a shallow cove. They might assist a mother dolphin by baby-sitting for her calf, or they can play group-type games. [lac-del][hrn2] The horse community in the wild is affectionate and herd-oriented. They have transferred these characteristics to their interactions with humans. They have a great desire to please and to bond with those who are their masters. Yet it seems that, however much they try, there is never an end to their labours or to the demands that are made on them. [lac-e][hrn2] The African elephant is a magnificent, gentle giant whose life is characterized by its extraordinary sense of community and cooperation. After the drenching downpour of the rainy season, there comes a time of lush green grasses, and the savanna is rich, vibrant and loamy. Suddenly and inexplicably, clans of all the different elephant kinship groupings (all the family members that have broken off from the original cow-calf group) come together. As many as 2,000 arrive at this festival. When they meet, it is with obvious rejoicing. [lac-loxod-a][hrn2] Many birds are very family/group oriented – flocks of birds. [sej-birds]

On the whole the attitude to the group is a positive one. I noticed last night that I was in and out of the room doing what I wanted to do and being part of the group as well. [aids][nl2] I feel really good, and I feel part of the whole group. [aids][nl2] Dreams of being in company and taking part in a joyous festival. [anan][a1] Felt more connection to the group. [ara-mac][sej7] Dreams of lots of people, of being included in the group. [cygn-b][sle-swan] Felt I did not want to leave group, usually can't wait to leave by late Sunday afternoon. [falco-pe][nl2] Missing the rest of the group – want to be with people but not to interact, just to be in a group with people I know. [lsd][nl-lsd] I feel as one with the group. [lsd][nl-lsd] Warmth and peace with others in group. [sal-fr][sle1] I feel more included in the group and an important member. [vacuum][es-vac] However, There can be a considerable conflict between the need for company and the desire to be alone. (*See Need To Be Alone II-9*) Tension between the sense of self and the need for expression. Expression of what is really oneself vs being an integral part of family and society. [ara-maca][sej-7] and much of the feeling of disconnection and isolation (*See Isolation II-8*) felt in the remedies comes from a failure to integrate with the group and with society.

I-5 Empathy & Clairvoyance

The vanishing of boundaries leaves a person open to external influences. This results in a sensitivity that can be an acuity of the senses and a clarity of perception (*see Clarity I-6*), or a hypersensitivity to external influences (*See Oversensitivity V-2*). It also results in a particular sensitivity to the feelings of others. Increased sensitivity to others. [irid-met][srj5] Very sensitive on an interpersonal level. [colum-p][sej-birds] Sensitive to other's emotions. I feel I know how people are feeling. [androc][srj5] Hypersensitivity. Very sensitive to people. [haliae-lc][srj5] Much more aware of the energy auras around people and energy beyond. Sixth sense is clearer. [agath-a][nl2] Seeing other people very clearly – their states and motivations. [ignis-alc][es2]

This sensitivity can go further and become a form of empathy. Feelings of empathy. Desire to share honestly and with feeling. [aids][nl2] Experienced a deep sense of compassion, feeling of real joy for other people's happiness. Very spontaneous feeling of pleasure. [limen-b-c][hrn2] During the proving, developed a true sympathy for the weakness of others. [hydrog][srj2] I was having lunch with a friend and she was telling me her marriage was probably ending. Even before this I got an emotional hit of her pain but when she told me I felt like I was experiencing her pain myself, physically and emotionally. [corv-cor][bdg1]

This in turn can be a form of clairvoyance. In some remedies, particularly the older ones this is described in general terms.

Extravagantly exalted fancy, ecstasy, prophecies, making verses. [agar][a1] Prophetic dreams. [cann-i][a1] Clairvoyance and clairaudience. [cann-i][c1] Clairvoyant and sensitive to mesmerism. [lac-f][wza1] Clairvoyance. [lac-leo][sk4] She prophesies, predicts with a sort of clairvoyance. [nux-m][k2] Thinks she is clairvoyant; can read character and understand motions. [pyrus][a1]

However, the main expression of this clairvoyance, especially in recent provings where it is clearer, is an intuitive understanding of how other people feel or think. Felt very connected with people. I walked into a room full of people and sensed where they were all at, intuitively. [adam][srj5] This proving has given me clairvoyance, feeling others pain, not as in this world as I used to be. I'm on the divide between two worlds with decreased attachment to the physical world. I can sense what's going on with other people. The feeling is hard to put into words but it is something like being not "in" this world as I used to be. [corv-cor][bdg1] Very sensitive to people. If I looked at them I would see their emotions written on them. [haliae-lc][srj5] Clairvoyance about people and what was going on with them. [haliae-lc][srj5] I felt I could see more deeply into people – beyond the roles they were playing. [hydrog][srj2] Psychic ability and intuition heightened. [lac-del][hrn2] I feel that my consciousness is heightened, my clarity of vision is higher. I've seen, or sensed very clearly what's happening in my patients today. I'm not using my intellect so much, using something else. [tung-met][bdx1] Birds are more emotional, feel connections, understand something of person's feelings. [sej-birds] Something like telepathic links with people, happening a lot. [vacuum][es-vac]

There is a breakdown of the boundaries between this world and others, particularly the world of the dead. (*See Death XII-8*) This produces a form of clairvoyance involving connection to those other worlds. Old symptoms from a long time ago are back – I saw fairies again today – haven't seen them for about 9 years (since I had Phosphorus). It feels good to see them again. [haliae-lc][srj5] Dream: Got a message in a dream, like it was a major revelation. [lac-del][hrn2] Increased intuitive awareness – saw what took place where my friend died. [urol-h][rwt3] Willows are associated with Water, the Moon, the Underworld and powers of divination. [sal-fr][sle1] During the proving, one couple saw a ghost, and two of the provers made a connection to a sibling who had died in infancy. [sal-fr][sle1] There is a Nux moschata symptom that is particularly descriptive of this simple connection to another place. Accurately answers questions quite out of her sphere, and on returning to consciousness knows nothing about it. [nux-m][vml2] In the Shark there is a feeling that the subject has psychic control over animals. Had the idea, and have had this idea twice in the last few days, that my thoughts could pentrate the wall and influence the rats or mice – to make them be quiet or make them die. [galeoc-c-h][gms1]

One of the most profound effects of electronic communication is the disruption of the steady flow of time. (*See Confusion about Time VII-6*) Many of the clairvoyant symptoms concern a confusion about time or its counterpart, synchronicity. She found that she was thinking or saying something at the same time or just before someone else was thinking or saying the same thing. [androc][srj5] Clairvoyance. I knew what someone was going to say when they came downstairs. I wrote the sentence on a piece of paper, they said the same sentence on entering the room. [falco-pe][nl2] Repeated prophetic notions of daily events before hearing of them, causing anxiety and discomfort; thoughts of a person not seen for months and found he had phoned a few days before, depression and sadness unexplained until heard of sad family news that had already happened. [neon][srj5] I have an inner vision of masses of fine, wave-like movement, stretching upwards into the light, dancing, twisting in spirals. Am I seeing things before they happen? [plut-n][srj7] I still have much increased synchronicity. [lsd][nl-lsd] This is often expressed by patients as a feeling of Déjà-vu.

The importance of communication in the modern world and in these remedies is reflected in the symptoms that concern psychic communication. Dream of ability to talk to and see sister who lives far away. Felt amazed. [germ-met][srj5] I was in an art class with my mother. (She had the same dream also that night.) [irid-met][srj5] I feel as if I am in psychic communication with another member of the group. [lsd][nl-lsd]

As with the need for spiritual connection the desire or need for psychic communication can result in a false and illusory sense of it. This effect is again most apparent in the hallucinatory drug remedies. Thinks each one he meets has some secret sorrow, and wishes to sympathize with him. [cann-i][a1]

Clairvoyance is clearly a very important aspect of the new remedies, especially the Birds, the Animals and the Drugs. It is also very important in many of the other miasms. In the Hydrophobic Miasm, particularly in Aconite and Stramonium, it is the power of great fear that heightens all the patient's senses and even his extrasensory abilities. The extra knowledge gained from this tends to be about the subject and his own fate. In the Sycotic Miasm the clairvoyance comes from a connection with the shadow side of the psyche, that which an astrologer might associate with Scorpio. This feeling is also driven to some degree by fear and also contains an element of self preservation. The clairvoyance found in the Tubercular Miasm is very similar to that of the AIDS Miasm. This is one area in which for example Phosophrus symptoms overlap the two miasms, just as in other areas Arsenicum symptoms overlap the Syphilitic and AIDS Miasms. The difference may lie in that the Tubercular symptoms involve a degree of exploration and a desire for such knowledge; whereas in the AIDS symptoms the openness is imposed upon the subject rather than actively sought. In the same way the fear and vulnerability in the other miasms to some degree drives the clairvoyance, while in the AIDS Miasm they are concomitant symptoms derived from a common source.

I-6 Clarity

The removal of barriers allows for improved perception of that which is around us. The word most often used to describe this in provings is clarity, and as this implies, it is the sense of vision that is most strongly affected and which provides the metaphor for the more general sensation.

The Eagle, the Falcon and the Wolf are known for their vision and this came up in the provings. In Native American belief, the eagle is a spirit of great vision, wisdom and power, one who sees clearly and travels high. [haliae-lc][srj5] Eyes feel like receptors to light the way a satellite dish is a receptor for stellar signals or microwaves, as if they are meant to capture light or receive it. Odd feeling. [haliae-lc][srj5] Sensitive to light but at the same time wide open to it, as if it is meant to be. [haliae-lc][srj5] Clarity to my vision. Usually my eyes have a soft focus, but since the proving, every so often they clear up and the focus is sharp. [haliae-lc][srj5] Vision quite clear – more sharp clarity than normal. [falco-pe][nl2] Sharp, outlines seem quite definite. Eyes getting caught by bright colours more than usual. [falco-pe][nl2] Wolves use all their senses intensely. Their sharp vision allows them to see and instantly memorize the height, weight, and shape of an oncoming intruder or friend. Wolves are particularly interested in colors that have red as a base, when these colors are perceived in a strong light. [lac-lup][hrn2] Birds see clearly especially those who fly high e.g. a hawk can determine a mouse a mile away. [sej-birds]

Clear vision was also important in many other remedies. Very clear eyesight. This is unusual, very much so in the morning. I feel like my eyes have been washed. [adam][srj5] Enlargement of stereoscopic vision, and of plasticity of reliefs. [anh][jl1] Things look clearer, better, fresher. [carbn-dox][knl3] Small details seem much sharper. Things look better. [choc][srj3] I see things differently than before – everything more clear and three-dimensional – more real. [choc][srj3] Felt I could see more clearly without glasses when I got up. I experimented with this on the way to work. I could not see more clearly, but could perceive better, which made me feel better. [dream-p][sdj1] Perception of minutest details. [galla-q-r][nl2] My eyesight improved. [lac-h][htj1] I also felt my sight was a lot clearer and there was a clarity of vision although everything was the same it seemed as if everything was more defined, everything was more in focus. Sharper. [lsd][nl-lsd] Clarity of vision, sharp delineation of objects. [positr][nl2] More interest in the finer details of things – how they are close up. [sanguis-s][hrn2] Vision extremely clear. [seq-s][vml3] For a time he was totally blind; but when his sight returned it was so keen that he could count the panes in a window said to be two miles distant. [meph][c1] Eyes felt different – felt different in focusing. Could take in more visually. [tung-met][bdx1] My clarity of vision is higher. [tung-met][bdx1]

Hearing is often enhanced. I realize my hearing is extremely acute. I can hear the silence all the time. [adam][srj5] Augmentation in auditory acuity. [anh][jl1] Fine perception, especially hearing. Good discrimination of various sounds. [lars-arg][fkw1] Acute sense of hearing. [limen-b-c][hrn2] Extreme sensitiveness to noise. [cann-i][c1] Hearing more acute, especially for deeper tones which have more resonance. [choc][srj3] Hearing for distant sounds much more acute than usual. [nux-m][c1] My hearing was really very strong and sensitive. [sanguis-s][hrn2] The scorpion can detect its prey's location with great accuracy by sensing vibrations through special sensors located in the legs. [androc][srj5] Pigeons can hear pin drop at half a mile. [sej-birds] External sounds very clear. [vacuum][es-vac]

As is the sense of smell. Acute sense of smell. The flowers had smelled exceptionally fine; cat pee in the study, shampoo in shower, all are acute smells. [limen-b-c][hrn2] Strong sense of smell. And liked it, a way of connecting. Could almost take the place of ideas. [limen-b-c][hrn2] Very acute sense of smell. [ipom-p][hr1] Sense of smell increased. [haliae-lc][srj5] Noticed I'm really sensitive to smell. [falco-pe][nl2] Sense of smell enhanced. [latex][nl-latex] Sense of smell heightened. Delighted in smells. [positr][nl2] Definite sense that my smell is a lot more acute. [tung-met][bdx1]

However, there is often a general increase in sensitivity of all or many of the senses. All senses heightened. [aids][nl2] Everything still looking crystal clear. All senses, hearing/smell heightened. [aids][nl2] All my senses are very acute, especially touch, smell, hearing. [adam][srj5] It is said that butterflies can see many more colors than humans can; can taste more with their leg-positioned taste buds (the Milkweed butterfly has a taste sensitivity 2,408 times greater than that of man); and can smell the most subtle scent. [limen-b-c][hrn2] Vision and hearing more acute. [choc][srj3] Senses of smell, touch and vision more acute and more dominating. [choc][srj3] Great acuteness of hearing; for a short moment I had the feeling of hearing, smelling and sensing everything in the room at the same time. [lars-arg][fkw1] All senses are enhanced, especially those of touch and sound. [mdma][hmd1] Moderate use is accompanied by increased speech and heightened perception. [pip-m][c1] Much more aware of the senses. [agath-a][nl2] Increased sensitivity to smell and all senses in general. [galla-q-r][nl2] The wolf's senses of smell and hearing are highly acute. [lac-lup][hrn2] Senses more acute. [lsd][nl-lsd] The senses of sight and touch are exalted in the same way as hearing. [nux-m][c1] Heightened senses. [plac][Biggs+]

This clarity is not purely of the senses but applies also to thinking, understanding and the emotions. Diamond is the substance that perhaps epitomizes the concept of clarity and clarity, especially clarity of thought, was important in the proving. Feel clearheaded, lacking confusion. Clear thinking. Notice my children are making clear choices. [adam][srj5] Clear fast decision making. Feel clear, incisive, perceptive, sparkling, attractive, connected. [adam][srj5] Clarity. Time to set my limits. [adam][srj5] Feel in center. Clear above and below. [adam][srj5] Just as visual clarity was strong in the bird remedies, mental clarity was also apparent. It's a kind of clarity about other people's feelings. [corv-cor][bdg1] My clarity and focus is much better. Not so many things distracting me. Life is much simpler, much clearer. [haliae-lc][srj5] Normally I walk around in a fog, thinking, in my head. In the proving state, there is an outward focus. I'm aware of people, and how they're moving, and what they're doing. Conscious of them and how they might effect me and I might effect them. Normally, I don't care. I like to be in this altered state. The ability to be in that state intensified since taking eagle. An animal awareness, very conscious of other people as animals. [haliae-lc][srj5] Clarity of thoughts. [lars-arg][fkw1] Feel there is a clarity or clearness of mind as I sit to do my homework. [falco-pe][nl2] But it is a theme that is found throughout the remedies. I feel a transformation in my acts and senses. I think everything clearer; I get to assimilate the things better, as a clarity of ideas. [lepd-s][rsi1] All his feelings of pleasure and pain seem exalted. [cann-i][a1] Clarity of mind – could resolve several issues. [coca-c][sk4] Clear and focused. [dream-p][sdj1] Clarity of mind. [mdma][hmd1] Increased clarity in expressing himself with words, communicating, and mental clarity in general. [germ-met][srj5] Thinking felt sharp and clear. [helo-s][rwt2] Aware of clarity of thought and calm mind. Feel very clear, noticeably clear, definitely not confused. Complete clarity of thought and mind. [heroin][sdj-h] Clarity of mind with increased ability for mental work. [lac-h][sk4] Feel very aware of what people are doing. [lac-h][htj1] Feel very energised and focused. Spent the whole day working on homework. Work that I couldn't be bothered to do three weeks ago. Nothing else seemed to matter, even observing my symptoms seem to he forgotten. [latex][nl-latex] I feel very energised again. My thinking was clear. I was very focused and able to complete lots of work today. [latex][nl-latex] Clarity of mental function. [latex][nl-latex] My senses and feelings were more acute. [plut-n][srj7] I have wonderful clarity of mind, too, and my eyesight is still good. [positr][nl2] Brain active, intellect clear, thoughts vivid, whole being intensified. [pyrus][c1] Clarity of thought. [seq-s][vml3] Feeling mentally clear. [galeoc-c-h][gms1] I feel very clear in general. [vac-uum][es-vac]

There is often a relationship between the clarity of thought and the clarity of vision. My thinking is quicker than usual and I am starting to get many thoughts and pictures of hedgehogs in my mind. Felt bright and efficient and excited, with clearer vision. [choc][srj3] There was a sudden clarity. During the proving I wore my glasses more and had dreams of windows. As though there had been a shift of focus to my own needs. [neon][srj5] Clarity of purpose and vision. [positr][nl2] I felt more alert and my mind was clearer. I feel that my consciousness is heightened, my clarity of vision is higher. [tung-met][bdx1] I can see clearly now, I'm realising the meaning. The universe helps me to go my way. [lars-arg][fkw1]

This clarity can take particular forms. In Adamas there is a sense of sparkles that clearly relates to the substance. After taking the remedy again, I was very struck again by sparkling – this time the sun in the shower. Before I took it, I seemed to be surrounded by dark and dirt. [adam][srj5] White frost this morning. At last some purity in this world. Every ice crystal sparkled like jewels. [adam][srj5] Strong desire for clear sparkling water, increasing throughout proving. [adam][srj5]

More generally there is a sense of vividness and the brightness of colours. This is very strong in Iridium whose name and nature are connected with the rainbow. I sat staring at the reflection of my hanging crystal in a picture glass. I thought it looked like a raindrop. [irid-met][srj5] Iridium was named from the Latin/ Greek word Iris, meaning rainbow. While in its solid form, Iridium is a silver-white precious metal, however, in marine acid, it becomes astonishingly multi-colored and iridescent, "emitting a light of extraordinary splendor." [irid-met][srj5] Attracted to men with pale skins, appear even more beautiful, luminosity, light shining forth. [irid-met][srj5] People said "You look radiant today." People came and chatted to me. Felt incredibly clear and colourful. Such a big grin on my face, my face hurts. [irid-met][srj5] Desire for sun, wanted rainbows, wanted rays of sun to create arcs of light. [irid-met][srj5] But it is found in other remedies. Objects perceived are too small, but more often violently bright. [anh][jl1] Increase and improvement of colour vision. [anh][jl1] Increased clarity of vision; colours look bright, intense and painfully pleasurable. [mdma][hmd1] Seeing colours more brightly. [lsd][nl-lsd] Colors seemed brighter to me. [sanguis-s][hrn2] Heightened sense of colors. [urol-h][rwt3] And in some dreams. Vivid dreams, partly agreeable, partly disagreeable. [agar][a1] Dream in vivid colors. [adam][srj5] Dream In a forest making a quilt with colors of purple, rose and blue. [urol-h][rwt3]

The truth is another important clarity issue. Generally fairly severe mood, very straightforward and will say what is needed to be said. [adam][srj5] Dreams of lies and deception. [adam][srj5] Throughout my life there had been a reticence to speak my truth. I'd felt it wouldn't be acceptable to speak my truth and there would be a punishment, not so much in a physical way. [ara-mac][sej7] A friend visited and I felt I wanted to tell her the truth. [choc][srj3] Validating truth, validating authenticity. Living in higher self. Daily life realities have shifted. Not caught up in pettiness. [lac-del][hrn2] Dream last night of a dilemma whether to tell my old friend that I really didn't like her new boyfriend. Odd truth or dare dream. Dishonest not to tell her. At the same time I was given a time sheet to sign for work I had not done should I sign it or not? I was tempted but unable to do either. [latex][nl-latex] Feeling like my truth is readily available, speaking what is true saying it like it is, with no affectations. [lsd][nl-lsd] Felt the remedy had to do with authenticity – what is real. [vacuum][es-vac] I've been very honest with people. It's like everything that should be said is being said. There is no wall no resistance. [vacuum][es-vac]

Coca-cola has been advertised as "The Real Thing" whereas the reality is of a patently manufactured product and one that lacks real nutrition of any kind. I asked for juice, and the waitress brought us an imitation, artificial fruit drink. We asked for something real, and she brought us a beautiful, delicious, red-coloured juice made from pinenuts (which I dislike). There was a lot of plastic. I wondered how one can make something wonderful out of something "yucky". I felt the people were strange and backward. Also felt that the world was too chemical and synthetic; we were in a country where the food should be real, yet it is synthetic. I wondered what the world is coming to, and felt that the earth is going to be lost if we don't change our behaviour. [coca-c][sk4]

Truth tends to be informed by the feelings of indifference and insensitivity. The desire to tell the truth at whatever cost often becomes a selfish or cruel rather than a virtuous thing. (*See Lack of Emotion III-4*)

This overall clarity seems positive but it easily crosses the line to a pathological form which is usually expressed as hypersensitivity. (*See Oversensitivity V-2*) There is also a compensatory reaction of a lack of sensitivity. This can be expressed as if perception took place through a veil or obstruction. (*See Obstruction of the Senses XII-2*).

I-7 Nature

One of the most important connections made through these remedies is the connection to nature.

Many new remedies are made from animals, birds and plants but it is not just in them that a connection to nature is found. This connection corresponds in many ways to the clairvoyant connection to people. I see plants in the house differently, very aware of them and want to give them more light. [choc][srj3] Since the proving, I know how it feels to be a animal or a plant. I know the feeling of daffodil, of flower, of hedgehog, of dog. [choc][srj3] Feel more aware and connected looking at the sun, trees and sky colors. [germ-met][srj5] Felt more with the environment. [helo-s][rwt2] Watch 'Predators'. A cheetah stalking and chasing its prey. I'm absolutely fascinated. The speed and agility of this beautiful animal really moves me and I'm quite thrilled by it. [heroin][sdj-h] Desire to be outside walking and to connect with Nature, especially attuned to the energy from the trees and flocks of birds. [lsd][nl-lsd] I can't stop thinking about animals. Can't focus, think about hunting birds. [lsd][nl-lsd] She loves animals and is very sympathetic to them: 'I cry if I see animals hurt or any kind of cruelty to animals.' [oncor-t][srj-case] Keep feeling very much in touch with nature, animals, the world, they are within me, I in them, a feeling of no separation to the same substance and energy. [positr][nl2] Saw a daddy longlegs and had a feeling of love towards it. I wanted to touch it as it fluttered by. [tung-met][bdx1] (*See Empathy & Clairvoyance I-5*) This feeling also relates to the concern for babies, children and animals. (*See Babies, Children & Animals IX-2*)

Sometimes there is an enhanced awareness and a clearer perception of nature. I am aware of nature, the profusion of wild flowers and insects, the feel of the wind and its sound, the song of the birds, the shadows of clouds across the sun. [falco-pe][nl2] Noticed nature quite distinctly especially trees and shrubs. Saw the outlines of their leaves so precisely. [helodr-cal][knl2] Very aware of the colour of the sky, the light, birds singing, flowers – like a pastoral ideal. Feeling of expansiveness, mentally cool, airy and light. [hydrog][srj2] Abnormal mental awareness, very conscious of nature, everything seemed very vivid, very lovely. [irid-met][srj5] Dream: Driving in a car over the hills while singing, very pleasant feeling. Beautiful spring scene in Sonoma County, blue sky and green pastures, blooming daffodils and plum trees. Intensely beautiful and happy to be alive feeling and awed at how beautiful the earth was. [lac-e][hrn2] The Mother Planet, our Earth, which I feel as beautiful, strong, female and benevolent, but so abused and disregarded. [positr][nl2] Heightened sensuality. [rhus-g][tmo3]

There is a particular affinity for birds and their ability to move in the air free of the constraints of the Earth. Feeling of delight and joy as the swallows and house martins have arrived. Sensation of oneness with them in their flying. [falco-pe][nl2] (*See Floating & Flying IV-8*)

There is also a desire to be in nature and to experience it. Pictures of the mountains make me homesick. Deeper than homesick. Feeling low, remembering the freedom of going to them. Missing mountains and the outdoors. [haliae-lc][srj5] Overwhelming desire to be in the country. [hydrog][srj2] Feeling of wanting to sit in open meadows and enjoy nature. [rhus-g][tmo3] In Rubber the desire for nature arises from a feeling of being separated from it. [latex][nl-latex] Very aware of the weather, keep looking out of the window to record in my mind what is happening. [latex][nl-latex]

The desire for nature ties in with the desire to be outside (*See Trapped IX-7*) and with the connection to the primitive (*See Youth, Beauty, Peace & Love I-8*) The desire to be in nature relates also to issues of solitude: both the need to get away from people (*See Need to be Alone II-9*) and the feelings of being isolated and separated from the rest of humanity. (*See Isolation II-8*) I felt very disconnected from people and found great solace in being alone with nature. There was a deeply spiritual aspect to it, and at times a real beauty in my isolation. [lsd][nl-lsd]

The overwhelming sense, however, is one of concern for the environment. Many of the remedy substances are themselves endangered species. Butterflies, Each species relies on a specific and often narrow food habitat. Thus, they are vulnerable to environmental modifications, especially ones that alter the availability of flowers. At the present time, in Europe alone, over 50 species are in danger of extinction. [limen-b-c][hrn2] Eagles, Today, though they are protected by law, bald eagles are still shot. More frequently, they are victims of accidental poisoning, environmental toxicity, loss of habitat and a diminishing source of food as other species upon which they rely are being destroyed, in particular the many species of salmon. [haliae-lc][srj5]

Falcons, DDE, a product of DDT breakdown, accumulated in the falcons and interfered with an enzyme that is important in the production of egg shells. The shells became so thin that they often broke under the weight of the brooding mother. [falco-pe][nl2] Wolves, The wolf seems to have been earmarked by humans for planned extinction. Many reasons have been set forth for this, such as the killing of children and mass slaughter of deer and elk, but as we have seen, these do not appear to be true. [lac-lup][hrn2] Sequoias. They were the dominant trees of North America. There are now only two species left. [seq-s][vml3] Whales, Dolphins, Elephants, Kauris and Lions could all be described as endangered even Ozone could be seen as endangered.

The microcosmic breakdown of the immune system seen in AIDS is reflected in the macrocosm. The breakdown of the immune defence system is mirrored in ecology by such phenomena as the ozone hole, monoculture diseases, (combated by agrochemicals in a manner analogous to the multiple drug therapies employed in the conventional treatment of AIDS) and in sociological terms, by abuse. Here the boundary of the self is violated. It is also worthy of note that Chiron, the asteroid associated by astrologers with wounding and healing was discovered at around the time that AIDS became known. [aids][nl2]

The feeling becomes one of despair over what seems to be the unavoidable destruction. There is a similar sense of destruction in the Syphilitic Miasm, but it tends to be more personalized. The subject feels that he or she and his or her immediate, personal world will be destroyed. In the AIDS Miasm there are no boundaries and no limit to the possible destruction which could extend to the entire planet and the whole of humanity. The appearance of AIDS in haemophiliacs and intravenous drug users indicated that it was an infectious disease and that the infectious agent was carried in the blood. The appearance of AIDS in female partners of high risk men, indicated that the infectious agent was probably present also in semen. The cases of babies suggested that breast milk might also be a carrier. The obvious conclusion was that all bodily fluids, including saliva, were possible carriers of the infectious agent. What had at first seemed to be restricted to a particular, and somewhat isolated, community; now came to be seen as a plague that would affect everyone. A simple kiss could be a death sentence. [aids][nl2] Dream: I was told ,"You've been selected to leave this dying planet." From the new world, which was beautiful and green with lots of butterflies like Eden, I looked back at the old world with sadness. I thought, "I've been brought here too soon; there's more to do." [adam][srj5] Dream: I saw a cautioning sign while driving by a cove of water in an industrial setting, which warned that swimming there would cause suicidal feelings. Felt alone, melancholic, as if the world was sad and dark, and it was all madness. Horrific dream about sick cows wasting away with a sort of "cattle aids". I had an awful, sinking, helpless, end-of-the-world feeling. [hydrog][srj2] A group of us were living in a space rocket, like Star Trek, big and round. We were up in space, looking down on earth and there was something that came over the Earth, like a shadow and was quite threatening to all of us and got quite worried and didn't know what to do. Everyone felt anxious. [agath-a][nl2] Although generally esteemed, goats are still considered the most 'destructive' and therefore the most dangerous pets. They eat grass to the very roots and often the roots themselves, while loosening the topsoil and making it easy for this layer of soil to be blown or washed away. They sometimes even climb trees and eat the bark and the leaves. Just as they had to adjust to the dangers of the desert in order to survive in the wild, as domesticated animals they tend to overexploit their surroundings and change them into a desert. In this way, habitat and animal are linked inseparably. [lac-cp][vml3] I felt connected to spirit, but after a few weeks I descended into a deeply despairing state, feeling the suffering of humans and the Earth. This was not a new state of awareness, far from it, however it was uncomfortably intense. [positr][nl2]

The feeling was as strong in the substances that might be held responsible for the destruction such as Coca Cola, Plutonium and Polystyrene, [coca-c][sk4] Expressed surprise that a colleague drank Pepsi-Cola, and then said, with a kind of serious and sleepy dismay, that Coca-Cola was what was wrong with the whole world, and that we had exported it all over the world. Then paused and asked my colleague if she understood this symbolic, rather drastic statement. [coca-c][sk4] Fear of ecological catastrophes. [plut-n][vml3] Frightful but beautiful dreams, of clusters of many coloured bubbles in an ellipse, swimming in the sky and which are supposed to be chemicals thrown by aliens to destroy the earth. [polys][sk4] As it was in substances being destroyed such as Eagles, Falcons and Ozone. I was anxious about so much rain. There was severe flooding in our valley, washing the bridge out that connected us to the rest of the world. I felt isolated; lives were decimated. I felt frantic because I couldn't be helpful. [haliae-lc][srj5] Deep sadness, so much light pollution. Can see so few stars. [haliae-lc][srj5] Car exhausts seem a thousand times worse than normal. [haliae-lc][srj5] Feel despondency over the state of the world. We don't respect our environment, we are destroying the planet, we have no respect for each other. [falco-pe][nl2] Feeling of clearly perceiving the aggressive nature of the city. All the stimulus, the noise, the exhaust fume stench, the ambulances and people's lack of consideration, like an increased sensitivity. [ozone][sde2] Dream of poisonous industrial snow. [ozone][sde2]

In Fire there is a general need for purification and cleansing and this applies strongly to the environment. Feel very sad. Feel that everyone needs to cry for the world's suffering – to cure the disease of the world. Tears of purification to cure the world's ills. A sadness, purification and celebration in the tears as they flowed. The destruction of forests, starvation, war, famine would all be healed if the world wept for it's own grief. [ignis-alc][es2]

I-8 Youth, Beauty, Peace & Love

The AIDS proving brought out a few particularly resonant phrases that are undoubtedly central to the modern state and to the entire Miasm. One of these was "youth, beauty, peace" or "youth, beauty, love". All I could think of was: youth, beauty, peace. [aids][nl2] The phrase, 'youth, beauty, love,' kept repeating in my mind over and over again. [aids][nl2]

The search for these great virtues, and that of truth (*See Clarity I-6*), is undoubtedly one of the major themes of life in the modern world. This is contradicted, or perhaps necessitated, by the current scarcity of these aspects of life and by the seeming inability of modern man to recognize them and to distinguish them from the false and deceptive substitutes he is offered.

The experience of these virtues can be similar to the experience of the Divine (*See Divine Connection I-2*) and the drug remedies, such as LSD, Mescaline and Ecstasy, are particularly strong in both effects. In this remedy "beautiful" illusions are typically seen. Grotesque experiences are much less marked. [anh][vh1] Excited fantasies, wonderful visions, now indescribably beautiful and wonderful forms, now frightful images. [coca][a1] When you're on E it's like you're dancing on the notes, and you just feel so up there it's like heaven. And you just feel so good, you love everybody, you look around and you think oh you're all wonderful! [mdma][saunders] Pronounced feeling of personal wellbeing; at peace with the world; deep sense of forgiveness and unconditional love. [mdma][hmd1] Big truth. Higher truth. Wider truth. Love. [lsd][nl-lsd] Reconnected with love, my cells are filled with love, I am love, I live love, I serve love. [lsd][nl-lsd] He hears voices, and the most sublime music. He sees visions of beauty and glory that can only be equalled in Paradise. Landscapes of sublimest beauty, with profusion of flowers of most brilliant colors, in contrast, to afford the greatest delight. Architecture of magnificent beauty and grandeur, and all giving a consciousness of happiness for the time, without mixture. [cann-i][a1] The last experience of which I had been conscious had seemed to satisfy every human want, physical or spiritual. [cann-i][a1] However, many other remedies also have this quality. Feel an unlimited flow of love. [adam][srj5] Taken a love-drug drug. [ara-mac][sej7] Rarely have this sense of goodness pervading everything. [dream-p][sdj1] Thought about what a proving of a rose would be like. Thought about all a rose symbolises – love, beauty; closed first, then opening out. [ignis-alc][es2] Now I felt no resistance, a harmony between heaven and earth. [neon][srj5] Feels rich in love – cherished, blessed and nurtured by family and friends. [plac][Biggs+] A feeling of love and warmth. [plut-n][srj7] When I thought about what I needed to help the pain I was feeling – a very strong powerful feeling – it was Love. [tung-met][bdx1] Felt totally desireless, nothing I need or want, a tremendous oneness. It felt like paradise. [neon][srj5] It was said that in the golden age, when man lived upon acorns, the gods lived upon Walnuts, and hence the name of Juglans, Jovis glans, or Jupiter's nuts" (Treasury of Botany). [jug-r][c1] My own experience included the realization of the existence of an opportunistic spirit – an all knowing but unintelligent entity capable of using matter for its own development. Spirit in a state of innocent being and pure love. [vacuum][es-vac]

This feeling is also often found in dreams. Dream: I was walking through a beautifully decorated house. It was decorated in pastels and white and had flowing curtains. [limen-b-c][hrn2] I imagined myself an aurora borealis, and could distinctly hear voices shouting, "Beautiful! Oh, was not that splendid?" [phos][a1]

The subject can feel that they are beautiful. I am receiving good energy and compliments from people, they tell me that I am beautiful. [limen-b-c][hrn2] Or they can desire to be or to make themselves beautiful. Go to town looking for sexy underwear. Feel womanly. Want to flaunt it. [heroin][sdj-h] In dreams, felt ever so beautiful, wanted to decorate myself. [irid-met][srj5] Desire to walk gracefully. [lac-h][sk4] Wants to look nice, been painting nails and dressing up. [tung-met][bdx1]

There can be a feeling of harmony and contentment and perfection. He feels very good, as if he can tackle the whole world. Everything in life works more perfectly. There is a new order in things. [aids][nl2] Everything seems to complement everything else; balance and harmony, and order and form in the universe. [adam][srj5] He hears music of the sweetest and sublimest melody and harmony, and sees venerable bards with their harps, who play as if it were the music of heaven. [cann-i][a1] Like us, they seem to have fleeting moments of joy when the mate is won, the game is played, the belly is full, and the sun shines on our backs. [corv-cor][bdg1] When dolphins sing, they harmonize flawlessly in the same pitch. [lac-del][hrn2] A pleasant, youthful freshness and vigor of body and mind. [pip-m][a1] I feel so good inside. I want to yell and shout thank you! I wish that the whole world were happy and full of peace, blessings and the sheer delight of being alive, in this place which is so beautiful, so full of abundance, humour and dancing! Am finding my singing voice again and wanting to sing! [positr][nl2]

But there is also an uneasiness, a sense that this state is unsustainable or a feeling that it is breaking down. Dream: bright, vivid color in the tropics and flowers. I never dream about the tropics. But beyond the flowers, it seemed there was something evil going on. [aramac][sej7] I feel like I never look beautiful. [corv-cor][bdg1] Life seems like hell. The beauty and order are gone. [haliae-lc][srj5] I felt so much love I didn't know how to focus it. It's like being in another state of consciousness. No one can come near and its frightening me. [hydrog][srj2] Out of this horror and cruelty, he needs to produce an illusion of an opposite state of beauty and peace so that he can survive. [cann-i][sk7] I had a thought after this dream how can such a beautiful place produce such a horrible experience. [cann-i][sk7] Or that the perfect world is somewhere else. Dream: Living in a different galaxy; the planet I was on had an immense beautiful forest and the other human inhabitants took great care with their environment. [urol-h][rwt3] Or that it is unattainable. Organized, I feel if I could get things neat and organized the world would be perfect, but I can never get to that point, because there will be a flow. [haliae-lc][srj5]

The breakdown of these feelings and the sense that they can never be reached are major themes of the Miasm which are explored later. (*See Lack of Confidence XI-1*)

There is a need and desire to create the states of beauty, peace and love. This can be general, I make beauty. [corv-cor][bdg1] or personal, I want to force people to smile. [galla-q-r][nl2] but are especially global. If these people make a revolution it is always with an avoidance of violence; they are followers of the ecological movements and whatever is mild and non-violent. [cann-i][vh1] Dreamt of speaking with Martin Luther King about suggestions and methods of creating world peace. I was giving the suggestion and felt hopeful. [haliae-lc][srj5] I went to a group meditation for world peace (first and last time). [plut-n][srj7] I want to experience love, lots of love and lots of different people's love and to express love. [vacuum][es-vac] The desire for beauty is particularly strong in Placenta. Want to see beauty, especially beautiful men. [plac][Biggs+] Searching for beauty, perfection and refinement. Craving for physical beauty rather than spiritual, looking for a face, a perfect face. [plac][Biggs+] Seeing beauty, a childlike innocence, seeing things afresh as a child would. [plac][Biggs+]

This feeling of wanting or needing to create a better place or world is also partly behind the desire for neatness and order. (*See Order & Chaos V-5*) This feeling also appears strongly in the Cancer Miasm. The differentiation is again perhaps one of boundaries. Carcinosin looks for this state in their personal bounded world and is less affected by the wider world; whereas AIDS looks for the same state in a global or even a universal context.

The need for love is an important issue and some of the remedies reflect this. Either as symbols of love such as Diamond and Mistletoe. Often referred to as, 'the stone or reconciliation,' it has, of course, from the very earliest times been a favorite stone for lovers. [adam][srj5] The plant also produced the arrow with which the Germanic sun god Balder, the darling of all the gods, was killed by his blind brother Hödur, with the agency of Loki the Bringer of Doom. The moment Balder died, winter began. He was restored to life at the request of the other gods and goddesses, and Mistletoe was afterwards given into the keeping of the goddess of Love [Freyja], and it was ordained that everyone who passed under it should receive a kiss, to show that the branch had become an emblem of love, and not of hate. [visc][vml3] Or as a substitute for love, especially Chocolate. Chocolate is often used as a substitute for love, an idea often exploited by the emphasis on romantic themes in chocolate advertisements. In patients the desire often arose at times of emotional stress especially regarding relationships. Research has showed a connection between chocolate and enzymes produced when people fall in love. [choc][srj3]

The feelings of youth, beauty and love are quite often asexual but they can also have sexual dimension. Often there is a confusion as to the exact nature of the sexuality. (*See Sexuality VIII-5*)

The modern obsession with youth can be beautiful, Feeling really sexual with a 19 year old boy. We got left alone. It was exciting. He had beautiful eyes. I was so surprised this guy liked me. We talked about things you don't normally talk about with a 19 year old. He had a white bottom beneath his tan line – beautiful. [haliae-lc][srj5] but it is often disturbingly close to the incestuous feelings that arose in many provings (*See Rape, Child Abuse & Incest IX-4*)

There is a sense of purity and a desire for cleanness and whiteness. I felt out of it. I need to read a lot, children's novels because of their purity, [adam][srj5] White frost this morning. At last some purity in this world. Every ice crystal sparkled like jewels. [adam][srj5] The botanical name originates from the Gr. hagnos and the L. castus: both mean purity [as innocent as a lamb]. According to Dioscorides the name came from a [= no] and gonos [= progeny]. To this very day in Italy the blossoming branches are laid on a novice's path when she is entering the convent to become a nun. [agn][vml3] Dream: everything is pristine and pure. Then I noticed dirt and evil, the intransigence of people who have the power. "How can you destroy this beauty?" Feeling powerless. [corv-cor][bdg1] Feel that I don't want any trappings. I want to be in a whitewashed cell. [dream-p][sdj1] Feel an urge to get rid of everything that isn't functional. [dream-p][sdj1] Dream of white lilies. Tall, proud stately, steely white lilies. Dreams of purity, desire to purify body. [irid-met][srj5] Dream I was on a mountain covered with snow. There was also an animal there. [lac-h][sk4] Dream of a lake of white milk and a baby polar bear. [lac-h][htj1] Dream of a freak snowfall over fields of yellow corn and oilseed rape. I was trying to save naked babies from the cold and being pursued by hungry fish type reptile. [lac-h][htj1] I feel totally clean inside and out. I have lost the unclean feeling I always had. [neon][srj5] Ozone is one of the most vigorous oxidizing agents know. It destroys bacteria, fungi, and algae. It is used as a water purifying agent and causes many colours to fade rapidly. [ozone][sde2] My partner shows me a colour chart – he's painting the house. I said: just paint it white I can't cope with colours any more. [plut-n][srj7] Image of a very clear, white space, ready to be decorated, everything was white. [sanguis-s][hrn2] I want everything to be organic uncontaminated by chemicals and pesticides. [vacuum][es-vac] In both the Vulture and in Fire the main theme is about the cleansing of a dirty world into one that is pure and clean. I am having dreams of dirty going to clean. [cath-a][rwt] Phoenix rising from the ashes. [cath-a][rwt] Suddenly overcome with a desire for the place to be absolutely spotless and perfect. So I started cleaning, scrubbed the place from top to bottom. Got loads of bleach – obliterate all dirt and possibilities of dirt. [ignis-alc][es2] Woke with a feeling of being born into the light. Feeling of having been in some dark place during the night and being born again to a new day – a new beginning. [ignis-alc][es2] There was snow today. It was beautiful, like a fresh start, a new world, all white and beautiful. [ignis-alc][es2] It's raining today. Noticing how clean everything becomes in the rain – purification. Wash away the ills and sins of the world. [ignis-alc][es2] Purity and virginity are of great importance. A great desire to be again a virgin. [ignis-alc][es2]

This sense is matched by an obsession with tidiness and order. (*See Chaos & Order V-5*) and with the polar symptoms to do with infection, dirt, and shame. (*See Infection X*)

One manifestation of the theme of purity that is particularly noticeable in the AIDS Nosode but which runs subtly through many other remedies is a sense of connection to primitive, purer societies. I felt like I had to keep my feet on the ground, the only way to describe it would be a as a delusion really – a tribal one; Cheyenne with tepees and people and it was pleasant and the sensation was very, very real to me and I had to force myself to get in the car and drive it, and I had to keep myself grounded. [aids][nl2] Everything felt natural, tribal natural – like the south sea islands with water but natural bare foot and nothing much underneath with flowers but natural with white, green and water. [aids][nl2] This connection is also partly expressed in a desire for nakedness and skin decoration, I felt like doing something mischievous. I had no embarrassment with nakedness. [aids][nl2] *(See The Skin XII-4)* and for music. The combination of the drug with music and dancing together produces an exhilarating trance-like state, perhaps similar to that experienced in tribal rituals or religious ceremonies. [mdma][saunders] *(See Music IV-9)*

There are also important feelings of great strength and power, I began to be lifted into that tremendous pride which is so often a characteristic of the fantasia. My powers became superhuman; my knowledge covered the universe; my scope of sight was infinite. [cann-i][a1] Constant desire to undertake vast feats of strength. [cocain][a1] It stimulates a heightened sense of balance and physical agility. [mdma][hmd1] Feeling like a warrior, sensing great hope for the goodness in the world. Decisiveness. Resolute. [sanguis-s][hrn2] Felt really good today, felt I was flying and there were no obstacles. [sal-fr][sle1] and invulnerability. I am invincible; there is a green aura around me to protect me. Someone with a samurai sword starts to stab me, but the sword is stopped by the green aura. I am invincible, totally whole, perfect, and one with myself – mind and body. [coca-c][sk4] I feel invincible when upright. No wavering – like a laser. [neon][srj5] The skunk would seem to be well aware of the effectiveness of this defence weapon, since it walks fearlessly in the open and is generally not bothered by predators. [meph][vml3]

There are also feelings that the subject is in possession of great knowledge or skill. Nothing seems a problem. Problems are just there to be solved! [adam][srj5] He imagines that he is possessed of infinite knowledge and power of vision, and then that he is Christ come to restore the world to perfect peace. [cann-i][a1] It felt like my mind was so expanded I could understand anything in an instant. [lsd][nl-lsd]

These feelings are definitely in contrast to the feelings of vulnerability, powerlessness and lack of confidence which lie at the centre of this group of remedies. *(See Vulnerability IX-1 and Lack of Confidence XI-1)* However, there is a sense of these contradictory elements coming together, where the very lack of protection is in itself a very powerful thing. Exquisite and precious mental pain – I had no shell for protection. [aids][nl2] Felt no fear but more aware of danger. Very strong desire not to be at home. Felt I had no protection —felt strong, not like a victim – nothing protecting me. [tung-met][bdx1]

I-9 Benevolence

There is in many of these remedies a feeling of responsibility. He was continually preoccupied with solicitous impressions as to the fate of his companions, for whom he feared the dose of Hashish had been excessive, and might even prove poisonous. [cann-i][a1] There has been a strong need to stand up against any form of oppression, whether it be to myself or to others. [falco-pe][nl2] Very strong sense of responsibility to family, more than duty, they are obliged to care and support. [buteo-j][sej-birds] This responsibility is particularly to those that are vulnerable. (*See Babies, Children & Animals IX-2*)

There can be strong sense that this responsibility is a cause of conflict and difficulty because it is beyond the powers and abilities of the subject. Thus, in Indian mythology, the lowly and despised rat has responsibility for the great god Ganesha. Ganesha, the great elephant-headed God, rides on the back of the rat. The rat has the responsibility to care for its holy charge and look ahead to problems they might encounter. [sanguis-s][hrn2]

The responsibility is unbounded and so becomes global but the subject has no power over events, they are often things that are out of the hands of individuals, or even of societies. I was anxious about so much rain. There was severe flooding in our valley, washing the bridge out that connected us to the rest of the world. I felt isolated; lives were decimated. I felt frantic because I couldn't be helpful. [haliae-lc][srj5] (*See Nature I-7*)

There is also a conflict between the feeling of responsibility and the desire to help and the lack of confidence felt by many subjects. I felt very "spacey" and my head kind of heavy. Afraid that I will make a foolish mistake that could hurt someone. [corian-s][knl6] (*See Lack of Confidence XI-1*)

The need to help and the sense of responsibility can also lie at the root of more generalized restlessness. Have the feeling that one shouldn't sit without doing any work, that "rest is the devil". [lac-h][sk4] There is the urge to avoid necessary rest and restful recreation, even though both may be of vital need. [querc-r][rcb4] (*See Speed & Rushing IV-12*)

There is also conflict between of responsibility and the desire to do something and the equally strong desire to for luxury and comfort. Conflict between what I am doing and what I am supposed to do. [polys][sk4] This feeling is particularly strong in Lac humanum. Constant dilemma of being highly spiritual and God fearing, against bouts of being unreligious and sinful – a turmoil. [lac-h][sk4] Persistent thoughts about how to improve my work, while at the same time the idea kept coming to me of being in a five-star hotel, and just watching movies on television. [lac-h][sk4]

There is in many of these remedies a powerful desire to be helpful. Dream of banking and shopping, gave it all away. [adam][srj5] Then he possesses the wealth of the world, and with a benevolence equal to his wealth, showers riches on all the needy around him. [cann-i][a1] Generous. Helped with snorkel stuff a lot. [lac-del][hrn2] Dream: A patient, who was paralysed, was lying in a dirty toilet with blood shot eyes. I had to pick him up, support him and take him for a CT scan to a diagnostic centre nearby. The man was very bulky, but I managed to reach him even though I had a tough time doing it. [lac-h][sk4] When I tried to imagine the remedy the words that came to mind were benevolence and detachment. [lac-h][htj1] Dream: I was teaching a friend how to deploy a parachute. He was going out for a flight with an older man in an airplane. I felt like I needed to offer him something, some sort of help or instruction. [lac-lup][hrn2] Feel like I have to help others less fortunate. I am so lucky, I have so much. I just want to help my friends and try and save their lives – help them have better, easier, healthier lives. [lac-lup][hrn2] Dreams of responsibility, blessed by a saint, saving people who are threatened by floods, being busy. [osm][stj2] I felt really loving towards people and I felt like being nice which is really unusual. [positr][nl2] Everything seemed beautiful including the people – wanted to share it and be nice and love people, not for any gain. [positr][nl2] Even though they are fearless they are very peaceful creatures. They move forward slowly and calmly and only spray when there is no other alternative. Being the sympathetic creatures that they are, they always give a warning before they spray. [meph][vml3] Dream: Inherited great deal of money and gave it all away; felt exhilaration. [urol-h][rwt3]

Even Scorpion, which is probably the coldest and cruelest of all the remedies, includes the symptom: Helpfulness. [androc][vml3] and Anacardium, another cruel remedy, is included under the rubric Benevolence.

The benevolence can be found in some of the substances. In ancient lore, the mystical power of the gem could only work when it had been freely given and would lose its power when stolen or taken by force. [adam][srj5] The Oak tree is particularly known for the shelter and support that it offers to a vast number of other creatures, Oak trees are rich in nourishment and shelter, they sustain many life forms in their vicinity and, through one of their species, even give "food" and sustenance to the work-oriented human mentality. [querc-r][rcb4]

and this is reflected in the remedy picture. The tree's richness also expresses the human reliability and loyal tendency to support others, as portrayed in the Oak mentality. [querc-r][rcb4]

The Oak is also a noble and kingly tree and the benevolence can have a sense of coming from a place of nobility or regality. Dream: I feel regal and generous. [haliae-lc][srj5] (*See Nobility VI-3*)

Milk is a substance that is a gift from mother to child giving nourishment and life and it is to be expected that the Lacs will have a tendency to benevolence. (*See Babies and Children IX-3*) The Placenta fulfills a similar role in relation to the unborn child. Contented slightly benevolent state. [plac][Biggs+]

Cereus Bonplandii, The Good Plant, is the remedy in which benevolence is strongest and perhaps most pure. Felt all day an astonishing inclination to be engaged in something useful. [cere-b][a1] Felt a desire to give something quite necessary to myself to another. [cere-b][a1] The main theme of Cereus bonplandii is that the person is very much attached to God, to the extent that he feels that he is under the powerful influence of a God-like person and that he can thereby help to relieve the suffering of mankind. [cere-b][Latha Iyer, I desire to be a useful remedy, Homoeopathic Links, 1/97]

Coca Cola also has great benevolence, Dream: Distributing food to stunned and unhappy looking Japanese people, who had been rounded up and placed in internment camps. Felt saddened by their plight and wanted to take care of them in the midst of their injustice. [coca-c][sk4] Very unusually calmly helping a person in front of me who was unable to put a key into a lock by putting my hand over hers and gently guiding the key in. [coca-c][sk4] Dream: Three men were trying to kill one man in an alley. I felt the need to go and help him. [coca-c][sk4] but Sankaran has described it as being less selfless than it appears. Sankaran in a seminar has said that the Coca Cola patient feels that he is lost and alone and that he needs to build a network of people that will help him. He does this by being helpful to everyone he can. His seemingly unlimited benevolence creates a net of people indebted to him. [coca-c][sk]

The feeling that the benevolence is not properly recognized or rewarded is very strong in Lac Humanum Dream: I was waiting at a bus stop with an elderly person who was unable to walk properly. I made way for him to climb in, when the bus arrived, but was myself refused entry when I tried to get in. I felt I should think of myself first, and then for others. [lac-h][sk4] and is also found in Positronium and Oak. There may be unceasing disappointments or lack of rewards despite efforts made. [querc-r][rcb4] I feel abused and used by my children – as if they are draining me. They take everything – I feel very taken for granted. [positr][nl2]

The feeling of benevolence is also expressed in indignation, anger or sadness at a lack of goodness or truth in people or in society. Thoughts about the 'veneer of civilisation' that inhibits how we really feel and keeps us from displaying what we're like beneath the surface. [choc][srj3] Deceit of others (common). [corv-cor][bdg1] Lack of integrity in others. [corv-cor][bdg1] I don't recognize myself as human. I don't know who I am. I feel so heavy and earthbound, stuck with human desires that are not my own. Why don't I fit? Where is the truth and justice they talk about? Why do humans lie and deceive? I feel a big thing about truth and justice. "Why don't these people just tell me the truth?" It feels like a game, not telling me what they really want and need. [haliae-lc][srj5] Watched programme, felt disgust at deceit of someone in the programme – really touched me, made me feel more miserable. [falco-pe][nl2] Feeling of revulsion for many people especially young parents with children, while wandering through town. Feel people are stuck in their lives. What a waste. [germ-met][srj5] They absolutely hate dishonesty. [lac-f][vml3] I feel angry and upset. Feel that people are laughing at me they don't understand and they don't want to listen. I feel that the people I am living with aren't in touch with reality they don't want to listen or understand people they just like quoting theories living their lives in their heads rather than facing the truth. [latex][nl-latex] Realize that feelings of empathy for animals, people or nature in pain or difficulty are much stronger and deeper. Feelings of disgust for the tastelessness of TV with its diet of sex, sensation and violence are very strong, sad and contemptuous. How can standards of integrity, worth and peace be passed to our children, when so much pollution (of the Planet, of our minds) surround them. It makes me want to go and live on a desert island. [positr][nl2] Lyrics of songs irritating me, a lot of them seem meaningless. A lot of songs using the word 'love' – but that is not what they mean. [vacuum][es-vac]

There is a particular and specific dislike for superficial small talk that comes up in a number of remedies. Didn't feel comfortable with superficial small talk. Imagined everything I said sounded wrong, gabbling. [aids][nl2] Repugnance to laughter and conversation. [ambr][a1] Frivolous chat makes me angry. [ignis-alc][es2] On Ecstasy small talk and flirting seem ridiculously hollow, and so this sort of behaviour has become taboo in rave culture. [mdma][saunders] Many subjects reported that their feelings were stronger after sessions and some said that they now avoid superficial social meetings such as cocktail parties. [mdma][saunders] I was at a party and everyone was talking in a most superficial way. I felt much deeper, totally alien to all that. I found it difficult to adapt. [plut-n][srj7] Have felt totally unable to make small talk with people. I look at people chatting and think, "How do you think of things to say like that?" [positr][nl2] Irritated by others' flippancy. [rhus-g][tmo3] Little tolerance for people into their ego. [urol-h][rwt3] Told boyfriend that his colleague was "full of shit". Felt annoyed at his superficial attitude and creepiness. [tung-met][bdx1]

II-1 Disconnection

I feel disconnected. [aids][nl2]

Another consequence of the dissolution of boundaries is a sense of disconnection. This can be seen as a consequence of the tension of opposites, of a zero sum universe in which any increase in the sense of connection inevitably leads to an equal and opposite sense of disconnection.

However, the path to this disconnection can be quite clearly mapped. A lack of boundaries also means a lack of definition. Just as the subject has no definite boundaries the people and things around him have no proper definition. I heard myself saying to a friend that the boundaries between myself and those that I love feel very fluffy, not hard and sharp, but a soft and diffused feeling of energy between myself and loved ones. My field interacts and penetrates theirs at the fluffy boundaries edge. [positr][nl2] When connection is made it is more complete, however, these fluffy boundaries are hard to identify and this makes connection very difficult.

There is a tendency for things to bounce off and not to stick or break through. I feel above it all, as if the harsh realities of the world can't touch me, they just register and bounce off. [aids][nl2] By the afternoon I felt above it all, serene, even rested, was able to listen to landlord being racist and let it pass over my head instead of getting worked up. [aids][nl2] No event disturbed his equanimity. [ars][a1] Sensation of a strong pure silence inside. No matter what happens it just ripples over me and is gone. I experience it, but there aren't any footprints left. [choc][srj3] During the periods of enjoyment, the phlegm of the chewer is marvellous; no degree of urgency or entreaty will move him; under the influence of the Coca the chewer is heedless of the thunderstorm which threatens to drown him where he lies or the roar of approaching wild beasts, or of the smoking fire which creeps along the grass, and is about to surface or scorch him in his lair. [coca][a1] Feel light and happy, as if nothing matters much, and I can't control anything. [coca-c][sk4] Things that normally would pressure me didn't. [helodr-cal][knl2] Time warp feeling and timeless feeling. Staring and pondering but not pondering about anything specific. I felt I was reflecting a lot. If there was a potential conflict I could see it but I did not feel it, sense of being unaffected by these conflicts. [lac-loxod-a][hrn2] I am easy going, nothing has got on my nerves. [ozone][sde2]

This in turn leads to a sense of calm and tranquillity. Unhurried and untroubled. I feel content and happy with the world – emotionally connected – much more settled. [aids][nl2] Foolish joy and absurd complacency, with himself and his labour; internal complacency, with smiles. [anan][a1] In India and Sri Lanka the oil of vetiver roots is known as "the oil of tranquility". [anan][vml3] Calm and equable mood. [ars][a1] Very relaxed and calm all day. [carbn-dox][knl3] Generally contented with a neither there nor here feeling. [haliae-lc][srj5] Tranquility. Reduces physical and emotional stress. [mdma][hmd1] Saw nothing and thought nothing most of the time. [falco-pe][nl2] Very spaced-out. The rest of the day was dreamy and calm, immersing myself in cooking. [falco-pe][nl2] I felt so mellow, like I could just flow with this and be. [falco-pe][nl2] Very peaceful with my situation. [lac-del][hrn2] Lying in a hammock, all anxiety left me. I felt connected and deep relaxation. [lac-del][hrn2] Still feel calm, high. In that ponder state it was a calm, still, peaceful feeling; even if I was in motion, I felt still. [lac-loxod-a][hrn2] More contentment and calmness. [lars-arg][fkw1] Feel very calm and peaceful inside, no desire to busy myself with a hundred things. [neon][srj5] I felt quite peaceful, and calmer. [plut-n][srj7] Deep meditative state devoid of thoughts or sensations. [positr][nl2] Have a feeling of peacefulness, my emotions feel calmer than they have done in previous months. [sal-fr][sle1] I seem to be able to maintain an incredible calm. [galeoc-c-h][gms1] I don't feel hurried or rushed which is unusual. [galeoc-c-h][gms1] I feel calm and sure of myself. [rhus-g][tmo3] Very content. [rhus-g][tmo3] From rising, feeling of serenity, calmness. [tung-met][bdx1] More calm than usual, less wound up in difficult situation. [tung-met][bdx1] Pleasant, serene, blissful, not fully awake. [tung-met][bdx1] I was feeling so calm, euphoric, a mellowness. [vacuum] [es-vac]

Anxiety is reduced. Calm, enjoyment, great excitement and a sense of fun in the hustle-bustle in which I am usually uneasy and fearful to be alone. [coca-c][sk4] It made her feel quiet and self-possessed; no fear of anything, is usually nervous and timid. [mosch][a1] I have lost all sense of anxiety almost to the extent that I do not know the meaning of the word. [positr][nl2]

This calm state extends even into dangerous situations, especially in Lac delphinum. Dream: House flooded and had to use rowboat to get to friend's house. I was using a rowboat to get to and from classes and visit friends and go back and forth. Water was everywhere, and this was my mode of transportation. Calmness, no sense of danger. [lac-del][hrn2]

This calm even extends, particularly in Arsenicum, to approaching death. Calm indifference; without caring about their approaching death, they neither expected nor desired to recover (secondary effect, in two suicides who had taken Arsenic). [ars][a1] A similar symptom is found in Coca Cola. Dream I realized I was going to die in two days, and was doing a last minute preparation. I was not upset, and was doing last minute jobs to clean things up. [coca-c][sk4] And at least one Eagle prover was able to see the connection between calmness and death. Is this true calm or the calm of the dead? [haliae-lc][srj5] (*See Death XII-4*)

There is also an actual need for calmness, it is not something that just happens but it must be actively sought. This is especially so in the Rat. Desire for a contemplative lifestyle and life experienced through the observation of coincidences. What would it be like: pure knowing, clear perception? Meditation: To know the beauty of the Goddess is to understand mathematics, geometry, and an abstraction from the material world. My mind wants to grasp this knowing. [sanguis-s][hrn2] I felt spacey, forgetful, and just want to sit still. [sanguis-s][hrn2] There can be a need for this calm and without it things are aggravated. Overpowered by indescribable anxiety. Feeling of anguish increased with failure of every effort to strive against the weariness; torment only diminishes with perfect rest. [coca][vml4] I was just in the present, very calmly. Anger increased with the children for fighting because they disturbed my calm. [haliae-lc][srj5]

Not only does the subject not want to be affected but he or she loses the desire to effect and becomes very passive. Desire to sit undisturbed and just look. [androc][srj5] Egocentric introversion. [anh][jl1] Passive state. [anh][jl1] I have the idea that life is fine without thinking. Mentally, there was a feeling of dullness, and not wanting to do anything intellectual. [limen-b-c][hrn2] Her disposition is particularly quiet, being otherwise very lively. [tell][a1]

This calmness seems to lie at the root of many of the other symptoms of contemporary disease and the new remedies. Perhaps the most important of these is detachment. Felt very quiet and calm. Almost detached. [germ-met][srj5] I felt slightly high, removed from reality, yet very alert, clear and calm. [hydrog][srj2] (*See Detachment II-4*)

It also leads to feelings of numbness, A kind of numbness, with a feeling of serenity, with retention of clear self-consciousness, and an instinctive desire to make no motions, not even to move a single finger, for an entire day. While in this condition there set in a sleep, full of strange quickly changing dreams, which could last an entire day without leaving any feeling of lassitude or restlessness. [coca][a1] and anaesthesia. While walking, a sense of mellowness and extreme calm, both mental and physical; almost a sensation of anaesthesia of the body. [coca-c][sk4] (*See III-3 Anaethesia)*

Another powerful manifestation of it is indifference. Good guys and bad guys. Drama of evil is set up by the bad guys. They always win, always a struggle to just keep going. That is where I came from. During the proving, I saw that even engaging in that struggle gives it power and meaning. If you stop and watch the game, eventually there won't be anyone playing anymore. Good and bad were still positions, but it was all the same game. [haliae-lc][srj5] Or not finding a parking place in China town. I just drove around until I found one. I didn't realize how often I feel hurried. I've had days off in a row before. Internal sense of not being hurried. I just didn't care. [helodr-cal][knl2] (*See Indifference III-1*)

II-2 Not Belonging

Flowing directly from the feeling of disconnection from a subject's environment is the sense of not belonging. He suddenly felt 'I don't belong here at all'. [aids][nl2] They are the type of people who feel, even at an early age, that they do not belong to society, that they are something apart. They become distrustful and resentful toward society, and they can easily fall prey to what can be termed an "existential anxiety". [anh][vh1] Feeling I don't quite know where I belong and what I should be doing. [choc][srj3] I don't belong. I don't feel at home any place. Feel lonely. I nearly always feel special – always on the side/outside of others. Either better or smaller than others. [germ-met][srj5] I don't belong; outcast – I should go; feel defeated. [phasco-ci][rbp2] I felt alone and as if everyone perceived me as odd. I felt strange, like an outsider and could not connect on any level. [neon][srj5] It seems to her as if she does not belong in her own family. [plat][a1] I felt alienated, as if I did not belong. [sal-fr][sle1] Feel very unreal for no reason. As if the earth were shifting under my feet. All the familiar things seem different. [galeoc-c-h][gms1] Feel like I don't belong or fit in anywhere. All I wanted to do was go off into the woods with the dog. [sanguis-s][hrn2] Sometimes I feel like I'm inside a mirror looking out and can't reach out. People can be sitting in front of me, I can see them and hear them but I can't reach them. Like being in a parallel world. [vacuum][es-vac] I feel like the space I'm in at present is very removed from everything around me. I see everything but I can't reach out and touch it. I can't connect. [vacuum][es-vac] This feeling is almost always accompanied by feelings of isolation and loneliness. (*See Isolation II-8*)

Since most provers are homœopaths or homœopathic students it is not entirely surprising that this feeling can manifest around homœopathy but it is also interesting that homœopathy should match the spirit of the times so closely. I've been very sensitive. Had a disagreement over homeopathy and my beliefs with my family and got upset, almost starting crying. I had to leave the room. I felt like an outsider to my family, that I didn't belong. Also that they did not even care to hear my viewpoint. It made me feel unimportant and incidental. [lac-lup][hrn2] Feel that homœopathy has alienated me from people because I don't see the world in the same way as they do. They don't understand what I'm saying or what I really mean when I say things. [positr][nl2]

This sense of not belonging is implicit in many of the substances. Some of the remedies include the notion of being a stranger within their names. Peregrine comes from the Latin peregrinus, strange or foreign. This was the term used for non-Roman citizens living in Rome and it later became the description applied to pilgrims. [falco-pe][nl2] The English name Walnut is partly of Teutonic origin, the Germans naming the nut Wallnuss, or Welsche Nuss – Welsche signifying foreign. [jug-r][vml3] Some substances, like the Oak Gall Wasp and Mistletoe are parasites, while many of the animals involved, such as the Housefly, the Rat and the Stingray, are scavengers. Some of the animals, particularly the Lion and the Eagle, are scavengers at heart but have disguised this with a compensatory emphasis on nobility. Those animals that are at the top of the food chain pyramid are by their very nature solitary and disconnected from the other animals around them. The herd animals on the other hand do need to have a community around them of which they feel a part. This type of isolation is taken to its extreme in the Scorpion which has adopted an evolutionary niche that is so harsh and extreme that no other animals has challenged it and it has remained unchanged for many millions of years. However, this niche is so harsh, that there is no room in it for more than a solitary inhabitant and no two scorpions will inhabit the same space except for a very brief mating.

This sense is sometimes expressed in the feeling of being an alien, of not belonging to this world. Driving back from shopping at nurseries. Beautiful day, warm sun. Almost seemed other-worldly. Is this a drug remedy? [carbn-dox][knl3] Parallel universes – all happening somewhere else. I felt maybe I was in a parallel universe and it's all happening the same somewhere else. Not lonely. Just what happens. [haliae-lc][srj5] Someone says that I have behaved as if I am from another planet. [germ-met][srj5] We're doing aliens milk aren't we? [lsd][nl-lsd] I felt as if I wasn't really on this planet, not in this reality. [plut-n][srj7] Vulnerable feeling. Strange feeling of being alien. [tung-met][bdx1] This feeling came through particularly strongly in the Butterfly proving but it is the feeling that the prover should be in another reality not just another world or universe. I keep thinking, "I'm at the wrong sphere of the universe, internally and externally." I felt I was in the wrong place, I felt gross and materialistic, the work I had to do, I mean. I had to organize some things; it felt gross, I didn't want to be there. I felt

I was beyond the material sphere, somewhere else. [limen-b-c][hrn2] I went to sit in some woods. I felt in the wrong medium. I wanted to be in another state, either planted in silence in the earth or existing in space. I wanted to be in a relative quiet state that comes in meditation, that seems to be the state that part of me is in. I didn't want to be at a mundane level. [limen-b-c][hrn2]

Plutonium has a particular version of this feeling that they do not belong. I feel as if perhaps I am the wrong way up. [plut-n][srj7]

There can be a strong desire to belong and the subject may make an effort, often ineffectual, to make some connection. At party made an effort to connect with people, but found no-one anything like me. [heroin][sdj-h] At the other extreme the subject can deliberately distance him or herself from the people around them. This remedy can induce the desire to dress publicly in a peculiar, grotesque manner, all the while hoping to impress others with their shocking appearance. [anan][vh1] There can also be timidity or bashfulness that prevents connection. The patient has an embarrassed air; the bashful state is very characteristic in certain connections. [ambr][a1] Bashful: timid: ill at ease in society. [coca][tl2] (*See Lack of Confidence XI-1*)

A common expression of the feeling of not belonging is the feeling that the subject is in a strange place. The feeling is that one is in a strange place. [cann-i][sk7] Feel I'm in a different space from everyone else. [falco-pe][nl2] I felt isolated and alone. I don't want to communicate, I feel in a different place from everyone else. [plut-n][srj7] This is often expressed in dreams of travel, journeys and foreign places. (*See Travel IV-13*)

Another expression is the feeling that everything is unreal. This is common, especially in drug remedies, but it is particularly strong in Hydrogen. Feeling of being out of reality. [hydrog][srj2] Feel distant and separated from things and they feel unreal. [hydrog][srj2] Everything, even themselves, seemed unreal; so that I did not feel certain that I was even in the room with them. [cann-i][a1] I felt as if I were removed from reality. [sal-fr][sle1] A shock that makes her feel things are unreal. [tax-br][oss1]

There are also feelings that things are artificial, Everything seems artificial. [anh][sp1] Dream I asked for juice, and the waitress brought us an imitation, artificial fruit drink. There was a lot of plastic. I felt the people were strange and backward. Also felt that the world was too chemical and synthetic. [coca-c][sk4] or strange, The most familiar objects appear strange and are not recognized. [cann-i][a1] or ludicrous, He stood still of mind, and on collecting himself everything about him seemed ludicrous. [nux-m][a1] or changed, Delusions: thinks everything changed. [nux-m][vml2] or simply not quite right. In a restaurant felt anxious that things weren't right. [androc][srj5]

These sensations can apply to people as well as to places and things. One very good friend said I didn't seem to be there. They seemed like strangers to me. [irid-met][srj5] This is one of the roots of the feelings of isolation that are so strong. (*See Isolation II-8*)

They can also be about time. The shrub blossoms and forms seeds when the soil becomes poorer in the autumn! [agn][vml3] Feeling that the time isn't right. [choc][srj3] This is perhaps a part of the more general confusion about time. (*See Confusion about Time VII-7*)

This sensation of not belonging applies in an important way to the subject's own body and physical self. Feels strange and singular in his whole body, but cannot describe the sensation. [tell][a1] This is manifested in the particular symptoms of a split, particularly a split between the mind and the body, (*See Splitting V-4*) and a deep confusion of identity. (*See Confusion of Identity VII-5*) The sensation can also apply to the voice, His voice seems strange, as if not his own. [cann-i][a1] but this is often an aspect of feminization and gender confusion. (*See Gender Confusion VIII-4*)

II-3 As if In A Dream

The sense of disconnection, especially the feeling of being disconnected from reality leads to a lack of distinction between the world of reality and the dream world. The sensation that the subject is "as if in a dream" is a well known symptom of Nux Moschata and of drug remedies, especially the Opiates, Delusions: everything is strange, as if in dream. "She performs all her duties and yet seems to be in a dream." [nux-m][vml2] but it is found in many of the remedies of the AIDS Miasm. He is always as if he were in a dream. [ambr][a1] Delusion that there is no reality in anything, all appears like a dream. [anac][c1] All his senses seem to vanish and he gropes around as if in a dream. [anac][k2] The peculiarity of Anhalonium in this regard is that the involuntary visions, which are often quite colorful, do not frighten the individual; furthermore, though he knows that the visions are unreal, he seems to experience and attend to them as if they were real. [anh][vh1] Reveries in the daytime. [conv-d][a1] Some of it felt dream like, as if I wasn't there at all. [falco-pe][nl2] I felt spacey, out of focus, odd, slightly, not there. Maybe in a dream. [germ-met][srj5] Felt similar to being in water or asleep, as if almost asleep or in a trance, aware, but floating in inner self, uncommunicative; like a near death experience, inner self is primary and separate. [irid-met][srj5] All day Friday was in a dream. [lac-h][htj1] Feeling as if in a dream. [visc][vml3] Sensation as if in a dream and all is unreal and through a kind of invisible veil. [tung-met][bdx1] I don't know whether I sleep and dream or think I am dreaming. [lars-arg][fkw1] The role that rubber has in separating the user of it from the world came through in the proving, especially as the feeling that the subject is in a bubble separated from the world. Aware again of ache in ears and feeling of not being able to hear normally. Everything seems clear and normal in a sense but distant as if being separated in a bubble. [latex][nl-latex] Am slightly spaced out not really in this world. [latex][nl-latex] Feeling of faintness and unreality. [latex][nl-latex] Felt head and thoughts swimming a bit. With the hearing still being poor and the muzzy head and difficulty in hearing I feel separated from everything, including myself. I feel in a bit of a dream, like being under thick murky liquid. [latex][nl-latex]

There is also difficulty in distinguishing the boundary between the dream world and the real world. I was really conscious all night about having to remember my dreams and having to disentangle whether I was in a dream, whether it was a dream, that sort of half-conscious state. [aids][nl2] Did not know if it was really real or a dream. Could not tell my dream from reality. [carneg-g][rwt1] I felt that the dreams were intruding into my life. [urol-h][rwt3] There are also dreams about dreams. Dreamt I remembered yesterday's dream but dreamt forgot it again. [sal-fr][sle1] and Plutonium and Adamas are the other remedies in the rubric Dreams of dreaming.

There is a tendency to push into the dream world things that are suppressed in the waking world. This was a particularly important symptom in the Heroin proving where the suppression of the conscious is so strong that the unconscious is forced to take up and explore important issues in the dreams. I cannot remember dreams, but I am aware that I am dreaming a lot. Before I awake, I know that the dreams are to do with things I am worrying about, even though I am not worrying about these issues when I am awake. When I was walking the dog this morning I thought about this, it is as if all my anxiety has gone into my subconscious and my conscious is anxiety free. I have decided that this is quite good. [heroin][sdj-h]

In the Wolf the general sense of disconnection is less apparent in daily life but it comes through strongly in the dreams. More impatient during the day but very patient and not caring in the dreams. Disconnected, unemotional in the dreams, opposite in waking life. [lac-lup][hrn2]

In Selenium there is the peculiar symptom of things are forgotten in the day, particularly matters of business, to be remembered in the dreams. Dreams of the occurrences of the day. [sel][a1] Very forgetful in business, but during sleep dreams of what he had forgotten. [sel][c1]

In Crack Willow and in Chocolate there is the strange sensation that the dreams that are dreamt do not belong to the dreamer. I have begun to remember my dreams. They are alien in character – I swear they are not my dreams. I usually remember my dreams in detail, but now they are flashes, snapshots- i.e. witnessing a murder, people being crushed, dripping boiling fat on self, a hanged man falling down an interminable lift shaft, injuries to myself when pregnant. [choc][srj3] Dreamless sleep – a change in their character when they do occur – I feel as though they've been stolen or as if they are someone else's dreams. [choc][srj3] Three fellow students who had spoken with me and another prover yesterday reported having had vivid dreams last night "which didn't seem like their own dreams". [sal-fr][sle1] In Lac Humanum the sensation is the other way round with the subject feeling that it is not him or her who is dreaming the dreams. Felt it was not me who was dreaming the dreams. [lac-h][htj1]

The sensations around dreaming contain features of the empathy and clairvoyance found in these remedies. (*See Empathy & Clairvoyance I-5*)

The connection between the dream world is an important one and though it can cause confusion it can also be a positive force. Must move freely between the world of dream and daily life, bridge the gap between these worlds [haliae-lc][sej-birds] (*See Death XII-8*)

II-4 Detachment

The rubric which most dramatically demonstrates the difference between the new remedies and the old is: MIND – DETACHED adam.; agath-a.; androc.; arizon-l.; brass-n-o.; carneg-g.; choc.; corv-cor.; falco-pe.; galeoc-c-h.; germ-met.; granit-m.; haliae-lc.; ham.; hydrog.; hyos.; irid-met.; kali-p.; lac-del.; lac-h.; lac-lup.; lat-h.; loxo-recl.; luna; nat-sil.; neon;1; olib-sac.; plut-n.; podo.; positr.; rauw.; rhus-g.; sal-fr.; sanguis-s.; sel.; sep.; sulph.; symph.; syph.; tax.; trios.; ven-m.; vero-o.; The classic texts give only Syphilinum for this symptom: A far-away feeling, with apathy and indifference to future. [syph][a1] There has been the addition of a few remedies such as Hyoscyamus, Sulphur and Sepia, but the vast majority of remedies are new ones and most of the recent provings have clearly demonstrated this symptom. This might be put down to language difference but while indifference and apathy are symptoms that do cover the old and the new; the idea of detachment does seem to be peculiar to the contemporary world.

This feeling is perhaps strongest in the Scorpion. Even more remarkable is the fact that, like no other species, they have remained unchanged for nearly 400 million years, indicating a remarkable success in the process of life and evolution. [androc][srj5] Felt detached, very interested in little things. Felt detached from everything, as in a dream. Reactions slowed down a lot. [androc][srj5] In the evening felt very lonely and desolate, although not alone. She felt separated, detached, disconnected and unreal. [androc][srj5] Felt disconnected from the human race, as if everyone were another species. Directionless. [androc][srj5] A sense of detachment was one prevailing symptom that appeared, detachment from other people, from the world in general, and from one's own pain and discomfort. There was a pervading disinterest in other people, in the opinion of others, and in one's usual sources of pleasure and intellectual stimulation. [Guess] [androc][vml3] I consider detachedness to be the keynote of Androc. They have the idea of belonging to another species than humankind. They may have the idea of being a kind of extraterrastrial. They feel like a bystander, experiencing some invisible barrier between themselves and the others. To find out their origins they may be deeply interested in the creation of the earth and in genealogy. [Zala][androc][vml3]

The detachment can be fairly general. I feel the separateness of me from the world, not my spirit from my body, the whole of me, I can't touch the world. [adam][srj5] Still feeling very removed and on the outside of things. [dream-p][sdj1] Feel as though I'm in a plastic bubble – didn't feel part of the world as though everything going on around me – nothing and no one can touch me. [dream-p][sdj1] Still less emotionality in reactions. Things not making an impression on me, for better or worse. [haliae-lc][srj5] There was a sense of detachment. [falco-pe][nl2] I have had a strange sense of detachment and a sort of cosmic view of things for a while. [falco-pe][nl2] Felt very quiet and calm. Almost detached. [germ-met][srj5] I was aware of feeling very contented with life, but detached. [heroin][sdj-h] Things going on around me and I don't feel part of them. Automatically doing things on one level, but "not there" on another. [irid-met][srj5] Feel a bit distant. Not felt at all conscientious, like riding over the top of something. [irid-met][srj5] Actually felt somewhat detached, and all the old stuff has not come up. [lac-del][hrn2] Felt separate from this, not a part of it. Felt really like I wanted to isolate. Feeling like a loner. Just stay on the beach and relax and not participate. [lac-del][hrn2] They become detached, and have a sort of numbness to life. [Assilem][lac-h][vml3] I have a feeling of detachment. [ignis-alc][es2] Feeling quite unreal, detached from everything happening around me. [latex][nl-latex] Felt distanced from my problems. They were there but I wasn't feeling the full impact of them. [latex][nl-latex] A strong feeling of detachment. [osm][stj2] Was assertive and non-interfering; quite aloof, detached, objective. Felt others should not get so involved. [polys][sk4] Constant strange feeling of being in a trance, as if my mind and body were separated or as if I wasn't in touch with things around me or with myself. [polys][sk4] Feel more detached like I am judging a situation without jumping into it emotionally. [rhus-g][tmo3] A little bit removed, not quite detached. I was very clear, able to move through decisions. [sanguis-s][hrn2] More able to detach myself. [carneg-g][rwt1] Anxiety that produces a feeling of not being in reality, detached and not present. [tax-br][oss1] It's like an independence of mind, being distant. I feel miles away. [tung-met][bdx1] Feel less attached to changing the world. feels detached, with a stronger sense of peace. [vacuum][es-vac]

It can be more specific and be from the environment, Dissociation from one's environment. [anh][sp1] or from people, Felt separate from friends today, which was unusual. I felt outside them. [adam][srj5] On any one speaking to him, it seems as if the persons were at a great distance. [coca][hl9] Felt dull, as if I wasn't in touch with the others. [coca-c][sk4] I feel that no one is responding to me. I'm in an indifferent state, quiet state. [helodr-cal][knl2] I feel separated from people and places. [germ-met][srj5] Felt detached in company, reticent to speak my mind. Sat and listened but didn't speak at the moments I usually would. [irid-met][srj5] In 8 years I have not had anyone collapse on me but the last week 3 patients have, also haven't had any violent incidents for a long time at work but this has happened in the last week. In both circumstances I seemed to cope more calmly and in a more detached manner than I would have expected. [latex][nl-latex] Emotional detachment, therefore saying what I feel like without fear of repercussions. [latex][nl-latex] That was also true with my dealings with patients. Even now I don't feel suppressed emotionally but I feel slightly detached. [sanguis-s][hrn2] Feel disconnected – felt withdrawn from friends and family and from myself – I felt withdrawn into a different level and did not care about others. [urol-h][rwt3] especially people with whom there should be a strong connection. Feel happy and emotionally connected, though still too detached from wife. [aids][nl2] Feeling of complete detachment from my family. They seem like a million miles away and I could be in another world. [lsd][nl-lsd] I dreamt I was going to get married to a man from another culture. I had to meet his parents. I had no feelings. [latex][nl-latex] Disconnected from people in my life. [urol-h][rwt3] It's a kind of detached state, distant, coldness to my partner who says I seem miles away. [tung-met][bdx1] It can even be from the self. An ongoing wish to communicate and not being able to explain my feelings. In the place of my mind, there was a possibility that I could operate my life from my feelings rather than my head. [limen-b-c][hrn2] A feeling of not being in myself. [positr][nl2] (*See Confusion of Identity VII-5*)

The detachment is often connected to feeling of lightness, It was a high sensation. I felt very detached and light. [agath-a][nl2] I feel lighter. Things don't affect me as much and I feel more distanced. [plut-n][srj7] (*See Floating & Flying V-8*) and also to the feeling of being tall or small. I felt not completely divorced from what was happening but I felt small compared to the enormity of what was happening. [aids][nl2] (*See Tallness VI-2*)

The sense of detachment clearly connects to feelings of isolation, (*See Isolation II-8*) but it combines them with feelings of indifference and a lack of feelings. The sense of isolation was very strong but did not worry me. [lac-h][htj1] (*See Indifference III-1*)

II-5 The Observer

One of the effects of detachment from the world is to make the subject an observer rather than a participant. Feeling detached from things, observing again, not touching the world. [adam][srj5] Ability to observe without being involved. [ara-mac][sej7] I feel I am an observer, compassionate and gentle, yet still an observer. The feeling of being divorced from the mental realm in some way "came up" for me. [limen-b-c][hrn2] No strong emotion when my acquaintance jumped the queue on being recognized by the attendant in charge, and went ahead of me. It was as if I was only an observer. [coca-c][sk4] I used to always be ready to tangle. Loved to argue even if it was a topic I didn't care about. Since the proving that is gone. I now actually enjoy listening to people express opinions I don't necessarily agree with. I continue to feel calm, able to listen, and not get caught up in the fray. [haliae-lc][srj5] Out for the day. Discover lots of new things. Keep coming across fast flowing water. Beautiful gardens with bluebells, wood anemones, etc. Like looking at it all but not moved by it, sort of accepting of it. [heroin][sdj-h] I feel kind of in an altered state. Like removed from myself, like an observer. I am putting away my feelings do I can just perform properly. [galeoc-c-h][gms1] Transient feeling of spaciness. I don't feel like I am really here. Its all just a movie and I am a detached observer. [lac-del][hrn2] I was more like a spirit watching – an outsider. [lac-lup][hrn2] Step-back point of view – observer. [plut-n][srj7] I seem to be quieter in myself and more observing. [positr][nl2] Hallucinations of being outside and looking in at night. [carneg-g][rwt1] Just wants to sit and observe. [tax-br][oss1]

The particular sensation of observing from above ties in with the sensations of floating and flying. There is a sense that he is separated from the physical world, which he is observing from above. [anh][vh1] I felt as though I was looking from above. [plut-n][srj7] On a motorbike at red traffic lights, seeing self from birds eye view. [tung-met][bdx1] (*See Floating & Flying IV-8*) This is of course to be expected in the birds to which this behaviour is central to their way of living, Watching myself from above. [buteo-j][sej6] Feeling of overview. [lars-arg][fkw1] and it is particularly strong in the birds of prey and especially the Eagle. They have one tree for their nest, and a different tree for perching-and-staring, an activity at which they spend a lot of time. The perching tree will usually be one snag that stands out above the others and offers a good view. [haliae-lc][srj5] Most of the time, when thinking of a place, I am looking down on it. [haliae-lc][srj5]

The sense of being an observer is found in dreams as well as in the waking life. Dreams as if a fly on the wall. [ara-mac][sej7] Am observing myself during sleep, and lift myself out of sleep through levels of consciousness to the surface where I awaken. [coca-c][sk4] Dream: I was visiting a friend in a large house 160 feet over the ocean. 160 stuck in my mind. Steps up to the house. My friend has a fear of heights. A feeling of being very high and overlooking the ocean. A very pleasant dream. [maias-l][hrn2] I realize my dreams are unusual because they aren't strong messages to me. Usually when I remember a dream it has a strong emotional lesson or impact on me, which these dreams don't. It's as if I'm an observer rather than a participant in them. Usually even as an observer I have more of an emotional connection to the other players in the dream. These dreams are flat emotionally. [haliae-lc][srj5]

The self is the most important object of observation, Observing oneself. [anh][sp1] Feel detached, separate, as if observing myself being here but not really being here. [dream-p][sdj1] Look at myself in the mirror and see clarity. I almost feel like I could see through my face. There is an objectivity of looking at my face. [haliae-lc][srj5] I became more and more an observer of my situation and myself. [falco-pe][nl2] Feel very calm and relaxed as if I am an observer in my own life. [galeoc-c-h][gms1] which leads to a sense of division and splitting into the observing self and the observed one. He seems possessed of a dual existence, one of which from a height watches the other. [cann-i][a1] Feeling of being both inside and outside my life. [heroin][sdj-h] He seemed to be two persons, and his real, conscious self seemed to be watching his other self playing. [nux-m][c1] (*See Splitting V-4*)

In Diamond the split is linked to gender which reflects the importance of gender division in the remedy. I realized I am observing a lot and have a feeling of being observed. The observer bit is female aspect, and the male bit is a critical voice. [adam][srj5]

II-6 Drugs

The feeling of detachment and many of the other feelings found in contemporary disease are similar to those of recreational drugs. (*See also Anaesthesia III-3; Floating & Flying IV-8; Confusion VIII-1*)

The drug remedies could all be categorized as belonging to the group of remedies useful in treating contemporary disease. This applies to the well known traditional drug remedies such as Opium, Agaricus, Cannabis and Anhalonium; and to the newly proved ones such as Ecstasy, LSD and Heroin. Morning Glory and Nux Moschata are examples of substances that have minor hallucinatory and drug properties. There are also many drugs that have achieved a degree of social respectability, Alcohol, Coffee, Tea and especially Chocolate.

The effects of many of the new and associated remedies are drug like. Often accompanying this state of detachment was a state of dreaminess or a feeling as of being drugged. [Guess][androc][vml3] Driving back from shopping at nurseries. Beautiful day, warm sun. Almost seemed other-worldly. Is this a drug remedy? [carbn-dox][knl3] The Mayas had believed that the drink made from the cocoa seeds would nourish them after death and the Aztecs believed that cocoa relieved their fatigue and stimulated their psychic and mental abilities. [choc][srj3] A feeling of intoxication with double sensations. Colours are stronger and hearing is sharpened but at the same time feel absent and removed. [choc][srj3] High as a kite. In the middle center of the brain. Pleasure center activated. Not spaced out. Euphoric feeling. I feel guilty as this is similar to illicit drugs, so pleasurable you only feel this when you are taking drugs. [haliae-lc][srj5] Free and easy euphoric type feeling in morning. Not with work focus. Felt carefree. [haliae-lc][srj5] I'm spaced out, peaceful or spacey. [haliae-lc][srj5] Feeling spacey, light-headed. [hydrog][srj2] I have a lot of energy and still have positive feelings. Almost like a false high. [vacuum][es-vac]

Provers often described experiences as being stoned or reminiscent of previous drug experiences, Felt drugged, as if my body had become very long, and I was falling fast through space. Later, felt introspectively "stoned" while talking. [coca-c][sk4] I felt very "spacey" and my head kind of heavy. [corian-s][knl6] Feeling spacey and disoriented, stoned, far away from reality; am I making this up? [haliae-lc][srj5] Drugged and stupefaction. [helodr-cal][knl2] Spaced out. Went to county fair yesterday. Felt like on drugs. Like stupefied. Didn't really care. [helodr-cal][knl2] Felt adolescent, but without the self-consciousness, inhibitions and hang-ups. Stoned. [falco-pe][nl2] Felt really stoned, ever since taking the remedy. [agath-a][nl2] Immediately on taking the remedy, as if on ecstasy – everything looks yellow; feel giggly. [phasco-ci][rbp2] Felt very heavy-headed all morning. There was also this calm feeling, as if drugged, accompanied by heightened senses, being very alert. [latex][nl-latex] Proving does feel like a drug. [lsd][nl-lsd] Recognized a change in awareness – a vaguely stoned, unreal feeling. [neon][srj5] State of mind similar to that of the opium-eater, entertaining no apprehension of the result, although aware of the presence of some danger. [nux-m][a1] Feeling as if I had taken too many strong drugs. [plut-n][srj7] A 'stoned sensation' (as if he had taken marijuana). [rhus-g][tmo3] Was kind of spacey. Husband even asked me, "What are you on?" because I was kind of out of it. [sanguis-s][hrn2] I definitely feel elated – like I was a little drunk. [vacuum][es-vac] and particularly like psychedelic or LSD trips, Sensation of being intoxicated, of being stoned – it felt like I was just going up on acid – like the beginning of a trip. Sensation of going into nowhere, into nothingness. [aids][nl2] On going upstairs, all colors seemed incredibly bright and the walls were pulsating in towards him and out again. This felt similar to an LSD experience years ago. [androc][srj5] Apprehensive about the shift in consciousness and nervous someone would notice. It is reminiscent of LSD, the 'shifting edges', before the full blown trip arrives – an uneasiness and unsureness about which way things will go. [choc][srj3] It's like an LSD or mushroom trip. You sink into the hallucinatory phase and you think that that's the way things have always been and will always be. It's "reality" and then something clicks and you're back to real reality so in a way it's as if I'm floating between two dimensions. [corv-cor][bdg1] Physically I had some sensations from the time I took the remedy, a sensation of taking LSD kind of feeling. [agath-a][nl2] Slightly depressed, but there are moments of universal happiness, love that would flicker in amongst the depressed state. It's slightly reminiscent of taking hallucinogens. Everything is O.K. The feelings would come and go in a minute, just long enough for me to acknowledge them, then they would be gone. [neon][srj5] I started to feel really strange – weird sensations as though I was on LSD. [plut-n][srj7] Feel a bit "tripped". I could imagine it ever so slightly. I feel as if I'm on an LSD trip. [tung-met][bdx1] It's like an acid trip out here, another world. [vacuum][es-vac] though sometimes like Ecstasy or Speed. Immediately on taking the remedy, as if on ecstasy – everything looks yellow; feel giggly. [phasco-ci][rbp2] Feeling of ease, as if tipsy, as if on speed. [ozone][sde2]

AIDS has, since its early days, been closely linked to drug abuse. The first men with the disease had tended to have a large number of sexual partners, a history of many episodes of venereal disease treated with antibiotics, and a substantial use of recreational drugs, especially amyl nitrate (a heart drug often used by gay men to heighten and prolong sexual arousal). [aids][nl2] AIDS and drug abuse have been closely linked since the first appearance of the disease. However, it is in intravenous heroin users that it has taken hold most strongly. In a number of cities in both the developed and developing worlds the problems of heroin addiction and HIV have almost merged into one. The isolation, the secrecy and the numbness of the heroin state, the only way out of unbearable pain, have a resonance with issues important in the AIDS state. [aids][nl2]

Condoms are frequently used as means of carrying drugs within the body and this came through in the proving. Dream: Someone was trying to get me to take drugs, wrapped like little pellets placed inside Durex. I was very upset that someone wanted to take drugs themselves. [latex][nl-latex]

There is also a need for drugs and for the drugged state, Desired alcohol and drugs, a feeling of wanting to escape. [androc][srj5] Got stoned, haven't smoked for about a year. It seemed to bring up the effects of the proving even more strongly. [positr][nl2] Have wanted to smoke dope, which I have not really had an urge to do for about six months. [positr][nl2] and a feeling of being addicted. Feel there's something addictive about whatever this is. I'm not feeling euphoric as I was the beginning of the week and I'm pissed off about it, want some more and would take another one if I could. Made me feel so great on Monday. [falco-pe][nl2]

Robbins in the Koala proving feels that this is so strong in the Koala that he calls it 'Nature's Drug Addict'. The Eucalyptus leaves, which constitute the overwhelming part of their diet contain over forty different chemical substances, including many alcohol's, aldehydes, esters, terpenes, phenols and ketones. Because of this an eminent Australian Zoologist Ambrose Pratt stated. 'Since all these substances are drugs of some kind, the koala is, in every sense of the word, a drug addict'. [phasco-ci][rbp2] Wanted to take heroin, the most strongly I have felt this in the last seven years. [phasco-ci][rbp2]

The Walnut has long been renowned for its ability to treat addiction. Walnuts are also said to keep people sober even when they drink large amounts of wine. In the past, every gift of wine was accompanied by walnuts. This custom still exists in Austria. [jug-r][vml3] Walnut teas are used to alleviate symptoms of withdrawal when eliminating coffee from the diet. [jug-r][vml3]

There is also a fear of the world of drugs which often implies a criminal and dangerous world. Dream of staying in a big house (our house, I think) with lots of friends. Drug addicts moved in next door. I could see them through the open doorway. Two of them in the bathroom – one shouting to the other (who I think was lying on the floor), 'are you okay?' I was worried about the influence on the children in our house (of them being enticed to take drugs?). [heroin][sdj-h] (*See Vulnerable IX-2*)

Many of the words that are used to describe drug experiences are also terms or concepts that describe the themes in the new and related remedies. Getting High, (*See Floating & Flying IV-8*) Stoned, (*See Grounding I-3*) on a Trip, (*See Travel IV-11*) and Spaced. (*See Space IV-10*)

II-7 The Past

One of the ways in which subjects appear to try to counteract the sense of disconnection is to increase the sense of connection to their own past. Recollections of the past; school and unhappy childhood. [aids][nl2] Flashbacks into the past: all of a sudden I was back in a farmhouse, remembering smells. [corv-cor][bdg1] Regrets for the past. [cur][a1] Experienced momentary memories of my past, 20 to 30 years ago. Unrelated pleasant memories, like opening a window on my past life for a second or two. [haliae-lc][srj5]

This connection is particularly to the subject's childhood. Journeying back to childhood – childhood memories. [aids][nl2] I've been travelling psychically through a lot of very early childhood stuff. [aids][nl2] Remembered events that had happened, and ideas that had passed through his mind when a child, as about toys. [cann-i][a1] All the thoughts and deeds of his childhood returned. [cann-i][a1] Went to bed, suddenly so focused on my teddy bear which lives on my bed, I realised it's the oldest possession I have, since I was two. Strange to notice her tonight. (More childhood stuff). [lsd][nl-lsd] Nostalgia – memories of childhood and children when they were young. [plac][Biggs+] Was getting a lot of flash backs to being a child. Feeling like I did as a child and seeing things around me with the eyes of a child. [vacuum][es-vac]

Though in Neon and Nux Moschata there is a disconnection from the past. Had the strong thought, "my connection with the past is dissolving". [neon][srj5] She speaks with intelligence about the things of the moment, but knows nothing of the past. [nux-m][k2]

The connection to the past echoes the connections made to childhood through childishness, (*See Childishness V-3*) and vulnerability. (*See Vulnerability IX-1*)

Both the past and childhood are important themes in dreams. Vivid dreams about old events. [anac][a1] Dream: Old friends from past. [lac-leo][hrn2] Dream about being little again and by the sea with my family, walking on a wooden promenade with a friendly white goat. [androc][srj5] A lot of dreams of childhood. [ozone][sde2] Dream: I am in the country of my birth in the fields that I played in as a child. [rhus-g][tmo3]

Perhaps the most interesting of these dreams are the dreams of previous lovers which are found in several remedies. Dream of an old lover. [corv-cor][bdg1] I dreamt of my ex-partner seducing me, imploring me. [heroin][sdj-h] Dreamed of a man she had been involved with in the past – felt she wanted to rid herself of him. [hydrog][srj2] I dreamt about a long lost lover, things from the past. [neon][srj5] Strange dreams, mostly of ex-boyfriend. [plut-n][srj7] Dream: Old boyfriends – first love, comfortable nice visit to the past. [urol-h][rwt3] Dreams of ex-boyfriend. [urol-h][rwt3] I dreamt I was locked in a passionate embrace with a pacifist I knew 30 years ago. [vacuum][es-vac]

II-8 Isolation

The ultimate expression of disconnection is a feeling of isolation and this is very strong in the new and associated remedies. Though the many of the new remedies are in the rubric Forsaken feeling , this rubric applies more to the feeling found in the Psoric and Hydrophobic Miasms. It is the sub-rubric Forsaken feeling – sensation of isolation, that is fundamentally more of the AIDS Miasm. That is not to say that it is exclusively AIDS Miasm, but it does contain a large proportion of the remedies.

Just as the Scorpion is the most detached of the remedies so it is the one in which the substance is the most isolated, Scorpions are loners and sometimes will eat each other, though they are immune to their own poison. The female has been known to eat the male after copulation and the mother may eat her young. It seems as though not even the most primitive form of animal association is known to them. [androc][srj5] They completely avoid each other or fight to the death. It has been said that if you find two scorpions under a rock they will either be mating or killing each other! [androc][srj5] and the one in which the feeling of isolation appeared most strongly in the proving. I feel entirely alone, that I am viewing the world through one hole, for it all seems just a picture, and the rest of the world shares a different viewfinder together. I don't want to join theirs though. [androc][srj5]

On the other hand many of the remedies have come from social or herd animals and a sense of isolation can, for them, be doubly distressing. Wolves are extraordinarily fond of each other, and the bonds between them are so tight that the actions of each individual profoundly affect the entire pack. Once in a while a pack member is rejected and sent out to become a loner. When this happens, that wolf may seek another loner and team up to start a new pack. [lac-lup][hrn2] Feeling slightly isolated and different from others. [lac-lup][hrn2]

The sensation of isolation is often found in a feeling of being shunned by friends, family or the group. Since I've been on the proving I've fallen out with everybody, especially at home. [agath-a][nl2] Too depressed to write my diary; feel like a monster; everyone I love hates me. [phasco-ci][rbp2] I've got no friends. Feel alien to one's own family. [phasco-ci][rbp2] Wanted to be with people but felt shunned. More detached, introverted yet still awareness of surroundings. Want to be in my own world, be inside myself. Preoccupied with myself. [lac-del][hrn2] I felt separate from people. I felt at a party that I was being cold-shouldered, which I was, but I really felt it. [sanguis-s][hrn2] As if she were alone and all about her were dead and still, or as if she had been forsaken by a near friend. [rhus-t][a1] This feeling is perhaps most strongly expressed in Lac Humanum. Feeling "cut off" from my friends circle; I don't want to be with them, or I am unable to maintain a relationship with them. I feel that if they do not want me, I should leave them alone and be free. I feel like I have done a lot of things for them but they give me nothing in return, that they reject me because I am of no use to them, that they have chosen their path and I must choose mine. [lac-h][sk4] Felt as if I was alone, there was no one there for me. "Wild" with anger on friends when they neglected me and sat amongst themselves, although I had reserved seats for them in the seminar. [lac-h][sk4] Dream: I had organized a picnic with a few friends. We spent the whole day enjoying ourselves; we had our lunch together. As the evening approached, I started to feel depressed. When I looked behind, I found that my friends had disappeared along with all their belongings. I was shocked, lonely, and didn't know what to do. [lac-h][sk4]

There is a general feeling of isolation. Not connecting with people, feelings of isolation. [aids][nl2] Loss of contact with the outside world, and escape into a fantasy world. [anh][jl1] A peculiar sensation of isolation from the outer world. [coca][c1] Her husband said to her, "You are like in a shell, in your own closed world, you don't seem to feel good." [corv-cor][bdg1] I feel so alone. I need company. Got a buzz when people started calling. It almost killed me. Loneliness is a major theme. [corv-cor][bdg1] A feeling of isolation and coldness inside. Shutting down to the outside world, separation from my partner. [falco-pe][nl2] A strong mind symptom was a sense of isolation. [musca-d][stew+] Feeling of being on the outside. [irid-met][srj5] Feel as if I am the only person. Feel like I'm in my own little capsule sitting very still and yet being moved. Thinking of nothing, just driving and staring at the road.

[irid-met][srj5] The remedy heightened my separation and isolation from people. [irid-met][srj5] She cannot bear to be alone. [lac-c][k2] Dreams as if left alone in the wilderness, or as if alone in the world. [lac-h][sk4] Awareness of how I am both insider and outsider. Want to be both but both are painful. [cygn-b][sle-swan] I have an intense feeling of loneliness. [ignis-alc][es2] On taking the remedy I felt that everyone and everything moved to twice the distance away from me. [latex][nl-latex] I have felt it impossible to connect with anything or anybody, including myself. The barrier has left me feeling isolated and discontented except when at home often where I have felt safe and more content. [latex][nl-latex] Disconnected from others around me. [lsd][nl-lsd] Feeling lonely, forsaken and abandoned. [lsd][nl-lsd] I feel that nobody is there for me when I need them; I'm there for everyone when they need me but no one is ever there for me. [neon][srj5] She thinks she is left wholly to herself, and stands alone in the world. [plat][a1] Feeling of Isolation. [plut-n][srj7] I feel very locked inside myself – as if in a prison. It is dark and hard, and very silent. I feel isolated, but it doesn't seem to matter. I'm not afraid or upset, that's just how it is. [positr][nl2] She feels separated from people, withdrawn and isolated. [tax-br][oss1]

This sensation is particularly strong in Germanium. I feel separated from people and places. [germ-met][srj5] I feel I have no real contact with people, I have no emotion at all except for a feeling of isolation and a concern that people may not like me. I wish someone would cuddle me. [germ-met][srj5] I have an intense feeling of estrangement and isolation, with a desire to start my life again. [germ-met][srj5] I don't belong. I don't feel at home any place. Feel lonely. I nearly always feel special – always on the side/outside of others. Either better or smaller than others. [germ-met][srj5]

Love is an important issue in the AIDS Miasm (*See Youth, Beauty, Peace & Love I-8*) and isolation is often expressed as a lack of love, of being unloved. Not connecting with people – feelings of isolation – felt, 'nobody loves me'. [aids][nl2] Delusion is unloved. [berlin-w][hmd2] If I were me, nobody would like me, so I try to be what I think others expect me to be. I don't think I can be loved with all the parts of me which are ugly and bad. Lonely feelings. [germ-met][srj5] Almost in tears with an intense forsaken feeling when my mother gave more food to my brother than to the rest of us. Scolded her saying that she cared for him and didn't love me. [lac-h][sk4] My disease is loneliness a need and desire for love. [lsd][nl-lsd]

The feeling is not always imposed from without. There is often behaviour on the part of the subject that leads directly to the sensation of isolation. In her indignation she looks at nobody, and does not want to hear anything. [ars][a1] Hid away from the world, felt my life would fall apart. Felt totally isolated and averse to company. [choc][srj3] Estranged himself from his family and friends and stopped all communication with them for a long period. Did not reply to letters and left no address. He seemed to hide away and literally disappear. The state of Isolation resulted from feeling that "I didn't exist as a human being". This behaviour was in strong contrast to his normal sociable disposition. [choc][srj3] Usually I feel very connected to people around me, enjoy smiling at them. Feel separate from others. Don't want to be noticed. I usually like to be noticed. Not now. [corian-s][knl6] Have noticed today, that it's been difficult to listen to people, I start to feel bored and switch off. Several times today I've had to ask people to repeat the last sentence. It's as if I lose the thread of the conversation. [heroin][sdj-h] I seem to want to avoid contact with people. I can listen but can't seem to engage in conversation. It's as if I have nothing to say to people – when normally I love a chat and can make conversation with all these people readily. The phone is not ringing, no one has rung me and I don't feel inclined to ring anyone. I feel hard done by, neglected. [positr][nl2] Felt withdrawn and disconnected from my friends I could care less if I was listening to them – people were not important. [urol-h][rwt3]

On the other hand the feeling can be there in spite of the presence of people. Strange feeling of isolation from all around him, with great sense of loneliness, though surrounded by his friends. [cann-i][a1]

The feeling of isolation can be the feeling of being an outcast, of being ostracized. Feeling like being banished. [lars-arg][fkw1] Dreams of not being needed and feeling excluded, on the outside. [plac][Biggs+] Feeling of separation; I felt separated from the group during the proving. Feeling like an outsider, or outcast. Pervasive feelings lasted over three months. [lac-del][hrn2] This seems to be strongest in Germanium and Oak Galls. Painfully aware of the feelings of being an outcast. [germ-met][srj5] Felt that I did not have the right to be with others. I feel that I'm sucking them out. Throwing my dirt at them. [galla-q-r][nl2]

The feeling of isolation also leads into many of the other themes of contemporary disease, including panic and insecurity, Feelings of panic and insecurity of separation and isolation. [aids][nl2] (*See Vulnerability IX-1*) and lack of confidence, particularly in Anacardium. He is separated from the whole world, and has so little confidence in himself that he despairs of being able to do that which is required of him. [anac][a1] (*See Lack of Confidence XI-1*)

II-9 Need To Be Alone

Although there is a strong feeling of isolation, the desire to be alone is just as strong. This might seem to be contradictory but one Plutonium expressed the connection very clearly. I want to be alone. It's when I'm in company that the feeling of separation from everyone becomes apparent to me. [plut-n][srj7] The need to be alone can also be an expression of the feelings of disconnection, isolation and not belonging. Had the desire to be alone. Felt different to and separate from other people. Felt very individual. [aids][nl2] I felt detached here after taking the remedy and I wanted to go off by myself. [agath-a][nl2]

The feelings of connection can also be overwhelming and the only way for the subject to maintain boundaries is to push people away or to remove yourself from them. Later on, in Lac felinum people, a behaviour pattern may develop of not wanting any further relationship with human beings, in order to preserve one's own independence intact. [lac-f][vml3] Obsessed about individuality versus group conformity. In a dilemma whether I should give more importance to my individuality and speak and question freely, or keep quiet like the rest of the group. [lac-h][sk4] I just want to go on a retreat or something – somewhere to be with my spirit, with no necessity to connect with people, and no responsibilities. [lsd][nl-lsd] These people tend to withdraw from life and keep themselves to themselves. They would rather hang on to their inner qualities and not bother with the dramas of the outside world. In a positive sense they are very good at abstaining. [oxyg][stj2] Wanting to be separate, not merged into regular society. [sanguis-s][hrn2]

The desire to be alone is clear in many remedies. I am enjoying to be alone – usually I don't like to be alone, since the remedy glad to be alone. [aids][nl2] I wanted to be alone. I felt better being alone. I wanted to be in the dark in bed. [adam][srj5] Desire to isolate one's self. [coca][a1] Desire for solitude. [conv-s][jl1] Wanted to be left alone. [haliae-lc][srj5] Feeling I want to isolate myself – want to be alone. [hydrog][srj2] Wanted to be in a snug place. Preferred to be alone. Averse to seeing any friends. [phasco-ci][rbp2] No urge for company. [lac-leo][hrn2] Desires solitude. [seq-s][vml3] Preferred to curl up in a ball and be alone. [urol-h][rwt3] Over the last four days, have noticed I feel reclusive, appreciate quiet, company can be stressful. Would almost rather be alone. [vacuum][es-vac]

In many remedies there is also be an aversion to company. Hypochondria, with dread of society; he seeks solitude and obscurity; does not want to see or hear anything. [anan][a1] Feeling like I don't belong in a crowd. [choc][srj3] Aversion to company; avoids the sight of people; shuts herself up. [cur][vml3] Aversion to society. [cur][a1] Aversion to people. Abrupt when obliged to speak. Had a consultation at

10 o'clock and really messed it up. I wish everybody would just go away and leave me alone. No contact. [germ-met][srj5] Aversion to company. [gink-b][vml3] Could not stand people around me. [galla-q-r][nl2] Strongly averse to company. Wanted to be alone to sit or lie down and weep. [lac-h][sk4] Want to reject the people around me and go away and be alone. [heroin][sdj-h] Love of solitude. [cact][a1] I know we have visitors at home and I am reluctant to go back. I am enjoying being alone and keep finding things to do to avoid going home. [ignis-alc][es2] Have a great desire for solitude to practice meditation. [ignis-alc][es2] Feeling "just leave me in peace". [ozone][sde2] Aversion to company. Aversion to talking. Self-centred. [positr][nl2] Distaste for society; no desire to speak to any one, or to be spoken to. [rhus-g][a1] Dread of society. [sel][c1] Has an aversion to people, wants to be let alone, cannot react adequately to people. [Whitmont] [visc][vml3]

The desire can also be for space. I really want my own space, but don't have it. I want to spend time on my own, have my own home. [aids][nl2] Wanting space, wanting to be at home, wanting to be alone. [falco-pe][nl2] Felt that I needed my own space – that I would set up my own tent. [galla-q-r][nl2] Aversion to having other people in my space/home. [phasco-ci][rbp2] Thinking about moving away from my family so I can be on my own. I'm allowed to. Arranged to move out for three months, with an option for a further three (a married woman with two boys). [phasco-ci][rbp2] I have felt my space has been invaded in the house. I felt so pissed off. I was there for peace and quiet, but the person I share with won't leave me alone. [positr][nl2] This aspect of wanting to be alone ties in with the feeling of being trapped and the desire to be outdoors. (*See Trapped IX-7*)

There is often an aversion to communication. Will not communicate. [berlin-w][evans] The prover is reluctant to call and talk about her symptoms. I have to encourage her to talk about her state. [haliae-lc][srj5] Didn't want any involvement with anyone, couldn't initiate a conversation because I felt that I had nothing to say, couldn't think of anything to say. I could respond if people spoke to me but not an active engagement as I normally would. [falco-pe][nl2] Friends coming around – don't feel like being sociable – don't mind them being there just don't feel like communicating. [lsd][nl-lsd] Am introverted, dejected, have no desire to talk with others, without contact. [ozone][sde2] Wanted to sit on my own quietly – not interact with anyone else. [positr][nl2] Don't feel very communicative. [positr][nl2] I've definitely got an uncommunicative air about me. [positr][nl2] She does not endure being talked to. [rhus-t][a1] Disinclination to talk or argue, as was customary with him. [jug-r][a1] Drove to college with fellow-prover. Didn't speak to each other at all. Couldn't think of anything important enough to break the silence. [sal-fr][sle1] Don't want to call/ talk to my kids. Don't want to go to work or socialize. [galeoc-c-h][gms1] This is very strong in Diamond. Wanted to be alone. Can't be bothered with husband. [adam][srj5] I want to be alone. I don't want to talk to or see people. [adam][srj5] I feel like I want to hibernate, not to be seen and keep warm. I want to curl up somewhere warm and forget the world. [adam][srj5] Did not want to talk to anyone. [adam][srj5]

There can be an aversion to physical communication, to touch. I don't want to be touched or talked to. [adam][srj5] Don't feel very loving towards the family, not enjoying a cuddle, pushing them away as quickly as possible. [irid-met][srj5] No feeling of contact or closeness with my partner. No wanting physical closeness or touch. A feeling that she's in her space and I'm in mine. [positr][nl2] (*See Touch XII-5*)

Heloderma has the desire to be left alone very strongly and when it is not it can react violently. The central idea of this remedy is expressed in the following: I am busy (industrious), centred (balanced) and speeding in my space but don't bother me or I will get irritable and lunge. [helo-s][rwt2] Dream: Circle of people and inside was a luminescent scorpion and everyone would scurry off; It would stay centered and content and in the middle and would keep people off. [helo-s][rwt2]

Ambra Grisea finds attention unbearable and is always made worse by company. One thing running through this remedy is that the presence of other persons aggravates the symptoms. [ambr][k2]

Sometimes it is possible to find the balance between company and solitude. I noticed last night that I was in and out of the room doing what I wanted to do and being part of the group as well. [aids][nl2] but it is more common for the balance not to be achieved. Want to get away from everyone, when on my own want to be with everyone again. [aids][nl2] Desire to be on my own but can't do it. I want people but I don't want the limelight. One person said aggressively 'Have you got a problem'. I started shaking. [aids][nl2] Wanted my partner to be there and close, but not too close. [irid-met][srj5]

The desire for solitude can be an expression of the sense of calm and disconnection. Wanted to remain alone and quietly. [Sankaran] [hir][vml3] I'm feeling quite self contained and in myself, as if I'm an element on my own. [positr][nl2] (*See Disconnection II-1*) It can also arise from the feeling of being too big or overwhelming. (*See Extremes VI-1*)

III-1 Indifference

The calmness and tranquillity that disconnection allows (*See Disconnection II-1*) can easily become a lack of caring about what is happening. This indifference can also rise in reaction to the constant state of vulnerability that a lack of boundaries causes. Unexpectedly you can be jumped at and caught, even though you have taken your measures. This is a state that is not bearable for a long time for an organism. So the pendulum can swing to the other side of indifference as a coping mechanism. [lac-cp][lsy+dmk] (*See Vulnerability IX-1*)

This indifference can be general. Feeling calm; abdicated all responsibility. [adam][srj5] He is very indifferent and unfeeling; neither agreeable nor disagreeable objects excite his interest. [anac][a1] Indifference. To pleasure; to suffering; to surroundings; welfare of others; opinion of others. [androc][vml3] Indifference to everything going on about him. [cur][a1] Feeling of not caring all day. [latex][nl-latex] Generally over whole of last two or three weeks, intensification of existing uncaring about what's going on in the world. Know about it more-or-less, but unmoved by it. As time is progressing, less seems to move me or bother me, generally. [positr][nl2] Lack of enthusiasm, and of interest; indifference. [sel][jl1] No life nor ambition to do anything. [xan][a2] In Lac humanum this indifference is specifically to everything. Indifference to everything around me. [lac-h][sk4] Indifference to all things and feelings. [lac-h][sk4] In Heroin it is not only to everything but is all encompassing. Disinterested in everything. [heroin][sdj-h] Arrive in Swindon. Husband asks have you enjoyed your day. I say yes, because I knew I had – but I hadn't felt I'd enjoyed it – a sort of take it or leave it feeling. [heroin][sdj-h] There is no fluctuation of feelings, joy, interest, inspiration, etc. Like I'm switched off, can switch on to talk to people but not 'to feel' but then seem to switch off. There's a general lack of response to situations. The loss of my son's university work in his bag. My friends operation. My mum's cat. My sister moving to Australia. [heroin][sdj-h]

In some remedies the provers stated that the indifference was to things that would normally upset them. By the afternoon I felt above it all, serene, even rested… was able to listen to landlord being racist and let it pass over my head instead of getting worked up. [aids][nl2] She who ordinarily felt so extremely solicitous about everything, is now quite indifferent. [agar][a1] Feeling indifferent about things that would normally upset me. [irid-met][srj5]

The indifference can have a particular focus. It can be to people, I didn't connect with the people I was with, couldn't feel anything for them, indifferent. [plut-n][srj7] Especially to loved ones. Have lost interest in my husband, feel totally indifferent. I have hardly spoken to him all weekend, with a desire to avoid him. [choc][srj3] Feeling of indifference, not very loving, unemotional, inwardly cold. [ozone][sde2] Indifference, he does not seem to care whether his absent wife dies or not. [plat][a1] Feeling as if I don't really care about some of my family members. I don't think I ever need to see them again. [galeoc-c-h][gms1] Or to matters of business. He feels as if nothing existed around him; he is dissatisfied with himself all the time; he is incapable of attending to any business; the things around him are entirely indifferent to him; while attending to his business, he is apt to fall into a thoughtless mood. [agn][a1] Is indifferent to business. [rhus-t][a1] Or to the opinion of others, which contrasts the more common feelings of lack of confidence and shame. (*See Lack of Confidence XI-1 and Shame & Humiliation XI-3*) Felt I didn't care too much any more about what others feel about me. [lac-cp][sk4]

This indifference is not generally a positive thing and can be very destructive, Great equanimity. Indifferent to joy or grief; more depressed, however, than composed. [ambr][a1] Especially in Scorpion. Felt depressed and destructive, did not care if things were broken. [androc][srj5]

The depth of this indifference is perhaps most extreme in Polystyrene. Dream: Indifference to being approached by four men who had the intention to rape me. [polys][sk4] In Dolphin also there is an unusual calm in the face of dangerous situations.

In Carnegia the whole thing comes full circle and the prover states: I am indifferent about indifference. [carneg-g][rwt1]

This indifference may be equated with a drugged state. Indifference to the world; the mind seems blunted. [cann-i][a1] Spaced out. Went to county fair yesterday. Felt like on drugs. Like stupefied. Didn't really care. [helodr-cal][knl2] For me there was an element of elation, tra la la, whatever feeling, like Valium slightly removed from every other thing... it didn't matter. [vacuum][es-vac] (*See Drugs II-6*) It can also be a removal from the pressing state imposed on us by time. Felt timeless, not caring [falco-pe][nl2] This is especially so in Hydrogen. All sorts of things have clicked into place since yesterday. Feel wonderful. Now I don't actually feel slowed down. Didn't hurry, just did things in my own time. Normally would have pulled out all the stops and rushed around. It doesn't matter if I'm late. [hydrog][srj2] My whole time scale has changed since taking the remedy, I've lost a lot of boundaries on time. Don't hurry, just do things in my own time. [hydrog][srj2] (*See Confusion about Time VII-7*)

There is often indifference to the state of things around the subject. Wasn't bothered as much by little things. This has lasted to the present. Little things now don't bother me as much, like having everything where I like it so I can find it the next time I want to use it. I'm not as picky at my work bench, in the kitchen, or with my office staff. [lac-del][hrn2] This morning I felt indifference about the dirty house. I left the dishes, and dirty hair in the bath. [neon][srj5] On the other hand there is a pronounced indifference not only to work but also to the things that make work something to be avoided. The subject doesn't care that he or she has to do things that would normally be unpleasant. Aptitude for work increased. [coca][a1] In a small dose, kava is a tonic stimulating beverage, producing an agreeable excitement, and affording support against great fatigue. [pip-m][a1] (*See Chaos & Order V-5*)

There is also indifference to injuries or to the subject's condition. In spite of very severe symptoms, not alarmed; passively indifferent. [helo-s][rwt2] During proving prover cut finger very badly. Supervisor's observation was that prover had no anxiety or concern: didn't get stitches or go to the doctor. Cut it to the bone, bandaged it up and drove two hundred and fifty miles home. [irid-met][srj5]

III-2 Apathy

Indifference is a lack of feeling of the passive function. There is a corresponding lack of action in the active function which is manifest as apathy. Insight increased, but volition absent. [anh][sp1] Diminution of willpower, apathy, and slow reactions. [anh][jl1] Felt numb to everything and everyone Apathy. [carneg-g][rwt1] Nothing matters, neither to go to work nor to keep an appointment. [gink-b][vml3] Koalas spend about 80% of their lives sleeping or resting and almost 20% eating, leaving less than 1% to move from tree to tree and do everything else. [phasco-ci][rbp2] Aversion to mental labour, on account of distracting fancies. [meph][a1] This is a sort of uncaring and not bothering feeling. What's the point anyway? [positr][nl2] He forgets and neglects much; also the writing down, and even the observing of the symptoms; it is all too much trouble to him. [tell][a1]

The apathy can be particularly focused on interaction with other people. Boyfriend, whom I usually talk to three or four times a day, says he doesn't want to be around me anymore and I don't care. Very apathetic. That's alright. [haliae-lc][srj5] Don't want to move, talk, laugh, engage at all. [falco-pe][nl2] She only answers, when spoken to, in a semi-conscious way. [plat][a1]

The apathy can be mental. Disinclination for mental exertion. [ptel][a1] Mental indolence. [jug-r][a1] But it is more often a wish not to do anything physical. No desire to work. [carbn-dox][knl3] Difficult to keep employed. [cere-b][a1] Detached, unreal feeling, disinclined to do anything. [heroin][sdj-h] No interest in any work, did not even feel like eating. [hir][vml3] Very lazy. Enormous aversion to any form of housework. [positr][nl2] Extreme lassitude; disinclination for mental labour or bodily exertion. [ptel][a1] Indolent, indifferent, no inclination to read. [pyrus][c1]

The apathy can come out of a sense of heaviness. Leaden feeling in the limbs, as though he could not move them. [cann-i][a1] Heaviness and tiredness all through the proving, morning and early evening. No power in me. [germ-met][srj5] Body feels very, very heavy and very tired with deep lethargy throughout my whole body, definitely aggravated by heat. Lost all desire to run and exercise as I usually do. [lac-del][hrn2] Or weakness. The provers remarked that everything felt too much. 'I can't do it, I feel totally exhausted'. [gink-b][vml3] Unable to go to work due to all round debilitation. [heroin][sdj-h] I drag myself about, total lack of any enthusiasm. So pissed off and joyless. [heroin][sdj-h] The patient was apathetic and sluggish. [phos][a1] Obliged to stop suddenly while sitting and working and lie down, without feeling any other effects than that it is quite impossible to do the slightest thing. [sel][a1] Indolence, with desire to stretch. [meph][c1] State of profound stupor and helplessness. [tax][a1] The Viscum patient is sad, tired, feels worn out, is apathetic but restless at the same time. [visc][vml3] Or of feeling aged. Premature old age, with apathy and melancholy. [agn][c1] Or a tendency towards slowness. Not reacting properly, not fast and not aware. [corv-cor][bdg1] Slow. Very slow in delivering account, long pauses. [heroin][sdj-h]

The apathy can be about personal appearance or cleanliness. Haven't washed my hair for weeks, I'm too tired – indifference about looking after myself. [falco-pe][nl2]

It can be manifest physically as constipation. No stool and no desire for stool since the beginning of the proving (six days), but no discomfort. [choc][srj3] Or paralysis. Strong tendency to paralysis, especially of the motor apparatus. [cur][a1] Reflex action is diminished or abolished the reflexes completely disappear. [cur][c1] Or mentally as indecision and procrastination. Refusal of self-responsibility. This remedy is helpful for children who don't want to anything for themselves when they are older. It is still mother who must lace up their shoes, wipe their behind, and so on." [Grandgeorge][cur][vml3] Postponing everything. [gink-b][vml3] Can't decide which order to do normal tasks in, it doesn't seem to matter. [lac-h][htj1]

The most common phrase used to describe this apathy by provers was "can't be bothered". Can't be bothered with anything, would like to lie down and read, – something sedentary. [aids][nl2] Cannot be bothered. Inability to do anything. [berlin-w][evans] "I don't care" sort of feeling. Can't be bothered to be worried about anything. [choc][srj3] Felt apathetic, born of a feeling of being trapped and like others felt why bother. [falco-pe][nl2] As I examine myself mentally I feel an underlying sense of futility – why bother? [falco-pe][nl2] Great awareness of "can't be bothered." [irid-met][srj5] Can't be bothered. [irid-met][srj5] Nothing bothers me. [lsd][nl-lsd] Received a long letter from a patient today; haven't even read it, can't be bothered. Very unusual. In terms of indifference, [neon][srj5] A sort of 'can't be bothered' feeling, have to push myself. [positr][nl2] Can't be bothered to do anything, wants to be left alone. [tung-met][bdx1]

There can be a recognition of how indifference leads to apathy and a wish to avoid it. Strongly started to accept that all changes come through conflicts and peace does not let you grow. If I had to choose between peace and conflict, I would go for conflict. [polys][sk4]

The apathy often leads directly to selfishness. Feels lazy, as if she would like to lie in bed and be waited on; selfish. [pyrus][a1] (*See Selfishness III-5*)

III-3 Anaesthesia

The indifference and the feeling of can't be bothered can become a lack of feeling and eventually an inability to feel.

At a lesser level this manifests itself as numbness. Cocaine is the root for many local anaesthetics and it has this symptom strongly. Lips and face so numb that she tried some time before she could speak. [cocain][a1] Anaesthesia (local). [cocain][a1] As do several other remedies. Have had a lot of numbness. Often it is in the parts that I am lying on but there is no motivation or desire to move. Just stay in one position and it gets even worse. [latex][nl-latex] Numb hands and face. [mdma][saunders] In the extremities there is numbness. [nux-m][k2] Propolis tincture can cause side-effects. Chewing the raw product causes an immediate numb sensation in tongue and mouth. [propl][vml3] I went to a burrito shop to get dinner and while I was waiting there, my right arm got numb. It kind of felt like I had slept on it, and I felt like I couldn't move it. [sanguis-s][hrn2]

However, this numbness can also be general, Numbness with sensation of deadness, lasting for most of the proving. [adam][srj5] There was no taste in what he ate, no refreshment in what he drank, and it required a painful effort to comprehend what was said to him, and return a coherent answer. [cann-i][a1] Feeling of numbness. [cann-i][a1] This animal does not bite frequently, but when it does it is understood that the result is a benumbing paralysis. [helo-s][rwt2] There was a numbness of the extremities, particularly the arms. [musca-d][stew+] Felt numb and spaced out. [hydrog][srj2] A sensation of numbness; in ears and throughout the body. [irid-met][srj5] And it is often emotional as well as physical. Felt emotionally numb and separated from things. [choc][srj3] A strange, unfeeling, benumbed state – a sense of inevitability. [falco-pe][nl2] Felt numb to everything and everyone Apathy. [carneg-g][rwt1] (*See Lack of Emotion III-4*)

The numbness can be as reaction to shock or danger to which the vulnerable state in many remedies makes the subject more likely to experience. While driving had an accident. Not had accident before, it threw me. I acted calmly. Just got back into my car, felt a bit kind of numb, shock state. [aids][nl2] Numbness, tingling and nausea throughout body during fear. [androc][srj5] (*See Vulnerability IX-1*)

This numbness can go much deeper to either a state of analgesia (in which the subject feels no pain) or to a state of complete anaesthesia (in which he or she feels nothing at all). These states are well known in the drug remedies, they could even be seen as the definition of a drug. A common docility and absence of susceptibility which was most remarkable. Thus one of them gave to another with whom he was but slightly acquainted a series of hard blows on the back, saying that he himself felt nothing of the Hashish, and asking whether the blows he inflicted were felt. On his part, he who received the blows took them all in good humour, uttering no complaint, and seeming, in indeed, insusceptible of complaint. Again, one of them, who sat writing, submitted to receive the infliction of two sharp blows, boxes on the ears, and to have his pen snatched out of his hand, without any expression of pain or even annoyance. [cann-i][a1] Again, anaesthesia extended all over his body, and now was added an automaton-like and rapid movement of the hands, one hand being pressed upon the breast, and rubbed actively on the back with the palm of the other hand. [cann-i][a1] Gradually total anaesthesia. [cann-i][a1] An hour after the entire quantity named has been taken, the sensibility of the limbs to external influences – which had gradually diminished from the first – became materially lowered, and neither pinches, pricks, nor slight burns with a heated wire could be felt upon the fleshy portions of the arms or legs. The trunk, however, never lost its sensibility to pain in any marked degree. [cocain][br1] While walking, a sense of mellowness and extreme calm, both mental and physical; almost a sensation of anaesthesia of the body. [coca-c][sk4] Traumatic memories, suppressed for years because they are too painful to face, may emerge and be looked at without terror. Insights into what is really happening in life can also occur. Pain may be reduced, especially if it is based on fear, such as the fear of death. [mdma][saunders] Analgesia. [mdma][hmd1] Although I have a headache I don't seem to mind about it. [lsd][nl-lsd] *(See Drugs II-6)*

These symptoms are not exclusive to the drug remedies but are also found in many others. Absence of the understanding and of the external and internal senses; he saw nothing, said nothing for many days, heard nothing, and understood nothing; when one shouted into his ears, he looked at those present like one waking from deep sleep. [ars][a1] Stranger, of it forms sudden is anesthetized. Of one moment for other, every area of the lips, upper and below, in the same intensity whole region, I feel as if it had won a place anesthesia of all the lips. I didn't place anything that can have anesthetic action. This picture a lot is impressing me, therefore it is completely anesthetized. [lepd-s][rsi1] Feeling a numbing effect physically. Feel submerged under anesthetic. [haliae-lc][srj5] Cannot feel pleasure or sorrow. Everything is Chaos. Cannot restore my energy. Totally meaningless. Feels like an empty battery. [germ-met][srj5] Playing on the beach, she gets stung by a bee. I pull out the stinger. No swelling no reaction. [lac-del][hrn2] Woke up feeling very relaxed again as if nothing could upset me – feel spacey in my head like I had taken morphine when in hospital – cut off from everything, nothing can intrude into your space i.e. disconnected. [latex][nl-latex] I felt happy and free from any pain. [nux-m][a1] Dream: Explosion from thumb: mud and rocks flying out. No pain, no emotions. [polys][sk4] According to Virgil and Galen, Roman soldiers took propolis with them on their military expeditions. It was used topically in the treatment of wounds, ulcers and boils, and as an analgesic. [propl][vml3] The bark of the willow contains salycilic acid, which has been used in herbal medicine, and as aspirin in conventional medicine, to relieve the pain of headaches, rheumatism and flu. [sal-fr][sle1] Death from Yew poisoning, says Cooper, is remarkably painless. [tax][c1] Bashed head violently on door, but didn't really hurt at all. [tung-met][bdx1]

The ultimate stage in this progression is the state of coma. This is found in some remedies particularly the older drugs such as Cannabis and Opium but it is not common. This may be because coma is end stage pathology that is not likely to come though in potentized provings. However, it may be that it is not so much part of the Miasm. The thing that distinguishes the venom of the Gila Monster is a lingering state of paralysis that does not progress to coma until the very end. This lingering nature of the action of the poison is markedly different from the snake poisons, which generally kill quickly if at all. [helo-s][rwt2] Very few persons bitten can speak after the first fifteen minutes, but unconsciousness seldom comes until a few minutes before death. [helo-s][rwt2]

III-4 Lack of Emotion

The physical inability to feel can be seen reflected in the more ubiquitous lack of emotional sensitivity. Absence of sensitivity towards others. [aids][nl2] Detached, totally cut off from emotions, no emotional connection with other people, just didn't feel anything. [falco-pe][nl2] It doesn't affect me too much – a sort of numbness – indifference to it all. [heroin][sdj-h] Disconnected from emotions, from things going on around me. Things were happening but I was apathetic: "Oh well too bad." [lac-lup][hrn2] Realized I didn't want to pass through emotions. Didn't want to feel them. [lac-lup][hrn2] A patient at work became very violent, grabbing a nurse by the throat. I ended up blocking his exit from the unit where I work while trying to explain the situation to irate relative waiting to come in to see someone else. I was surprisingly casual about the intensity of the violence and this concerned me as I was not being careful enough about my own safety. At lunchtime I removed myself from the unit to take stock as I felt I needed a dose of reality! [latex][nl-latex] Disconnected from my emotional process. [lsd][nl-lsd] In the Oak state, emotions may be held at bay, as one struggles to uphold one's duties and loyalty. [querc-r][rcb4] Feel like an onlooker, completely passive, no emotions, very little reaction to things going on around me. [plac][Biggs+] Calmness almost to the point of no reaction – no worry, no emotion. [plac][Biggs+] I lack any emotional response to anything. [plut-n][srj7] No strong emotions or fears. [polys][sk4] The music that I have been learning and which I could feel in the depths of my soul does not touch me any more. I think and sing, rather than being involved in the music. [polys][sk4] I allowed my car to close in extremely close to another. It is unusual for me to take rather than avoid a risk. It didn't perturb me at all. [rhus-g][tmo3] Heroin is the most powerful of all analgesics and it is not surprising that it is the remedy in which the lack of feeling both mental and emotional is strongest. There is no fluctuation of feelings, joy, interest, inspiration etc. Like I'm switched off, can switch on to talk to people but not 'to feel' but then seem to switch off. There's a general lack of response to situations. The loss of my son's uni work in his bag. My friend's operation. My mum's cat. My sister moving to Australia. [heroin][sdj-h]

The lack of emotional involvement is often expressed in relationships where feeling should be stronger. Unfeeling in relationship and sexually. [adam][srj5] Generally numb emotionally, and unusually uncaring about how I came across to other people, found myself treating people I knew well quite outrageously, although part in jest. [positr][nl2] Extreme tiredness and sense of disconnection. Irritable at work. Sarcastic and rude to colleagues at work. Don't care if I get the sack. [positr][nl2] But it can be towards the rest of the world as well. This is particularly so in Lac humanum which is not surprising as the issue in the remedy is about caring for the world and ignoring the world to care for the self. Indifference to the suffering of others. [lac-h][vml3] No reaction to anything on the news, unusual for me. [lac-h][htj1]

A lack of feeling can lead to decisiveness and an ability to do things and regard them as right regardless of the consequences. This is a particularly important aspect of Polystyrene and of Rubber where the subject is insulated from normal restraining pressures. Practical, able to take immediate, point blank decisions without getting involved or thinking what the other person would feel; also without any afterthought, like an executive. Felt always that I had done the right thing. [polys][sk4] Dream: Was on an outing in a religious place, with no religious feeling. [polys][sk4] I don't give a damn about anything my friend phoned up and I must have sounded quite cold and unfriendly. I am either very in touch with other people's feelings or I feel completely shut off, cold and hard. [latex][nl-latex] This can be extremely liberating. No embarrassment in situations that would have earlier been embarrassing. [polys][sk4] Feel I can say anything without inhibitions. [tung-met][bdx1]

The lack of sensitivity can combine with Chocolate's obsession with truth, with Diamond's clarity or with Fire's purity, with the result that the possibility of hurting others becomes less of a matter of concern. I wanted to ring a few friends and tell them what I really thought about them. [choc][srj3] I'm ready to speak my mind – I don't care if people cease to like me. [choc][srj3] Generally fairly severe mood, very straightforward and will say what is needed to be said. [adam][srj5] Find myself being sharp with people, saying things the way they are without beating around the bush. [ignis-alc][es2]

This trend becomes general hard heartedness. The world appeared a cruel place to me, and I felt I had no place in the scheme of things. I became selfish, impatient and intolerant. [choc][srj3] Moral weakness (in two provers). [conv-d][a1] I spanked the kids for the first time in years because they had been fighting, I wanted to make a point. The strange thing was that I did not feel remorse, as usual, for spanking them. [haliae-lc][srj5] A very real danger of taking Ecstasy is that you may do or say something you will regret, or that will upset someone else. [mdma][saunders] I have been removed from the strong connection with my conscience. [vacuum][es-vac] My sense of compassion was neutralised. [vacuum][es-vac] Tremendous irritability. Desire to be silent, taciturn. Easily irritable, rebellious, rude in speech and behaviour, back answering and hurtful to those around. [lac-h][sk4] Feeling of objective detachment. I must say what I am feeling even if it hurts others. [lsd][nl-lsd] Feeling that relationships are mostly selfish and that people try to utilize and take advantage of others; that love and care does not matter but how useful you are or not. [polys][sk4] Feel harder, more rebellious. I will do what I want. Inconsiderate and unsympathetic. [adam][srj5] The name is derived from two Greek words, *ana* – without, and *cardium* – a heart, because the pulp of the fruit, instead of having the seed enclosed, has the nut growing out at the end of it. [anac][vh1] I think I'm a bit bossy at work – this is not normal. [falco-pe][nl2] I have been feeling very assertive, quite aggressive. [falco-pe][nl2] Kind of fearlessness and not worrying about things. [falco-pe][nl2]I notice I haven't the usual concerns about pussyfooting around so as not to offend or speak out of turn, and no remorse about what I've said. [heroin][sdj-h] I feel harder and less caring. [lsd][nl-lsd]

The hard hearted feeling is often described in terms of coldness. Furious cold anger when money stolen from me. [adam][srj5] A basic pattern I discerned is that many woman felt abused and neglected, reacting by rebellion and independent behaviour. They have a "I don't need anybody" attitude. [lac-f][wza1] Especially in Falcon, A feeling of isolation and coldness inside. Shutting down to the outside world, separation from my partner. [falco-pe][nl2] I feel paralysed on the sexual level and it is almost a relief when we don't have sex because of my obstacles. I'm not happy about this. I feel ugly and my body looks ugly. My partner has dubbed me the ICE QUEEN. [falco-pe][nl2] and Cocaine. Icy coldness. [cocain][a1]

A small feature of this trend which comes through in several remedies is a propensity to swear. Swearing and cursing. [adam][srj5] A curious symptom is a great propensity to swear and blaspheme in persons not usually addicted thereto. [anac][c1] My language has got worse – I do swear, but it's got much worse. [falco-pe][nl2] Attacks of rage, cursing and swearing at slightest provocation. [lac-c][al2] Desire to curse and swear. [lac-h][htj1] Also I use swear words more than usual, they just seem to slip out. [lsd][nl-lsd] Scolds and rages till she falls unconscious. [mosch][c1] He used improper language in a loud tone. [nux-m][a1] Involuntary blasphemous mood. [opun-v][a1] Fit of swearing at evening after coming home; praying in the morning. [opun-v][a1] Unusually expressive of my irritability without any remorse. [polys][sk4] I was swearing a lot. [sanguis-s][hrn2]

There can be the reverse effect in which the lack of strong feeling allows the subject to remain apart from the need to express himself. A debate starts up in the pub. I listen to both sides. I have an opinion of my own, but it doesn't seem to be able to stir me, I can't work up any strong feelings. [positr][nl2]

The lack of emotional involvement can lead to a concentration on logical, left brain activity. Thinking becomes much more important than feeling. Logical. [polys][sk4] Normally my delight is in music, colours, art, poetry and all that is associated with right brain activity or the female side. Now it is quite the opposite. I read avidly, watch science programmes on TV, listen to radio serious talks and enjoy mind teasing games. I feel a need for accumulating as much information as possible on various subjects, some of which I was never really interested in before. [positr][nl2] The remarkably brain-like appearance of the nut has given rise to the notion that it is a "brain-food". [jug-r][c1]

There can be a split between reason and emotion. (*See Splitting V-4*) But there is also a split between feeling and doing which leads to automatic actions. Things going on around me and I don't feel part of them. Automatically doing things on one level, but "not there" on another. [irid-met][srj5] I am beginning to notice a strange sense of fuzziness where time seems to stop. The fuzziness is detached, almost hypnotized feeling. I'll be driving or writing and going through the motions but not mentally aware, kind of robotic. [lac-loxod-a][hrn2] I feel like a clockwork doll, all movements and actions automatic. [ozone][sde2] Felt as if I was mechanically living my life. [polys][sk4]

III-5 Selfishness

A lack of sensitivity and a hard hearted attitude to the feelings of others is likely to result in a concentration on the needs of the self. There is definitely a sense of selfishness, of egoism in this desire to express himself, where he will insist that others listen to what he has to say concerning these visions. [anh][vh1] I usually care, want to be helpful. Don't give a shit about my friend. Don't want to be here with this stupid broken down car. [corian-s][knl6] I am less reserved than normal, more confident; but my boundaries have altered. I get less drawn into other people's emotional problems, less sympathetic. [irid-met][srj5] When you sit and wait for the cat to snuggle in your lap, it is nowhere to be seen, yet you can't get rid of it at the very moment it doesn't suit. [lac-f][vml3] Loud, dominating speech. Making others do whatever I wanted them to. [lac-h][sk4] She was being bossy, impatient and abrupt. [lac-h][htj1] Still feeling a little self-centred, in other words find it easy to say what I need. [latex][nl-latex] When they have been encouraged to resort to crafty cunning, to have every whim gratified from infancy to eighteen years of age they become fit subjects for Mosch. [mosch][k2] Feel that the person I am conversing with should shut up and listen to me. Curtly dominating. [polys][sk4] Had the feeling that no one would take me for granted or dominate me, and the person who tried would get a firing from me and I would beat him and pull his hair. I felt that I must be prepared in case anyone tries it. [polys][sk4] Desire to pamper myself. [positr][nl2] Lovely job – non stop, full steam – intolerant of slow people. [positr][nl2] Feels lazy, as if she would like to lie in bed and be waited on; selfish. [pyrus][a1] I've been barely on time to class, unusual for me. Tonight I'm feeling relaxed about time, people can wait a few moments. [galeoc-c-h][gms1] "Fuck everyone else, what's in it for me?" has been the unnerving impetus of thought. [vacuum][es-vac] I feel I won't go to work tomorrow if I don't want to, as it really doesn't suit. [vacuum][es-vac]

This is perhaps strongest in the Scorpion, Scorpions are loners and sometimes will eat each other, though they are immune to their own poison. The female has been known to eat the male after copulation and the mother may eat her young. It seems as though not even the most primitive form of animal association is known to them. [androc][srj5] Feels much more self centered. Have given up all the permanent favors I do for people I don't want to do any more. Feel I need more time for me. I must feel guilt but I don't think I do. I feel the nasty side of my character is emerging much more aggressive and domineering. I don't want people's good opinion of me as someone who is nice. Very unusual. [androc][srj5] and the Koala Bear. My needs are important to me; I did what I wanted to do. [phasco-ci][rbp2] No concern for others feelings. Selfish. [phasco-ci][rbp2]

Sometimes the selfishness is unrecognized, Inability to realize my rudeness towards family members. Totally self-oriented. [lac-h][sk4] Partner says I'm aggressive and aloof. I'm feeling happy and independent. [positr][nl2] but often it is just something that the subject does not care about. I feel selfish, but don't really feel bad about being selfish. Unfeeling – able to say straight what I feel without considering the other person's feelings at all. [heroin][sdj-h]

This selfishness is not always negative. Sometimes it allows a clarity as to what is really important. Decide to simplify my life by not encumbering it with charitable obligations. [aids][nl2] Exceptionally strong desire to leave my marriage and children, to live a clear unmuddled life alone. [adam][srj5] Noticed lack of wanting to overextend myself. Usually do overabundance of things and will be committed. [carbn-dox][knl3] Sudden thought as to why I was being so considerate, "taking shit" from everyone, taking what they are saying to me without answering. [polys][sk4] Can't tolerate anything that doesn't suit me – liberating! [positr][nl2] Or it allows the subject to recognize what he or she really wants. It's crystal clear! Clarifying female roles. Clarification of issues. Realization – anger and depression in the past, had to do with conditioning, not saying what I wanted, not having my needs met. [adam][srj5] Very resentful of husband and demands of life. Actually told husband did not think I could go on with the relationship. Feeling of being overwhelmed. [lac-leo][hrn2] Expressed irritability which I usually suppress; was happy to do it. Felt how dare people tell me these things for no fault of mine; they had no right to. [lac-leo][sk4]

Selfishness can also be manifested as a tendency to be critical. Get angry when criticized, yet easily critical of others. [adam][srj5] He is vexed about every trifle, and constantly talks about other people's faults. [ars][a1] It is this inner drive for perfectionism that leads him to be very critical, very censorious of others. He readily criticizes anything done by anyone else, and his keen perception readily brings any existing imperfection to light. He is exhaustively fault-finding. [ars][vh1] Strong inner critical voice. By letting it out, I felt better but did not want to do it. Felt bad being critical of things, even small things that normally would not bother me. But it was not a release because I did not like that I was being picky about things. It all seemed so trivial. The things that were making me uptight. [lac-lup][hrn2] I am still feeling critical overall. I still want to fix things and contribute. Sort of critical and helpful at the same time. [lac-lup][hrn2] Strong inner critical voice. [lac-lup][hrn2] I couldn't seem to stop myself nagging and finding fault. [positr][nl2] In a meeting this morning, I felt critical, censorious. [galeoc-c-h][gms1] However, this critical attitude is also likely to be turned back on the self. Needs to criticize others and himself. [gink-b][jl1] Criticizing every aspect of self and others. So threatened do I feel because of disconnection from self and source. [lsd][nl-lsd] (*See Lack of Confidence XI-1*)

III-6 Cruelty

The feelings of indifference, selfishness and apathy reach their combined apotheosis in feelings of cruelty.

Anacardium is the remedy traditionally associated with cruelty and this is just one of the features of this remedy that leads me to believe that it is related to many of the new remedies. A strong feature is that all moral feeling is taken out of him. [anac][k2] He feels cruel. [anac][k2] Can do bodily injury without feeling. [anac][k2] Cruel, malicious, wicked. [anac][k2] Anacardium is also one of the first remedies to consider for cruelty. These people can be extremely cruel to both people and animals. They are capable of torturing animals and can be indifferent to the torture of humans; they may even enjoy seeing others suffer violence. It is as if they are devoid of all ethical feelings of morality. [anac][vh1]

However, Anacardium's place as the cruelest remedy has been

usurped by the Scorpion, even its name The name is derived from Gr. *androktonos*, killing people [androc][vml3] puts it ahead of Anacardium which merely means "without heart". Every day things disappear from my mind. Am free from pressing, nagging responsibilities, just a black thunder sits within me, and I feel afraid of what I might do next. My eyes are staring and full of hate. Just looking at the children sends them frantic. [androc][srj5] Dream that I murdered my grandfather by poking a knitting needle through one of his eyes when he was asleep. He died peacefully and it appeared that he had had brain hemorrhage. I confessed and no one believed me. A close friend explained he was 86 anyway and I had children to look after and responsibilities, I couldn't afford the luxury of easing my conscience and going to prison. I did confess properly to the police and they refused to prosecute. I wanted to be punished, yet felt no remorse myself. The confusion of what I should do took more time than thinking of poor grandfather. It frightened me. [androc][srj5] One of the main features of the remedy is a total lack of guilt and remorse, unfeeling. This is more so than in Anacardium. Cold knife-edged violence, desire to stab things or split them open. [androc][vml3] God/Satan; hell, darkness. [androc][vml3] Mutilation, blood and sadism. [androc][vml3]

Many of the new remedies are predator animals that might be expected to contain a cruel streak. The Falcon, My son pushed me down to the ground. I reacted so indignantly and angrily over something so small and playful. I told him I felt the whole family just used me and abused me, took me for granted and that I felt like just walking off and leaving them. [falco-pe][nl2] I have responded with irritation and anger when I have felt that my boundaries have been under threat, or when challenged. [falco-pe][nl2] and the Eagle, I was in a gallows humour, cruel but funny. My friends had never seen that side of me before. Like I was on speed. I had no control. They asked me not to cut up vegetables, not to use a knife. I was waving the knife around. I threw the knife at a potato. [haliae-lc][srj5] I wanted to really hurt somebody or something , no respect for the person, anyway that I could. There was another part of me that couldn't believe I was doing that. It was like a horror movie. I got to that place of no boundaries or responsibility to life. It didn't matter what I did. Indifferent. Like ice, no feeling. Just like if I killed someone there would be no regrets. [haliae-lc][srj5] A god-like place or a devil-like place. Why do I have these things? [haliae-lc][srj5] I have to kill the children. They are not obeying me. [haliae-lc][srj5] Had a peculiar experience during the day. While playing with one of my dogs, I started to wonder what it would be like to crush her. Suddenly I thought how sensual it would be to crush its little head and rip its flesh. There was something very sensual about the idea of crushing flesh and bones of a soft creature that would not be able to fight me off. It was not a strong, powerful impulse, but there was something compelling about the idea. [haliae-lc][srj5] I look at rabbits and birds in a different light. Wondering how a rabbit would taste raw. What would the fur taste like? [haliae-lc][srj5] Caring equals oneness. A scary point about that acute phase yesterday – there was no caring. It didn't matter. Nothing mattered. I was alone and wanted to be that way. To have caring, there must be an attunement with the oneness of the universe. Is that where Hitler came from? The crack in the universe? [haliae-lc][srj5] These are powerful examples of this, as is the Lion. Felt I wanted to crash the face of people who stared at me. [lac-leo][sk4] and the Shark. Hard feeling toward cat's cry, usually I would get up quickly to let the cat out, can't stand the cry. Today I would prefer coldly throwing the cat against the wall to shut it up. [galeoc-c-h][gms1] On waking son, today, I just say "Time to get up." and leave in response to his scowl. Usually I sit with him, stroking or rubbing his feet for gentle wake-up. [galeoc-c-h][gms1] However, many other animals have this element of cruelty. Had a very brutal, ugly dream: a witness to the rise to power of Al Capone. Was passive and impotent and was impotent to his acts of brutality as he murdered everyone on his way to the top. It was about the nature of good and evil, that evil becomes powerful when there is no good to oppose it. [ara-mac][sej7] Sensed there was cruelty and hatred within me. [cygn-b][sle-swan] Others noticed that I had become contemptuous and was acting superior. Was deliberately using complicated words which people wouldn't understand, and was getting a lot of satisfaction when they would ask me for an explanation. [lac-cp][sk4] Wondered what it would be like to twist the head off of a living bird. [urol-h][rwt3] It is found even in the cuddly Koala, Dream: Strangling my ex-boyfriend; pushing my thumbs into his throat. [phasco-ci][rbp2] Dreams of animals being butchered; packed into a box. [phasco-ci][rbp2] Hard and cruel; callousness. [phasco-ci][rbp2] and the lowly Worm. Dreamed I was traveling to classes and the hospital. I asked for a T.V. in the room and I was planning to steal it. I stole everything that I could fit in my bag, even the remote control for the T.V. [helodr-cal][knl2] The other dream I remember is looking into a cage and there were two white duck like creatures that were bloody and had deep cuts in their bodies. They were in the cage with some other animal that was furry and the one that was torturing them. The interior of the cage was bloody and dirty and couldn't see the details of the animals. I felt it was so cruel to have put these animals together and allow this to happen. [helodr-cal][knl2] Even the Milk of Human Kindness is not always so. Dream: Raping a junior colleague because she had teased me. [lac-h][sk4] Dream: Threatening my professor that I would kill him if he failed me. [lac-h][sk4] Was unnecessarily unkind to a colleague. Sharper tongue than usual. [lac-h][htj1]

Some of the non animal remedies also display an unusual degree of cruelty. I wanted to kill everyone. [aids][nl2] I feel cold and empty and very angry, almost cruel. [adam][srj5] Dream: Very violent, trying to kill people but they don't die. [adam][srj5] Sarcasm. [anh][sp1] Fascination with cruelty. [berlin-w][hmd2] Extreme aggression: towards self and others. [berlin-w][hmd2] Humourless, intolerant – almost cruel. [choc][srj3] The world appeared a cruel place to me, and I felt I had no place in the scheme of things. I became selfish, impatient and intolerant. [choc][srj3] Irresolute, false, and deceitful characters. [coca][a1] There's cruelty in me. [heroin][sdj-h] Withdrawal of generosity. I had got a plant for a friend and decided not to give it to her. Feeling cruel. [heroin][sdj-h] Found the cats had been at the rubbish. Picked up one of them and threw him. He hit his head off a wall – I found this funny. [ignis-alc][es2] I had this angry feeling all day. I was very irritable in the morning and then really angry at people and things all day – mainly people. This was connected to a great sense of self-confidence – it felt right to be angry. I thought " I have a right to be angry and tell everyone, I don't care what other people think!". It was a healing kind of anger. I felt like ringing people I'm angry at and saying, "This is bad!" [latex][nl-latex] Got up late in a horrible mood and reproached my partner again. I hurt him but I didn't care. I felt indifferent, malicious and vindictive, full of hate. [neon][srj5] Thoughts of accidents having happened to others, these thoughts grow upon him, as if he were to do the same injuries to others. [osm][a1] I had a fight with my wife, felt I was mean to her, cruel. [plut-n][srj7] Violent hateful, revengeful thoughts. [polys][sk4] Dream: I am beating up a friend and feeling very happy. [polys][sk4] Feeling evil and malevolent. Feel as if it would be a pleasure to hurt people and things. [positr][nl2] Dream: Killed one man by cutting his head off. [carneg-g][rwt1] I feel hard hearted, as if my heart is like a rock. [rhus-g][tmo3] Dreams of quarrels, of an unnatural horrible cruelty. [sel][a1] I can see things going with people that allowed me detachment from myself. My safety net wasn't there; that part of my psyche that's saying that's bullshit. It's the same kind of detachment someone has from killing someone, like in Kosova or Jews in Germany. If I wanted to do anything, an action I wanted to do without caring about the consequences. [vacuum][es-vac]

The cruel feelings are often turned upon the subject's own self. This is particularly so in Germanium, Feel envious of a colleague who I feel manages so well. When I compare with myself I feel worthless and nothing. I feel like talking badly about her to my friends and I do this, even though she is not present. [germ-met][srj5] I'm desperate. I want to die. Feel the power to kill. Feel like a wild animal locked in. It's strong, so intense. I hate so strong, feel a terrible disgust and I'm afraid of what I'm able to do. It's completely impossible to be in it and impossible to get out of it. [germ-met][srj5] but the same feeling lies behind many of the symptoms of self destructiveness. (*See Self Hatred & Self Harm XI-4)*

The cruelty is also the obverse side of the fear of cruelty and the Plutonium feeling, Woke up from a dream. I was looking for an alibi because I was a serial killer. The idea of knives and duality came into my mind. [plut-n][srj7] and is the other side of the feeling that came through strongly in the related remedy of Positronium. Have become paranoid that one of my students is going to stalk and murder me. There has always been something a bit creepy about him, but I have managed to push the feeling to one side. He has become obsessed with serial killers and devours books on them. He talks about walking down the street, realizing that no-one is aware of his existence and how he has the desire to smash someone across the head with a hammer or drop a heavy shopping basket on a babies head, then they'd notice him. This really freaks me out because I know he has been attracted to me since the beginning of the course. He was staring me all the time in a really unnerving way and not taking notes as he usually does. Now I'm paranoid that he's going to turn into a serial killer like the characters he is so fascinated by, and I'm going to be his first victim. My big fear and delusion is that I'm attracting this in some way because it's part of my energy field and unless I do something about this, my energy is going to attract this more and it is going to happen, but I didn't know what to do so it's a bit scary. [positr][nl2] I was reading a Sunday supplement which contained an article about a woman who married a man who had been imprisoned for murdering his family. He was the perfect husband for about 15 years. Until she became depressed and he murdered her then killed himself. I became paranoid and scared that my partner had a lot of suppressed violence and that he would murder me at some point. [positr][nl2] and in several others. (*See Vulnerability XI-1 and particularly Rape, Child Abuse & Incest XI-4*)

III-7 Despair

The ultimate result of all these feelings, especially of the sense of isolation is despair. Despair, and disgust of life. [ambr][a1] Black, hopeless depression. [berlin-w][hmd2] Great despondency; becomes reckless about himself. [cur][a1] Felt life is a hopeless dump. [musca-d][stew+] Immediately after taking the remedy, everything stopped. I become very subdued and depressed. It felt like a void. No joy in birds singing. [neon][srj5] But I really noted my lack of hope, optimism, enjoyment. [galeoc-c-h][gms1] I feel no connection with God or higher self or anything. I feel I've seen out there and there's nothing – only fractals. [vacuum][es-vac] If I disappeared in oblivion, nobody would know the difference. [vacuum][es-vac]

This despair is often related to thoughts of death, She is very sad, and keeps repeating that she will soon die. [agn][a1] Great sadness with a fixed idea of approaching death. This fear is not of immediate death as with Aconite, but the patient thinks it is sure to come after a while, and there is no use in doing anything. [agn][c1] Sadness and restlessness, with fear of death and of the future. [anan][a1] I am probably incurable and that's my own fault. [germ-met][srj5] She spoke of nothing but that she must die. [mosch][a1] and it may be expressed as a wish to die, or in a suicidal disposition. There is also a tendency to suicide by shooting. [anac][c1] Disposition to suicide. [cur][a1] Feeling a total failure, I would prefer to die. Very unmotivated. [germ-met][srj5] About two months after beginning the proving, developed an extreme range of mental symptoms that he had never had before. These included severe depression with strong alternations of moods – high then low – with suicidal tendency, desire to jump from a high building or cut wrist. [hydrog][srj2] Feeling, on being scolded, as if people don't care, or as if I am alone. I feel they can't understand me and that I should commit suicide because it does not make a difference whether I live or die. [lac-h][sk4] Despondent, hopeless; thinks her disease incurable; has not a friend living; nothing worth living for; could weep at any moment. [lac-c][al2] Irritable, depressed, quarrelsome, with family and friends over trivial matters. Felt they were self-centered. Sudden thought that I should die since it is of no use to live. [lac-h][sk4] *(See Death XII-8)*

One of the most despairing of remedies is Mare's Milk. The depth of the despair in an animal that is so beautiful and tries so hard to please is deeply disturbing. What the proving tells us is that this abuse aimed at horses has resulted in a central state of frustration. Nothing seems to go right. All that is attempted is thwarted. The horse (or the Lac equinum patient) struggles to do his duty but never gets a sense of satisfaction. This proving was an incredibly difficult experience for everyone involved with it. The initial provers found the state unbearable and were eager to end the proving. One prover said, "Felt frustrated and overwhelmed by everything. Wanted to quit school, quit work, get divorced, stay home and do nothing." Some provers had to take their constitutional remedy to get over the effects. [lac-e][hrn2] Struggling and struggling, but I am losing ground. Sense of doing my duty, doing the things I have committed to and following through, but my life is crumbling around me. Felt desperate rather than sad. Feeling of apathy, exhausted. I can't deal with this and I don't care. Hard to sort out what is what. Life is hard. [lac-e][hrn2]

IV-1 Dispersion

Sensation of going into nowhere, into nothingness. [aids][nl2]

Boundaries separate but they also contain and it is the lack of containment which follows the breakdown of boundaries that provides the greatest number of symptoms in contemporary disease and in the new remedies.

There are many descriptions of boundaries dissolving or opening up. During meditation: suddenly felt my energy body rising above my physical body, then my head opened and golden angels ascend from it, forming a powerful choir above me. [aids][nl2] I feel an expansion of my boundaries; my mind feels expanded and taking on more work. [adam][srj5] As if expanded, opened up, muscles relaxed, body changed shape. [adam][srj5] Pleasant feeling of being expanded and boundless, not limited by the body. [coca-c][sk4] The borders are breaking loose. I know I have a part of me that does this. My big fear is that I'm really crazy, that I'm making all this up, that I'm just crazy (i.e. that the remedy is a placebo). [haliae-lc][srj5] Release of "Body armour". [mdma][hmd1] I feel weird – like as if my body isn't right, as if the top part of my head isn't the end of my body – that it goes on further. [vacuum][es-vac]

The feeling that this leads to is one of disintegration. Desire to be dissolved, especially the trunk (after three hours). [cere-b][a1] Mind – delusions – body is falling to pieces; [lac-c][se70] Feel as though my heart is disintegrating. [lsd][nl-lsd] Imagined tongue was disintegrating. [positr][nl2] Thinks he is several pieces, and cannot adjust the fragments. [phos][c1] Feel on the verge of hallucinating, of things disintegrating but not scared. [falco-pe][nl2]

This is often linked to the experience of death. I am deeply in touch with a self-destructive sense inside. The part of me that wants to disintegrate and die. Dis-integrate; the opposite of integral oneness, the opposite direction. [haliae-lc][srj5] Sense of impending dissolution; besought me piteously not to let her die. [nux-m][c1] Indescribable sensation at 4 p.m., thought I was dying, whole body seemed falling to pieces, could not walk straight, the atmosphere seemed blue, light flashed before my eyes, body seemed elastic and as if on the stretch, tongue seemed to alternately expand and contract, distant ringing in left ear, could not eat but craved ice-water, which relieved the nausea. [xan][a2] (*See Death XII-8*)

The disintegration can be linked to a split between body and mind. The soul seemed to be separated from the body, and to look down upon it, and view all the motions of the vital processes, and to be able to pass and repass through the solid walls of the room, and to view the landscape beyond. [cann-i][a1] (*See Splitting V-6*)

Linked to this disintegration is the feeling that things are moving, or that nothing can be held onto. The room moved, as if I was being torn apart. [coca-c][sk4] Sitting by the ocean, I had a strong feeling of despair about the passing of time. Everything is fleeting. change happens so fast. We cannot hold onto anything. Even the finest experiences are immediately lost, similar to a feeling I've had after orgasm. [lac-del][hrn2] Felt all things were moving. Had to hold my head, with both hands in order to visualize an object properly. [lac-cp][sk4] Everything that she looked at seemed to move. [mosch][a1]

There can be a sense that there is not a centre or that the centre cannot be found. No sense of my centre; not centred. I feel on the edge of losing it; total ungroundedness; just floating or cut adrift. [phasco-ci][rbp2] This is especially so in the Gila Monster. The idea of centeredness vs. being out of balance (expressed on the physical level of vertigo) seemed to come up repeatedly during the proving. [helo-s][rwt2] Could not find center or get centred. [helo-s][rwt2]

The dispersion can also be of ideas and thoughts. Greatly increased tendency to theorize and philosophise, especially concerning esoteric matters. [hydrog][srj2] (*See Confusion VII-1*)

IV-2 Air & Water

Of the four traditional elements it is Air and Water that require boundaries to be contained. Earth is by its nature grounded and static and does not move unless forced. Fire needs fuel to exist and cannot move from the source of the fuel that feeds it. Water, however, moves freely in two dimensions and air in three. If they are not contained they will continue to spread and disperse forever.

Many of the remedies considered here are gases or are animals that live in the air or water.

Water images and feelings are important. (*See Water IV-3, Waves IV-4 and Thirst & Dryness IV-5*) As are floating and flying and a lack of substance. (*See Floating & Flying IV-8 and Emptiness & Lack of Substance IV-7*)

There is also a crossover between the two elements. Harmony above and below. Outer and inner space. Oceans and skies. [adam][srj5] It is often expressed as flying in water, or swimming in air. Cloud, skies, floating, swimming in air, water. [haliae-lc][srj5] I can play in air, like in water. [haliae-lc][srj5] I had one dream that was a bit vague, but I can see this man walking across a stream, he was able to walk on top of the water. [agath-a][nl2] Dream: I had a powerful dream about being underwater and suddenly realizing that I could breathe underwater and being delighted because I had finally come home. [lac-loxod-a][hrn2] Dream: Swimming in a clear pond with many different colored fish. I'm underwater with the fish, no trouble breathing, swimming around, no strong emotion. [lac-lup][hrn2] Water dreams – Swimming and floating – flying emerging from the water and flying out of the water. [urol-h][rwt3] On going to sleep, felt like I was suspended in the sky just above water, turning in a 360 degree tumble/spin – a lovely feeling, not resting on anything. I felt like a bird then felt like I was half in water then half in the air above it. [vacuum][es-vac]

Some of the remedies such as Rhus tox and Walnut are so unbounded that they can exercise their effect at a great distance. Actual contact with the plant is not necessary in order to produce its effect. [rhus-t][a1] An acrimonious vapour, combined with carburetted hydrogen, exhales from a growing plant of the Poison Oak during the night. It can be collected in a jar, and is capable of inflaming and blistering the skin of persons of excitable constitution who plunge their arms into it. [rhus-t][a1] Its plantation should not be too near dwellings, as some persons are affected by the powerful aroma of its foliage. [jug-r][c1]

Radiation remedies, which include Plutonium and Positronium, likewise have an insidious effect that it is almost impossible to contain. Berlin Wall has been credited with radiation like effects.

Some of the animal substances have a relationship with perfumes which disperse and have their effect at great distances. It is also used as a base for perfume. [ambr][vh1] The well-known power of Musk – the perfume – to produce fainting in some by the mere smelling of it, gives the chief keynote for its use in homoeopathy: Faints easily; faints dead away from the least excitement. [mosch][c1] Since time immemorial scents have been used as aphrodisiacs. [meph][vml3]

Butterflies not only live in the air as the birds do, but they are symbolic of the breath, the soul and the air. The ancient Greeks used the word, "butterfly," synonymously with the word, "soul" (and breath). [limen-b-c][hrn2] They also rely on the mechanism of scent dispersed scents. The females release pheromones (odorous substances) which attract the males. They then flutter together in a highly ritualized and graceful courtship dance. [limen-b-c][hrn2]

IV-3 Water

Many of the remedies are associated with water and might be expected to contain water connected imagery and symbolism.

Thus there are dreams of water in Salmon, Dreams of floods. [oncor-t][srj-case] in Stingray, Water dreams – Swimming and floating – flying emerging from the water and flying out of the water. [urol-h][rwt3] Dream: Swimming in a clean pool with wife; staying under as long as we could; much fun; made love in the pool; thought she might get pregnant. [urol-h][rwt3] in Shark, Dreams of playing baseball underwater. [galeoc-c-h][gms1] in Dolphin, Dream: House flooded and had to use rowboat to get to friend's house. I was using a rowboat to get to and from classes and visit friends and go back and forth. Water was everywhere, and this was my mode of transportation. Calmness, no sense of danger. [lac-del][hrn2] and in the Seagull. Dreams of water and the ocean. [lars-arg][fkw1]

There are also substances that bridge the border between earth and water. Water imagery is found in the Willow, Willows are associated with Water, the Moon, the Underworld and powers of divination. [sal-fr][sle1] Whenever I talked to the provers on the phone, and subsequently when we met, I noticed that they were using water metaphors in their speech. Drifting and floating were common words and there were statements like: "I felt like I was in the prow of a boat going forward through the water." Several provers had important experiences in swimming pools. [sal-fr][sle1] Woke feeling reflective. Thinking about the sea – desire to go to the sea. [sal-fr][sle1] and the Beaver. Of all mammals, the beaver is the most efficient and technically proficient when constructing its dwelling. The animal converts his living environment into different levels of water. This protects him against enemies on river banks and guarantees a quick escape through the underwater entrance to his lodge. [castm][mp4]

The Placenta supports the human being during that stage of its life when it lives in the medium of water. Dreams of water, sea, swimming pool. [plac][Biggs+]

The cactus is of the desert and is even the symbol of the desert in America, but it can only survive by storing vast amounts of water and water dreams are important in the remedy. Because of the great amount of water that the cactus contains, it is referred to as the "cactus camel". They weigh as much as nine tons. Their great weight makes them top heavy and they easily tip over in storms. [carneg-g][rwt1] Dream: Ankles were glued together and the sensation that my body was moving rhythmically to swim and be mobile; mostly my torso; felt like I was possessed by a dolphin. [carneg-g][rwt1] Water World dream; there was a world flood; we were all accustomed to the flood and it became a way of life. [carneg-g][rwt1]

Shore connects water dreams to the birds in general and they are certainly very strong in Falcon and Eagle. Dreams of water. [sej-birds] By the sea. Strong emotional response to looking at the sea: the waves and the sun reflecting off the water. [falco-pe][nl2] Dream: I'm in a swimming pool – I can't find the right tunnel leading into water. [falcope][nl2] Dream: Swam underwater for a whole length of a swimming pool without actually swimming, just dived in and glided to end. [falcope][nl2] I either feel totally in flow with the universe, or floating aimlessly down a river. [haliae-lc][srj5] I was anxious about so much rain. There was severe flooding in our valley, washing the bridge out that connected us to the rest of the world. I felt isolated; lives were decimated. I felt frantic because I couldn't be helpful. [haliae-lc][srj5] A dream of water everywhere, pools overflowing, an abundance of water, playing, trying to move the water from one pool to another. It was not a frantic or fearful feeling, just working and playing. [haliae-lc][srj5] Dreams of water. [ara-mac][sej7]

However, most of the animals have water dreams. Many provers had dreams of water. Water was a theme that kept repeating itself in the many ways in this proving. [musca-d][stew+] Dream: Going fishing. I have to walk down a large mountain and as I come to the river I see that it is dry. I look farther upstream and see the lake is dry. I am sad. [lac-e][hrn2] Many dreams of heavy rains and floods. [lac-h][sk4] Dream: I had a powerful dream about being underwater and suddenly realizing that I could breathe underwater and being delighted because I had finally come home. [lac-loxod-a][hrn2] Dream: Water dream: An immense swimming pool, more like a slow-moving river with current, a strong current, but gentle. [lac-lup][hrn2] A lot of dreams with water. Feeling of soothing. [lac-lup][hrn2] Dream: Lots of water, the ocean, and putting on a life jacket. Very realistic dream. [lac-lup][hrn2] Dream: Swimming in a clear pond with many different colored fish. I'm underwater with the fish, no trouble breathing, swimming around, no strong emotion. [lac-lup][hrn2] Very vivid remembered dreams of water. [meph][a1]

Even the desert dwelling lizard, Swimming underwater. [helo-s][rwt2] Dreams of ocean and water. Dreams of rain. [helo-s][rwt2] Water dreams (rain, waterfalls, pools, snow). [helo-s][rwt2]

Almost any of the remedies under consideration might have such dreams or feelings. Overwhelming desire to be at/in the sea. [adam][srj5] Dream: In quite a large boat on a big lake which at times becomes the sea. [adam][srj5] He is attacked with a feeling of vertigo when crossing a running water or walking by the side of a ditchful of water; he fears he will sink down. [ang][a1] Dream of tidal wave. [germ-met][srj5] Long to live somewhere close to the coastline, and enjoyed playing with the children at the water's edge. [heroin][sdj-h] Dream of great expanse of silver sea. [ignis-alc][es2] Felt similar to being in water or asleep, as if almost asleep or in a trance, aware, but floating in inner self, uncommunicative; like a near death experience, inner self is primary and separate. [irid-met][srj5] Felt cold water running through my arms and legs and out; though it didn't make me feel cold. [irid-met][srj5] I dreamt of water. [irid-met][srj5] I had a smell of water throughout the whole of my dream, like a waterfall dream. [agath-a][nl2] I had a strange sensation last night when we went swimming that I was a piece of polystyrene, that I was a polystyrene float, I felt very very buoyant on top of the water and very relaxed as I was swimming, it didn't feel as if it was any effort at all to swim. [agath-a][nl2] I had one dream that was a bit vague, but I can see this man walking across a stream, he was able to walk on top of the water. [agath-a][nl2] Dreams of rivers becoming oceans. [neon][srj5]

Although thoughts of water can be happy, Thoughts of rivers and oceans and being very happy by them. [neon][srj5] there is often an acknowledgment of the danger of water. Ocean crashing down on streets. [coca-c][sk4] I was anxious about so much rain. There was severe flooding in our valley, washing the bridge out that connected us to the rest of the world. I felt isolated; lives were decimated. I felt frantic because I couldn't be helpful. [haliae-lc][srj5] Dreams of water, flooding and a characteristic fearful waking from dreams. [gink-b][vml3] Dream: Someone tells me to come along and I join a group of people who are going on the water in a boat that is leaking and filling up with water. [urol-h][rwt3] Dreams of saving people who are threatened by floods. [osm][stj2] This was especially so in the Shark. I fear the power of the ocean and fear of being taken over. [galeoc-c-h][gms1] Depth of ocean is a void and it's scary and petrifying. [galeoc-c-h][gms1]

The worm in its burrow is in particular danger from flooding and this was manifest for one of the provers. Our land we purchased recently was under water. So we couldn't build our home on it. I felt concern and upset/lost. [helodr-cal][knl2]

The fear of a lack of water is also important, though this is more commonly manifested in a physical symptom, thirst. Relief that it's been raining, I was worried about the water running out. [falco-pe][nl2] (*See Thirst & Dryness IV-5*)

IV-4 Waves, Circles & Cycles

One of the particular manifestations of water imagery is in waves.

There are dreams of waves. Dreaming about remedy, ebb and flow, taking hold and letting go. [irid-met][srj5] Fearless on big waves. Plunged through giant waves. [lac-del][hrn2] Dream: Waves were taking over; got tossed and beat up by the waves. [carneg-g][rwt1] Dream: Waves trying to wash over high castle walls, as if the waves were alive. [urol-h][rwt3]

Images of waves occur, Sensation of things undulating – as if the grass was undulating, like wind blowing on a field of corn. [aids][nl2] It seemed as if the grass was undulating and then it expanded a bit. The grass wafting around with the wind and changing colours in front of us. [aids][nl2] Delusion on a roller coaster. [ara-mac][sej7] particularly in Cannabis. Heard the noise of colors, green, red, blue, and yellow sounds coming to him in perfectly distinct waves, the sensations it produced were those, physically, of exquisite lightness and airiness. [cann-i][a1] The alternation from obscurity to lucidity is like the effect of a sea-wave; a lucid wave is followed by a dark overhanging way on which the mind is shipwrecked, and carried with the sensation of a melancholy floating towards forgetfulness and oblivion, to be roused instantly by the passage over it once more of the wave of life and light. The dark waves chase each other so long as they continue. [cann-i][a1]

In a number of remedies the symptoms and sensations are described as coming in waves. Numbness and headache waves still there. [corv-cor][bdg1] Next wave of lung symptoms. [corv-cor][bdg1] Waves of heat coming over my body while lying, as if a furnace suddenly came on inside. I throw off the cover, too warm. [haliae-lc][srj5] Feelings both physical and mental, came and went in waves. [falco-pe][nl2] Waves, quite high then down again. [falco-pe][nl2] Concentration comes and goes. "Like water," I said thinking of waves. [irid-met][srj5] Waves of nausea throughout the day. [irid-met][srj5] Waves of pins and needles. [agath-a][nl2] In morning nausea when walking. Came in 2-3 waves. [lac-del][hrn2] Warm wave travelling through the right arm, and then through the left arm. [lac-h][sk4] Pain comes in waves with mental muzziness. [lac-h][htj1] Sexual desire increases and decreases in waves. [ozone][sde2] Or of being wave like. Wave-like sensations in muscles and organs. [buteo-j][sej6]

Another of the attributes of water is that it circulates, that it moves in cycles and in circles. Sherr has noted that cycles are a keynote of Salmon. I'm inclined to start at the end of my story rather than at the beginning. [oncor-t][srj-case] Wears many rings. [oncor-t][srj-case]

It also came through as important in the proving of Koala. Dreams recurring in cycles. [phasco-ci][rbp2] Provers going through the same states in different cycles. [phasco-ci][rbp2]

Falcons move in circles or spirals as they climb to the height from which they can make their deadly stoop. I drive home (usually I ask him to drive because I don't like driving). The first roundabout we come to I ask "which way do I go round it?" I really couldn't think for a few seconds which way I should go. I've never done that before – not even when I was learning. [falco-pe][nl2] On the way back from the party, I got lost several times and found myself driving around roundabouts two or three times. [falco-pe][nl2]

Dolphins also circle but theirs is usually a defensive manoeuvre. Occasionally, the mother dolphins have a strong need to free themselves from the constant responsibility of caring for their calves. They will then go off on their own to play, explore, and fish. To do this safely, they leave the calves with the "aunties" (non-pregnant or nursing females) who, while baby-sitting, will form a circle and swim round and round the calves to protect them from danger. Thus, the feeling in the dolphin is that there is calm and safety in the center of the circle, even though there is danger outside. [lac-del][hrn2] Dream: A woman and I were walking in a circle clockwise, around the perimeter of a crowded mezzanine in a mall. I asked why was she walking in a circle, and she said enemies were coming to get her, and she has to keep going so enemies wouldn't catch up to her. [lac-del][hrn2] Dream: On a merry-go-round, going clockwise. [lac-del][hrn2] Dream: Going to a horse racetrack. Again, the animals were racing clockwise. [lac-del][hrn2]

In Swan the feeling of spinning was related to an important theme of the remedy, that of being part of a group. Sense of spinning in and out of the group. [cygn-b][sle-swan]

One of the feelings that comes out of circular movement is that of going round in circles and of getting nowhere. Monomania, as for rowing about in a boat, dressing or walking out in a grotesque manner, always frequenting the same places and doing the same things. [anan][a1] Again last night I became quite directionless, going round and round, picking up things, putting them down again, doing something else, then dropping it. [falco-pe][nl2] Had to go round a roundabout twice having missed an obvious turnoff. [sal-fr][sle1] Got lost and was going in circles. [urol-h][rwt3]

Circles and spirals are the shapes that most are most clearly defined in AIDS Miasm remedies. The corresponding pattern in Syphilitic remedies is the straight line and particularly parallel lines.

IV-5 Thirst & Dryness

Corresponding to and balancing the excess of water in dreams and imagery there is a physical dryness in many of the remedies. Thirsty, with a dry feeling all over the system. [ptel][a1] It is a desert icon used by artists, cartoonists and film makers. It is also an ancient symbol for the Southwest lowlands desert. [carneg-g][rwt1]

This dryness often relates to the portals, the places where inner and outer connect. Thus dryness is felt particularly in the mouth, His mouth and throat were as hard as though made of brass, and his tongue, it seemed to him, was a bar of rusty iron. Although he seized a pitcher of water and drank long and deeply, his palate and throat gave no intelligence of his having drunk at all. [cann-i][a1] Dry mouth and loss of appetite are almost universal. [mdma][saunders] Dryness in mouth all day with increased thirst for gulps of cold water. [germ-met][srj5] At dinner mouth dry, great thirst, felt he could not drink enough to quench it. [nux-m][c1] Often there is a sensation of dryness when the mouth is moist. [nux-m][k2] Dry mouth. Lips parched – drinking great quantities. [positr][nl2] Mouth and throat very dry. [ptel][a1] Tremendous thirst for cold water in the evening, mouth felt so dry. [sal-fr][sle1] Burning and dry feeling in mouth and tongue. [xan][a1] Excessively dry sensation in the mouth, glutinous, with violent thirst; though he drank much water the thirst was not relieved. [phos][a1] and throat, Inability to drink, in spite of great thirst, on account of spasms in the throat, which contracts and feels tight as soon as he hears anything said about water, or sees shining objects. [anan][a1] Dryness in the throat. Parched sensation. Sudden onset. [limen-b-c][hrn2] Throat, dryness, like a ball in my throat, in center. Dry, hard to swallow. [lac-del][hrn2] Mouth very dry mornings – could hardly speak. [vacuum][es-vac] but also in the vagina. Intercourse at night; seemed dryer than usual. [sal-fr][sle1] *(See Portals XII-6 and Mouth, Anus & Vagina XII-7)*

The commonest expression of this dryness is thirst, which is almost universal in these remedies. Violent and constant thirst, with sensation as of suffocation when drinking. [anac][c1] Violent thirst, could not drink enough. [castm][mp4] Thirst increased, afternoon and evening. [choc][srj3] Thirsty for cold water. [conv-s][jl1] Thirsty for ice cold water. [haliae-lc][srj5] Very thirsty. [helodr-cal][knl2] Intense thirst with dry mouth. Desire for cold, refreshing drinks: fruit juices. [mdma][hmd1] Increased thirst. [helo-s][rwt2] Thirst. [heroin][sdj-h] Thirst. For large quantities of cold water [Raeside]; for small quantities [Sankaran]. [hir][vml3] Feeling quite thirsty, but no desire to drink. [lac-lup][hrn2] More thirst than usually. [lars-arg][fkw1] I was really hot and thirsty for cold water again. [latex][nl-latex] Tremendous thirst (for Pepsi). [polys][sk4] Increased thirst. [propl][vml3] Extremely thirsty, wanted tea. Unusual to drink 2 large mugs at that time. [tung-met][bdx1] Thirsty for water, glugged it down. Desires cold fizzy drinks. [tung-met][bdx1] Energy is good, not especially hungry but very thirsty. [galeoc-c-h][gms1]

In Diamond the thirst combines with the remedy's general theme of sparkle. Strong desire for clear sparkling water, increasing throughout the proving. [adam][srj5]

IV-6 Clouds, Balloons & Bubbles

The airiness found in the remedies is, in some of them, expressed through the idea of clouds. Sensation of being like a cloud. Image of a white billowing cloud. [aids][nl2] He seems to himself to be transformed into a vegetable existence, as a huge fern, and to be surrounded by clouds of music and perfume. [cann-i][a1] Still really noticing clouds, and the colours and shapes of nature – fascinated by the shapes of trees. [lsd][nl-lsd]

Often the cloud symbolism includes an element of heaviness and anxiety. I felt as if a heavy, grey cloud with red specks descended down to my chest entering into me. [adam][srj5] I had a feeling that something bad was going to happen. It was beautiful all around me. The sun was bright and the hills, the ocean. Then I saw the black storm clouds approaching us. [cann-i][sk7] Driving in this ecstatic state under beautiful clear twilight sky with bright stars, when I noticed a humongous dark cloud enveloping the whole sky in front of us consumed by an anxiety and an apprehension for the group of what was ahead – as if part of the proving was about entering the Dark Night of the Soul. [lsd][nl-lsd] (*See Anxiety, Fear & Paranoia IX-5*)

Another common expression of airiness is through images of bubbles and balloons. I was reading someone's hand and the analogy I used was of a bubble in water and rising to the surface. [aids][nl2] Desire to run away – in a balloon – up and out of it all. [adam][srj5] I had a wonderful time blowing bubbles with one of the bubble pots I had bought in the shop. [falco-pe][nl2] Felt like I was bubbling over, had to restrain self in company. [irid-met][srj5] Felt that I could fly away – As if I was a balloon filled with air. [galla-q-r][nl2] I'm at home – I'm walking – a balloon is swaying above me, then the air comes out. I tell myself that its soul has gone away. I thought a friend had died and it was true. I watched her being prepared for her funeral. [galla-q-r][nl2] Lightness, being out in space. Alienated from the earth. Bubbles of joy. [lsd][nl-lsd] Joy. Feel high and expansive. Happiness bubbles near the surface – as if I'm going to erupt with it. This light energy almost uncontainable. [lsd][nl-lsd] Feel light and bubbly – like bubbles rippling near to the surface within me. [lsd][nl-lsd] Car drive home: I feel like a helium balloon, wanting to be set free. I'm held only by a thread. [lsd][nl-lsd] Frightful but beautiful dreams, of clusters of many coloured bubbles in an ellipse, swimming in the sky and which are supposed to be chemicals thrown by aliens to destroy the earth. [polys][sk4] Dream: Flew up in the sky in a hot air balloon; the basket fell and I was left holding the strings. [carneg-g][rwt1] Balloons are made of rubber and condoms can be inflated just like balloons, it is not therefore surprising that this imagery came through in the proving of Rubber. Business is going on as usual around me but I feel very separate from it, like being here but in a bubble. [latex][nl-latex]

This imagery can be physically manifested as bloating and distention. A lot of flatus with distension. [aids][nl2] I am with the swollen abdomen, they already do some days and it is plenty, seeming that am pregnant of 5 months. [lepd-s][rsi1] Fullness, distension, aching. Bloated with pain. [carbn-dox][knl3] Appetite good, he would eat more if there were more room, the abdomen being filled with water. [conv-a][ll1] Distension of abdomen after eating ever so little. [lac-f][vml3] Flatulent distention of the abdomen. [lac-h][sk4] Bloated constantly, affected breathing. [lsd][nl-lsd] Enormous bloating – all food turns to gas. [nux-m][vml2] There are few remedies which cause flatulence and bloating of the abdomen more markedly than Jug. r. [jug-r][c1] Still have flatulence, upper and lower abdomen. [galeoc-c-h][gms1] Sensation of bloatedness earlier felt in the stomach seems to have gone to the brain. [germ-met][srj5] Bloated abdomen. [opun-v][c1] After eating I feel bloated. [vacuum][es-vac]

As the Contemporary Miasm is about the dissolution of boundaries, bubbles and balloons, which are about containment are particularly important because their boundaries are so fragile and almost inevitably break. Thus the imagery of bursting is as important as that of the bubbles themselves. Sensation of popping – image of seed pod popping open – of a bubble popping. [aids][nl2] It was a sensation like a bubble going up and then it popped and was all colourful, like a rainbow, and it left a wetness over everything. The growth thing, things coming out and then it popping. [aids][nl2] Bubbles and dreams are bursting. Feel guilty about partner and kids, feel I am doing it all wrong, have let them down. [falco-pe][nl2] Mental tension; feeling as though the head were enlarged even to bursting. [pip-m][c1] There is a sound in my body like a bursting balloon. [plut-n][srj7] As if something exploded in head. [phos][c1] Sometimes it seemed as if I was beginning to bloat, and then I could hear a multitude of voices saying in high glee, "Fill him up a little more and he will burst", followed by demoniacal laughter, which made the cold chills run over me. [phos][a1] Prover woke up first night with a sensation that a bubble came up to the surface and opened. [urol-h][rwt3]

IV-7 Emptiness & Lack of Substance

The balloon image is sometimes found applied to the body, especially the head. Head feels full of air, "achy" sensitive, as if headache is coming. [choc][srj3] Sensitive as if wind in head or head full of wind. [choc][srj3] The depression is still with me. I am a fully functional shell. I have been like a kind of shell, inside sometimes the most phenomenal blackness, but I have been functioning, like a functional shell. [falco-pe][nl2] Head feels full of air. [germ-met][srj5] Becoming aware of the whole inside of my skull. As if my brain were gone. A really nice feeling of cleanliness and emptiness in my head, instead of having it cluttered up with brains. [ignis-alc][es2] Sensation as if mind were void. Thought confused. [irid-met][mp4] My head feels like a marshmallow but I can see very clearly. [agath-a][nl2] My chest felt enlarged as if air was blowing into me through my sleeves; I felt blown up, as if I would be lifted up. [galla-q-r][nl2] Empty head – clear mind but hollow. [galla-q-r][nl2] Sensation of emptiness. [galla-q-r][nl2] Feels filled with air – stare for long periods of time. It was as though there was a spaciousness in me where I could leave and do something like that. [lac-loxod-a][hrn2] Feeling of emptiness within me. [ozone][sde2] Vacant sensation: out of my head, spaced out. [plut-n][srj7] I had the sensation of a space opening up over my palate inside my skull, a feeling of expansion upwards. [plut-n][srj7] It's funny when we are meditating, there's a huge empty space in my head. [positr][nl2] Hollow feeling in nose. [galeoc-c-h][gms1]

One of the symptoms of AIDS is a dramatic loss of weight, in Africa the disease was, for a time, known as Slim for this reason. Actual weight loss occurs in some remedies. While taking the medicine, I lost in weight seven and one-half pounds, which I did not regain for some weeks. [cere-b][a1] A long-term side effect experienced by ravers is weight loss which, for some women, is a motive for using the drug. Loss of weight is presumably caused by the combination of exercise and loss of appetite. [mdma][saunders]

However, it is more often expressed as a feeling. Especially the feeling that the subject is immaterial, Has non-material body. [anh][sp1] Strange feeling of being a spirit. [ignis-alc][es2] Delusion he is immaterial. [lac-c][lrp1] or transparent. Dreamt I was invisible. [adam][srj5] It seemed as though I was transparent. [cann-i][a1] Estranged himself from his family and friends and stopped all communication with them for a long period. Did not reply to letters and left no address. He seemed to hide away and literally disappear. [choc][srj3] My forehead was the only part of my body I could feel – the rest of my body seemed to have disappeared. [ignis-alc][es2] Feel the fragility of the material body. Sometimes don't notice it's there. [ignis-alc][es2] The doors in two different shops wouldn't open for me. The sensors didn't register my presence, compounding my feelings of unreality, being invisible. Once maybe accidental but twice seemed more profound. [latex][nl-latex] Shopping in Tesco. My perception is that everybody is in my way. I can't go down any aisle without people pushing in front of me. It's as if they can't see me, as if I'm not there. I'm getting more and more irritated by everyone. [positr][nl2]

Vacuum is a substance, or rather a lack of substance, that encapsulates this concept and the proving revealed a number of symptoms that illustrate this. A classmate came in and asked if I had been at the morning session – she thought I wasn't there! [vacuum][es-vac] I feel like I'm growing lighter, more delicate – transparent, almost. [vacuum][es-vac] I'm invisible today. [vacuum][es-vac] It was particularly apparent in a number of references to black holes. Dreams in space – black holes. [vacuum][es-vac]

This feeling of invisibility can imply powerlessness, All evening feeling physically wobbly and nauseous, like I could easily crumble, and emotionally wobbly, like the slightest puff would make me crumble. Emotionally weak, like the outer shell could easily break. but there are no emotions contained within the shell, it's hollow and empty. [heroin][sdj-h] Feeling really powerless and insignificant. [vacuum][es-vac] especially in Germanium. Sometimes I feel I disappear. I am not in my body. My hands feel gone. My feet are cold; I don't like them. Yet I feel I have great power inside, especially I feel it when I get angry or when I sing. [germ-met][srj5] I am no person. Feel I have no power when I meet people. [germ-met][srj5] (*See Vulnerability IX-1*)

These feelings, which are widespread in contemporary society, are often expressed in the form of eating disorders. Bulimia and Anorexia encompass these concerns but also express confusion and the tendency to move towards extremes. Feel like I'm gaining weight, but am actually losing weight. [haliae-lc][srj5] Thus the feeling of emptiness can be felt strongly in the stomach. Another sensation that keeps recurring is a feeling of absence in my abdomen. A band between my lower ribs and below my navel gone. It's as if there is nothing but a space there. [ignis-alc][es2] Funny feeling in abdomen. Felt my whole abdomen was a box with nothing in it – empty in the middle. [ignis-alc][es2] Still funny feeling in stomach – the polo mint stomach – no centre. [ignis-alc][es2] I felt an enormous empty feeling in my stomach. I didn't want to get up but eventually I was driven out of bed by the hunger. I had some soup to fill me up. Went back to sleep immediately. [latex][nl-latex] Or there can be a contradiction between the emotional and physical sensations. Feel a joyless indifference. Emotionally hollow and empty. Yet my stomach still feels full – little appetite. [heroin][sdj-h] (*See Confusion VII-1 and Extremes VI-1*)

Other things can also appear to be transparent. After waking, pattern on walls became fluid in movement, in air. The wall lost solidity; could easily move through it. [adam][srj5] Everything is transparent. [anh][sp1]

This can allow a deeper and clearer view of them. (*See Clarity I-6*) Material objects appear to lack substance. I see molecules. [adam][srj5] Impression that objects and his own body are transparent: sees his own internal organs. [anh][jl1]

The extreme form of this type of symptom is one of unreality, that nothing exists, that life is just a dream. Delusion that there is no reality in anything, all appears like a dream. [anac][c1] Some of it felt dream like, as if I wasn't there at all. [falco-pe][nl2] Cannot feel pleasure or sorrow. Everything is Chaos. Cannot restore my energy. Totally meaningless. Feels like an empty battery. [germ-met][srj5] Nebulous condition, with the impression of unreality. [gink-b][jl1] Not mentally aware, almost in remote control and time seems to have stopped as though I have been doing this thing forever. Time stops flowing the way it usually does. This sense comes and goes quickly. It is like a vacuum. [lac-loxod-a][hrn2] (*See In a Dream II-3*)

IV-8 Floating & Flying

There is in many of the new and related remedies a sense of floating and levitation. Sensation of flying gently, of floating, of being uplifted. [aids][nl2] I feel above it all, I feel that I am floating. [aids][nl2] I felt I had to ground myself. [aids][nl2] Enjoy the powerful night force. I can fly in the dark. [adam][srj5] She felt lest dense, floating. [ara-mac][sej7] Elevation of spirits, with a feeling of lightness in the body in the evening. [cann-i][a1] Produces a sensation of levitation. [cann-i][c1] Had a sensation of floating. Lightheaded, mentally spacey feeling. [maias-l][hrn2] A bit floaty still, but good. [dream-p][sdj1] I was flowing in the car. Driving to a destination and not being driven. More a sense like floating without the tension of driving. [haliae-lc][srj5] Difficulty focusing my attention while driving, with a sensation of gentle floating. [germ-met][srj5] I was listening to a patient and felt that my body was very light and that I was floating. [ignis-alc][es2] Walking effortlessly, easy, as if not touching the ground. [irid-met][srj5] Sensation as if ascending. Sensation of floating upwards. [irid-met][srj5] Floaty feeling, not really with it. [agath-a][nl2] Felt like I was floating on Alladin's carpet. [agath-a][nl2] When walking, seems to be walking on air; when lying, does not seem to touch the bed; legs as if floating. [lac-c][al2] It affects the whole body, as if she were swimming or floating in the air, spirit-like. [lac-c][k2] I felt incredibly light and incredibly free. I tried to put myself back into the earth but I couldn't because it was almost as if my gravity was too light to be on earth anymore. [lsd][nl-lsd] I also felt a lot of lightness and floatiness. [lsd][nl-lsd] Vertigo, as if everything were turning in a circle, at first very slowly, then faster and faster; at last it seemed as though she were floating in the air, then she became stupefied, and in this stupefaction it seemed as though she fell from a great height, and she lost her consciousness. [mosch][a1] As if falling from a height. [mosch][c1] Walking was effortless, light and free, with a sensation of walking uniformly. I feel so different in my body. I am all in the now, especially in lower legs and feet. At last, I touch the earth. [neon][srj5] Delusions: floating in the air. [nux-m][vml2] Sensation of floating. [ozone][sde2] My head feels very light, feels as if it will float off. [plut-n][srj7] Dream. I was rising out of my body with a fear of falling. [rhus-g][tmo3] Dreams of flying through the air. [rhus-g][a1] Felt high and floating in the air. [urol-h][rwt3] Felt very ungrounded; floating above my head. [urol-h][rwt3] Sensation in bed as if I were sunken deep, on sitting up sensation as if floating. [xan][a2]

Coca and Cocaine have a particular connection with height and are the specific remedies for altitude sickness. Great lightness while climbing a mountain, without any respiratory troubles. [coca][a1] Altitude sickness, almost a specific for this problem, especially where the respiratory power is depressed. [coca][mrr3]

The floating can come out of the split between the spirit and the body which frees the spirit from the mundane forces of gravity. There is a strong sense that the person is separated from his physical body, that the body is immaterial, and that he is floating in the air. There is a sense of being double, or that objects are double, or that he is separated from the physical world, which he is observing from above. [anh][vh1] (*See Splitting V-6*)

This place is also one where you are an observer. Dream: Flying – being above, looking down on my life as a young child. [vacuum][es-vac] (*See The Observer II-5*)

There are many dreams of flying. Dream of an old friend who is piloting a plane in the fog, she does it via instructions on the radio. [aids][nl2] Dream: Flying of friends at a party. [adam][srj5] Dream of flying, looking for something (searching), flying made it easier. [choc][srj3] I was floating around the room in my home in Ireland, although my feet were on the ground. I could see all my family, yet it seemed that no one saw me. [coca-c][sk4] Dreams of flying along a lighted street. [conv-d][a1] I'm so slow and heavy on earth and so light and swift in the air. [haliae-lc][srj5] Dream: I was teaching someone else to freefall and felt fine about it. This was astonishing as I have such a fear and strong physical reaction around heights. [falco-pe][nl2] Dream: Traveling from place to place – I seemed to be floating. [urol-h][rwt3] Dream: I have wings attached to my body on the back with piano like hinges – I can fly and I do. [urol-h][rwt3] I dreamt I was flying over hills and woods and up a swollen river that rushed down with incredible force. [plut-n][srj7] Dream of swimming in the air. [plut-n][srj7] Dream: Flying in the sky free and content. [carneg-g][rwt1] Dream: I was able to fly; flew up to the top of a tall building but wasn't sure how to get down; finally I jumped and floated to the ground. [urol-h][rwt3] Dream that I could fly. [tung-met][bdx1] Dreamed of flying about over tops of houses. [xan][a1] They are particularly prevalent in Dinosaur which is perhaps a little surprising though the birds are thought to have evolved from them and so perhaps there was always this drive in them. I've never flown before in a dream. I was zooming, looking down at the world, seeing everything, at about 1,000 feet. Soaring, seeing things. Lots of fun. [maias-l][hrn2] Dream: I was flying with a lot of flapping and soaring. Then I became anxious about how to land. [maias-l][hrn2]

Being high is one of the many terms used for the state induced by recreational drugs and the connection between the two is important. High as a kite. In the middle center of the brain. Pleasure center activated. Not spaced out. Euphoric feeling. I feel guilty as this is similar to illicit drugs, so pleasurable you only feel this when you are taking drugs. [haliae-lc][srj5] The drug causes a feeling of buoyancy [pip-m][c1] Excited, as if intoxicated, in the evening in bed, and a feeling as if the head were floating in the air. [jug-r][a1] (*See Drugs II-6*)

Birds and bird like states are important in the bird remedies. Feel free as a bird. [haliae-lc][srj5] Felt high like a bird. [falco-pe][nl2] Feeling of delight and joy as the swallows and house martins have arrived. Sensation of oneness with them in their flying. [falco-pe][nl2] Dreams of birds, eagle, owl, water birds, geese. [buteo-j][sej6] I had the feeling I was flying, very high up in the air. [buteo-j][sej6] Dreams of flying. [lars-arg][fkw1] Another strong theme was that of flight, flying, and floating. The feeling was that of feeling calm, centered, peaceful and content while flying. [cath-a][rwt] When on the ground however there is danger. The vulture is vulnerable on the ground. The ground is not safe and one can fall through. [cath-a][rwt]

The Housefly also had flying dream/sensations. She fell asleep for a nap and dreamt that she was flying all over her house. [musca-d][stew+]

However, they occur in many non-bird remedies as well. He thinks he can fly through the air like the birds. [cann-i][a1] Talking about flying. I would like to be a bird or a bat or in a plane. [choc][srj3] Much more aware of birds. [choc][srj3] Acutely aware of bird song. [germ-met][srj5]

Keep noticing ducks, love watching them and other birds. [heroin][sdj-h] Mental image: I am inside an egg – a bird, wet feathers, at the point it is smashing through its shell, bursting out; a chick, wet crumpled and hot, shell flying all over. The relief – getting to the air, refreshing, cool. Inside it was humid, stifling. Stretching vast wings, enjoying feeling the air dry them out. [irid-met][srj5] Sensation as if pair of wings, sensation as if folded, can be aware of them behind my shoulders. Measured seven feet by seven feet not open. [irid-met][srj5] Notice flocks of birds, their movements, patterns and numbers. Feel high, as if my cares have all receded. [lsd][nl-lsd] Nature feels very close to me – enhanced connection with it. Particularly noticed the birds – ravens, crows and pheasants. [lsd][nl-lsd] I had thoughts of albatrosses circumnavigating the earth without having to touch the ground. [neon][srj5] Even the Elephant which is so heavy that it cannot jump and so is completely earthbound dreams of flying like a bird. Vultures flying above me and they seemed high up, and I was watching them and I felt I had become them, as though I was in their body and flying with them. Felt the downward movement. Being a bird in the sky. [lac-loxod-a][hrn2]

IV-9 Music

The art form that is of the air is music. It is created through the movement of air, is insubstantial so it is of the instant and it permeates the environment in an unbounded manner. Music is important through many of the new remedies. The house that I was organizing the renting of had lots of music in it. A modern room, big room, and very beautiful. [aids][nl2] Danced all night in a frenzy, could not keep still, and was frustrated when the music finished. [androc][srj5] Much more sensitive to music – especially happy music. It gives me incredible pleasure. [choc][srj3] Fits of ecstasy at night, as if caused by hearing music. [cur][a1] I felt I wanted to move in a rhythm – and moved my feet as if to music. [falco-pe][nl2] When dolphins sing, they harmonize flawlessly in the same pitch. [lac-del][hrn2] Sensitive to music, could hear more deeply, enjoyable. [lac-leo][hrn2] Wolves use song extensively by howling in different tones and pitches to convey emotions and information. They signal their location, their excitement, their mournful sadness at the death of a pack member, and their tremendous joy in life through their singing. [lac-lup][hrn2] Began to listen to pop and rock music (which I have never listened to before). [polys][sk4] Strong urge to listen to music – spiritual music. Played piano with more competence and fewer mistakes, the notes were clearer. So I feel excited, joyful, exhilarated, imagine myself as a virtuoso. [tung-met][bdx1] Birds make music. [sej-birds]

Music and drugs have been closely linked, especially over the last 40 years. They respond enormously to music. They may have the sensation of being carried out of their body by listening to music. Drums may produce euphoria. [anh][vh1] He sings, and extemporizes both words and music. [cann-i][a1] He hears music of the sweetest and sublimest melody and harmony, and sees venerable bards with their harps, who play as if it were the music of heaven. [cann-i][a1] Music of any kind is intensely agreeable to him. [cann-i][a1] When you're on E it's like you're dancing on the notes, and you just feel so up there it's like heaven. And you just feel so good, you love everybody, you look around and you think oh you're all wonderful! [mdma][saunders] Music important, played it loud. [lsd][nl-lsd] Strong desire to listen to loud, fast music. [lsd][nl-lsd] Driving – I desire very loud techno and a party. [lsd][nl-lsd]

In some remedies, particularly LSD and Mescaline, music becomes confused with colours and vision. The chief feature of the drug's action is the production of coloured visions of most over-powering brilliancy, associated with moving shapes of fantastic design, the motion being regulated somewhat in time by music. [anh][c1] (*See Confusion of the Senses VII-2*)

Music crosses many boundaries, even the boundaries between the species. Lawrence further discusses another special feature of wolf vocalizing, which involves the wolf's distinctive relationship with the raven. The raven's caw alerts the wolf that there is a herd or weak animal nearby. The wolf then makes the kill, and the raven comes in for his share of the meat. In mutual celebration, both raven and wolf sing together in a song that Lawrence calls haunting, spiritual, and primitive. [lac-lup][hrn2] Music can ameliorate. Very sensitive to music. During a black mood, almost any sort of music will shake me out of it. [androc][srj5] I felt better when driving the car fast with company and loud music. [hydrog][srj2]

But it can also aggravate or there can be an aversion to it. Aversion to music. [lac-cp][sk4]

In Coca Cola the power and pervasiveness of music leads to the symptom. Tormented by music. Unless I gave in and listened only to music, I felt tense and harassed by it. [coca-c][sk4]

IV-10 Space

Taking the imagery of air and flying to its ultimate conclusion leads to the imagery of space. Dreams of being in outer space. [aids][nl2] Attracted to dark night skies. Stars seem more visible. [adam][srj5] Delusion of galaxies spiraling. One, then two, then four. [adam][srj5] Dream of body behaving as if it was a ball bouncing in outer space. [adam][srj5] Deep sadness, so much light pollution. Can see so few stars. [haliae-lc][srj5] Dream: I was above a huge galaxy that was spiraling slowly clockwise beneath me. Then, I was beneath it, and it spiraled down into a huge vortex. The shape of the warmer air of thermals is the same shape as a nuclear mushroom. I was riding the thermals. As I got closer to earth I realized nuclear mushrooms are the shape they are because it's hot air. I ride above it and it feels fine. I feel regal and generous. [haliae-lc][srj5] Felt that I was one of a large string of beads, suspended in space. [galla-q-r][nl2] I wished I could explain how I feel right now – I am in a spaceship, cruising gently between the stars, sometimes I wished I could anchor somewhere. [heroin][sdj-h] All day felt spaced out but can't bring myself to Earth (I normally can). [latex][nl-latex] Lightness, being out in space. Alienated from the earth. Bubbles of joy. [lsd][nl-lsd] Meditation: In blackness of space. I feel the vastness of space, see the stars. Look back and see the earth. Feel expansion and limitless. I look at the earth, but space feels my home. Feel light. Try to put myself back to earth – cannot, I'm too light. [lsd][nl-lsd] I'm moving along a path of light that weaves gently into infinity. [lsd][nl-lsd] Meditation – was standing on edge of earth, space before me, wondered how the earth is called flat when it looks round, but felt at peace with space before me and green earth next to me. Thought I'd return home, and someone would tell me my dad had died. [lsd][nl-lsd] I was very still – felt as if I was far out in space, gazing out into deep space. [plut-n][srj7] Dream: Having to do with the sky and the earth – in a space craft and looking down at the earth; it was just brown. [carneg-g][rwt1]

The main constituent of space is nothing and the remedy that most approaches this, Vacuum, has a lot of space dreams. Dream: Space ship in the sky – like a meteorite going along the sky. [vacuum][es-vac] Dream of space and galaxies. [vacuum][es-vac] Dreams in space – black holes. [vacuum][es-vac]

In the Shark proving the idea of alien abduction seems to be important. I think I experienced alien abductions as a child. During the proving this came back to me. It is like the shark, beings that are superior in the food chain and not deep in the sea but the opposite, deep in space. Feeling of something higher up and something we don't know about. [galeoc-c-h][gms1]

We live in the 'Space Age' and with 'Space Age Materials' and many of these have great potential as remedies. Iridium has been used in Voyager 1 and 2, Galileo and Ulysses spacecraft, in a protective capacity. It provides protective cladding for the fuel, as well as a coating on the visors of space helmets, to guard against UV rays. [irid-met][srj5] A few years later positrons were found among the particles generated by cosmic gamma rays, radiation from outer space. [positr][nl2]

Being spaced out, like being high, is a euphemism for the drugged state. Space metaphors are often entwined with descriptions of the drugged condition. You're like a different woman – all high and giggly, like a space cadet. [aids][nl2] This dissociation may also be responsible for a dream state the Cannabis patient may experience in which he feels as if he is falling into a dark abyss, into empty space. [cann-i][vh1] Felt drugged, as if my body had become very long, and I was falling fast through space. Later, felt introspectively "stoned" while talking. [coca-c][sk4] Empty space around me. As if in space. Spaced out. [corv-cor][bdg1]

IV-11 Travel

The world seems an exciting and strange place. [aids][nl2]

The lack of boundaries in the world today allows and encourages us to travel.

Dreams of travel are common in the new remedies. Dreams of traveling. [adam][srj5] Dream of traveling on a train. [adam][srj5] Dreams of journeys. [anan][a1] Dream about a foreign country. [corian-s][knl6] Dream of traveling and making choice of which home to return to. [haliae-lc][srj5] Dream of a journey. [ignis-alc][es2] After remedy new themes developed in my dreams. During my travelling dreams I was aware of routes and rail tracks, which I have never dreamt of before. [positr][nl2] Unusual dreams of foreign countries. [positr][nl2] Dreams of travelling. [propl][vml3] Dreams of journeys. [sel][a1] Dreams about trips. [urol-h][rwt3] Dream Traveling from place to place – I seemed to be floating. [urol-h][rwt3]

As is the desire to travel. Ardent desire to travel. [anan][a1] He would like to go travelling in great style. [cur][a1] Strong desire to travel comes up again, it's unsettling. [lsd][nl-lsd] Desire to go travelling – leave reality behind, be content in nature. Only thing which makes me feel better is simple tasks, painting and cleaning. [lsd][nl-lsd] A tremendous desire to travel with someone very close who would care for me. [polys][sk4] She has always loved to travel. She has traveled all over the world. [oncor-t][srj-case]

Or a tendency to do so. I thought I will have to go a long way away. [hydrog][srj2] During the first four weeks of the proving I was away each weekend traveling great distances and thinking nothing of it. [irid-met][srj5]

Again there is a drug connection, particularly with LSD where the experience is often referred to as a trip. During the homœopathic proving many spoke of the experience as a journey, a trip! [lsd][nl-lsd]

The travel of the AIDS Miasm is different to that of the Tubercular Miasm, which is primarily driven by a desire to explore; or that of the Cancer Miasm, which is driven by the desire to find a better, more perfect place. In the AIDS Miasm travel is almost forced upon the subject because there are no boundaries which means that the idea of the local and that of the distant become one. This is apparent in air travel where all that lies between two airports literally disappears. Birds and perhaps fish and sea mammals are the only other creatures to have discovered this. Migration and travel with superior navigation. [sej-birds]

The concept of instant travel is found particularly clearly in Neon and Cannabis. Aversion to TV, radio and cars. TV and radio seem to interfere with the coherence in my brain. Cars seem a very gross way to travel. I've been having the delusion that if I closed my eyes I could be anywhere that I wanted to be, so why do we need cars? [neon][srj5] Dream of a man with the ability to teleport. [neon][srj5] After the walk which I last recorded, the former passion for travel returned with powerful intensity. I had now a way of gratifying it, which comported both with indolence and economy. The whole East, from Greece to farthest China, lay within the compass of a township. No outlay was necessary for the journey. For the humble sum of six cents I might purchase an excursion ticket over all the earth; ships and dromedaries, tents and hospices, were all contained in a box of Tilden's extract. Hashish I called the "drug of travel", and I had only to direct my thoughts strongly towards a particular part of the world previously to swallowing my bolus, to make my whole fantasia in the strongest possible degree topographical. [cann-i][a1]

IV-12 Speed & Rushing

In several remedies there is a feeling of speed. Full of drive, steaming through my commitments. [aids][nl2] Outer space and moving fast; everything is fast; didn't need air; feeling of speed. [helo-s][rwt2] I felt better when driving the car fast with company and loud music. [hydrog][srj2] Usually I am nervous in the car while going fast, but I really enjoyed going fast. [irid-met][srj5] Driving unusually fast, wanted to overtake all other vehicles on the road. [lac-h][sk4] I felt like I was travelling a lot, very, very fast. [lsd][nl-lsd] I feel this overwhelming urge to get into the car and drive. I wanted to go faster and faster – cursing the Sunday drivers. [vacuum][es-vac]

This is particularly so in Falcon, which of all the animals, attains the fastest speeds reaching well over 100 miles per hour during its dive on its quarry. Drove back from the party (had had some wine but not too much) quite fast but well, changing speed as necessary. It seemed faster to the others in the car than to me. [falco-pe][nl2] Was very speedy. [falco-pe][nl2] It is also seen in the Shark, one of the fastest fish. Some species of shark have attained speeds of 40 miles per hour. Only a few species of animals can move faster in the water. [galeoc-c-h][gms1] Feel like everything's been accelerated. [galeoc-c-h][gms1]

Amphetamines, which are known as Speed, clearly deserve a mention here. The substance provings indicate that appetite confusion and lack of feeling as well as detachment are all important issues. Ecstasy is a closely related remedy with some of the same issues. Other remedies aslo have reference to Speed. Unable to focus in on mental work. Restlessness, want to be physically active. Feel as if I'm on Speed! Running around trying to finish decorating [lsd][nl-lsd] (*See Drugs II-6*)

Speed when it is linked with detachment and a lack of feeling produces recklessness. When I was driving home I felt quite reckless, I had to keep on bringing myself back. It was a floaty sort of feeling and I had to remind myself that I was in control here. [aids][nl2] Some run and walk involuntarily in the most dangerous places. [agar][a1] Nowadays chocolates are given to sweethearts on Valentine's Day, anniversaries or birthdays, wrapped in heart shaped boxes. In some of the popular TV adverts, men will enter into extremely hazardous exploits, just because the ladies love it. [choc][srj3] Erratic driving, Pwar that was close, but it didn't matter. [falco-pe][nl2] I drove home that evening in a record time of 1hr 10min, a journey which usually takes me 1hr 30min. I drove at high speed, I was aware of the speed but I didn't care. At one stage I spotted a police car in my mirror, fully aware that I was well over the speed limit, I carried on. I remember thinking, well I would be done for that and it would be a shame since I have never had any endorsement on my licence. [falco-pe][nl2] I have this real urge to be reckless. I want to party all night and watch the sun come up. Feeling mischievous and carefree. [latex][nl-latex]

The sense of speed is most likely to be expressed as a feeling of rush. This can arise from confusion about time and the disruption of sequence caused by electronic technology. Felt rushed; so much to do. Overwhelmed. [adam][srj5] Hurried in mind and action. Whirling thoughts. [adam][srj5] Feels like cycle of life has speeded up, with no way of stopping. [adam][srj5] Feverish haste in all his actions. [anan][a1] Impatient watching others, wanted to speed them up. [androc][srj5] Did everything in a hurry. [androc][srj5] Dreams of great activity. [coca][a1] Activity in the mind; wired and speedy. [coca-c][sk4] Feel hurried and speeded up like on caffeine. [haliae-lc][srj5] Speediness, clenching teeth, irritable with the kids. [germ-met][srj5] Feeling rushed. [helo-s][rwt2] Feels like a 'quickening'. [lsd][nl-lsd] In writing a letter, felt a curious and unusual disposition to hurry through with it as quickly as possible, hardly taking time to write the words. [ptel][a1] I feel restless and agitated, like I'm in hurry to do everything. [sanguis-s][hrn2] I was always in a hurry, not for any particular reason. Things were taking too much time. When getting ready in the morning, there was too much to do in the morning, for some reason. [sanguis-s][hrn2] (*See Confusion about Time VII-7*)

There is in some remedies a sensation that the subject cannot do everything in the time available. All day feeling and saying that there isn't enough time for anything, to do anything. [carbn-dox][knl3] Anxious about being late. Feel that I am late a lot, even though I am not. Feels hard to get somewhere on time. [lac-e][hrn2]

There is a strong feeling that other people are not moving fast enough. Impatient watching others, wanted to speed them up. [androc][srj5] Felt quick and was frustrated at the slowness of others. [irid-met][srj5] Continue to be impatient and confrontational at almost every encounter. I am intolerant of any delay and will confront anyone whom I feel is to blame or is the cause of delay. [lac-e][hrn2] Feeling competitive, impatient, disliked people getting ahead of me, and being delayed. Felt confrontational repeatedly. I needed to be first on the bus, first off the bus, first into the rental car office. I was feeling impatient, irritable; confronted the clerk as to why I was not the first person called, even though I was the first person in line. [lac-e][hrn2] Hurried, others seemed too slow. [polys][sk4] Lovely job – non stop, full steam – intolerant of slow people. [positr][nl2] Sensation of things not moving fast enough. [positr][nl2]

And a general impatience. Irritable at the slow pace of the day. again. [coca-c][sk4] Impatient with my patients, with unhelpful salespeople. A feeling of impatience. [lac-e][hrn2] Impatience with idiosyncrasies of patients, detached, "get on with it" feeling. [carbn-dox][knl3] Impatient and hurried. [lac-h][sk4] Feel very impatient others are so disorganised. [lac-h][htj1] Dream of impatience. Clients wanting to come in and shoot the breeze. There is an elderly fellow lazing around on the treatment table. I tell him, irritably, that he has to leave, make an appointment and come back. [sanguis-s][hrn2] Impatient and vexed at every trifle. [rhus-t][a1] Impatient disposition, which scarcely allows of the least intellectual contest. [tax][a1]

This feeling when less defined becomes a general restlessness. This is well known in the older remedies Arsenicum, Platina and Rhus tox. Anxiety and restlessness in the whole body. [ars][a1] Very restless disposition, so that she could not remain anywhere, with sadness, so that the most joyful things distressed her. [plat][a1] Very restless mood, with anxiety and apprehension, that constantly clawed at her heart. [rhus-t][a1] Restless, sleepless nights, must move about in bed constantly. [rhus-t][a1]

And it is found in several new remedies. Restless generally. [aids][nl2] Impulse to change about from place to place. [cann-i][a1] Ill at ease, restless. [cere-b][a1] Do not know what to do with myself. [cere-b][a1] Restless and wanting to do something, but not knowing what. [haliae-lc][srj5] Produces also restlessness. [mdma][hmd1] Restless and anxious. [agath-a][nl2] Restless desire in pains to change the position. [pip-m][c1] I find it difficult to meditate, too many thoughts, no depth or connection, very restless mind. [lac-e][hrn2] Have the feeling that one shouldn't sit without doing any work, that "rest is the devil". [lac-h][sk4] I feel anxious, like I need to get something done, but I am not sure what. [lac-lup][hrn2] Strong inner restlessness. [ozone][sde2]

V-1 Instability

Boundaries contain and organize, without them not only do things become dispersed but they also lose their stability and order.

There is an instability in modern life and disease which makes it very hard for anyone, homœopath or allopath, to grasp let alone to treat.

There is a tendency for symptoms to change or alter suddenly and quickly. Symptoms appear suddenly. [choc][srj3] Excited fantasies, wonderful visions, now indescribably beautiful and wonderful forms, now frightful images. [coca][a1] Feelings both physical and mental, came and went in waves. I do seem to be flipping from feeling quite trippy, to carefree, to calm, to emotional, to despondent, very changeable, much more than usual. [falco-pe][nl2] Very lively and energetic, feels exhausted suddenly; shivers, feels depressed. [hir][jl1] All night I had wandering pains of small joints. [galla-q-r][nl2] Symptoms erratic, pains constantly flying from one part to another; changing from side to side every few hours or days. [lac-c][al2] When the peculiar Moschus symptom of the face is present, viz.: one cheek red and cold, the other pale and hot, there is certainly some hysterical perversion in the mind of that patient. [mosch][k2] Symptoms appear and disappear suddenly. [propl][vml3] Pains seems to move in meandering lines. [pyrus][a1] A recurring theme in the proving was that of friendly characters or animals turning into those that are sinister and dark. [carneg-g][rwt1] Wandering pains. [seq-s][vml3] Many of the pains and symptoms of Tell. come and go suddenly. [tell][c1] Always complained of pains, but did not designate the locality. [phos][a1]

The same applies to moods and emotions. Keep getting mood swings, one day extremely happy and full of energy and the next, bad tempered, easily angered and tired, with little energy for anything. [adam][srj5] When possessed by that feeling, he has no courage to undertake anything; and when free from it he feels exalted, would like to read like an orator, etc. [agn][a1] Constant alternation of depression of spirits and vehemence of temper; this prevents him from having a calm mood. [ambr][a1] Frequent changes in his mood and turn of thought, even to idiotism. [anan][a1] Very changeable moods. One moment extremely friendly, nice and amiable, then irritable. [androc][srj5] Irrational sudden changes of mood. [anh][jl1] The disposition is very changeable. [coca][a1] Emotions flicker rapidly from happy, to frightened, to angry. [coca-c][sk4] Extreme mood swings. [mdma][hmd1] Erratic mood swings, can't account why. [irid-met][srj5] I keep changing. Loved everyone last night; bolshy tonight. [irid-met][srj5] Yo-yoing mood swings. I'm either giggling and high or zapped. [irid-met][srj5] Wandering features in the mental sphere, wandering and alternating states. [lac-c][k2] Mood flipped between the fuzzy and really aware states. [lac-loxod-a][hrn2] Big changes of my mood. [lars-arg][fkw1] Seem to be dipping in and out of being spaced and in this time zone and being somewhere else. [lsd][nl-lsd] Cries one moment and bursts into uncontrollable laughter the next. [mosch][fr1] I started to notice my emotions were changing rapidly, subtly, but pervasively. Ranging from happy to lost to desperate. [neon][srj5] Variable mood. [nux-m][a1] Increased and frequent changes of mood. [ozone][sde2] Vacillating mood [plat][a1]

States or symptoms can alternate. Moods fluctuating/vacillating between morose and exhilaration. [aids][nl2] The symptoms of Agaricus are apt to appear at the same time on opposite sides of the body but diagonally right upper and left lower, or vice versa. [agar][c1] Change of states; alternate states. [anac][k2] Alternating moods, at times loquacious, at times taciturn, sometimes prostrate, sometimes restless. [buth-a][jl1] Indignation, alternating with mildness. [ars][a1] Extremes of emotion, activity alternating with lethargy. I would become tense and wired up, running around for days, then feeling worn out and collapse with exhaustion. [choc][srj3] Condition alternates between wellbeing and depression. [hir][jl1] Alternate state: hectic activity on the one hand, doing many things in a short time, and lack of enthusiasm on the other. [lac-h][sk4] Changing moods; sad and gay alternately; laughs and cries by turns. [plat][c1]

Or they can become mixed up. An impulse to laugh overcame him in bed, owing to an indescribably mixed sensation of happiness and misery. [agar][a1] Foolish merriment, interrupted by fright and weeping. [cur][a1] Contradictory, hysterical states. [meph][vml3] He laughs when he should be serious. [anac][a1] Was obliged to laugh against her will while she was sad. [phos][a1] (*See Confusion VII-1*)

Another manifestation of this is capriciousness, desires are as changeable as moods. Anxious and disconnected. Yearning for I know not what – love, fun, peace! [aids][nl2] Desires this thing and that, but is disgusted with everything brought to her. [ang][a1] Desires something, and when everything is done to fulfil his wish, the least trifle is sufficient to change his mind, and he will not have it. [ars][a1] Restless and wanting to do something, but not knowing what. [haliae-lc][srj5] The well-known unruly behaviour of goats, particularly the bucks, is reflected in the word capricious, which is derived from Capra, goat. [lac-cp][vml3] Desires objects and rejects the same when they are offered. [lac-h][sk4] I don't know where I want to be and with who. No imagination. I have got 2 apples and don't feel like eating them. No attachment or desire of any kind. [lsd][nl-lsd] A great feeling of not knowing what I want to do. Want to eat and not – to be active and to lie down. Don't care what I say. Don't really know what I want to do. [lsd][nl-lsd] Very capricious, sensitive. [phos][a1]

These changing desires can never be satisfied. I felt grumpy and moody. I can't be pleased. [adam][srj5] Can not be satisfied. [rhus-t][a1]

The subject is unable to accomplish anything. Particularly in Nux moschata. At one time he wishes to do something, but when he is about to accomplish it changes his mind. [nux-m][a1] He never accomplishes what he undertakes, but remains standing in one place, absent-minded. [nux-m][a1] (*See Waves, Circles & Cycles IV-4*)

This capriciousness applies to appetite. Very difficult to decide what to eat. [haliae-lc][srj5] Felt that I wanted something to eat, now! Wanted something, but do not know what it is. [lsd][nl-lsd] Voracious rapidity in eating, with a disposition to find fault with everything (to detest everything around himself). [plat][c1] (*See Appetite VI-7*)

The ultimate expression of this instability is a loss of control. Anantherum is a remedy that stimulates the lower passions of man, most specifically the sexual passions, to such excess that an individual so affected may be driven mad by the sheer force of his desire. It creates an insatiable desire to satisfy the sexual urge, driving the person to repeated sexual contacts. If this urge cannot be satisfied, he is driven to masturbation. The desire is pathological, indicative of an organism completely out of check, impulsively driven to actions which could very well lead to its rapid self-destruction. [anan][vh1] Felt out of control. His emotions took over. [androc][srj5] Had no control over her temper. Bellowed and lashed out at everyone. [androc][srj5] In the evening, furious for no apparent reason. Wanted to kill her husband and children, banged doors and threw things. By bedtime, she felt fine but the intensity of her evil thoughts was very frightening. [androc][srj5] I have no control over my emotions. Argumentative. Pursued conflict almost with relish. [androc][srj5] Complete absence of will so that volition has become autocratic, divorced from any mental control. [anh][sp1] Impulses to do something bordering on the grotesque. [cact][a1] A feeling of being lost, a feeling of things going out of control and the need to find control. [cann-i][sk7] A woman friend who took E at a party reported that Ecstasy made her feel unpleasantly out of control and gave her a nasty headache, even though the pill appeared identical to that enjoyed by her friends. She went home early and felt depressed for the next two days. [mdma][saunders] Anger – uncontrollable. Felt I could burst out at anyone. [lac-cp][sk4] Feel out of control, as if time is moving relentlessly and remorselessly forward and I'm stuck behind, unable to keep up. Panic, guilt, constant anxiety that I won't get it all done, including keeping up this journal. [neon][srj5] Or a fear that control will be lost. Fear of insanity; losing control. [mdma][hmd1]

V-2 Oversensitivity

In an unstable situation there is a tendency for things to have an inordinate effect. The result of normal input becomes an abnormal or pathological effect.

Subjects are sensitive to outside influences to a degree that becomes a powerful symptom. Oversensitive. [dream-p][sdj1] Too alert. Psychically alert to everything. Very energetic. Too up. Had a glass of wine to relax but it had no effect. Very up and alert. Over stimulated. [haliae-lc][srj5] Extreme sensitivity of the whole nervous system. [mdma][hmd1] My skin feels very sensitive and I don't want anyone to touch me. [heroin][sdj-h] Sensitive to the hardness of the chair, almost painful. [heroin][sdj-h] For nervous, restless, highly sensitive organisms. [lac-c][al2] Sensitive to hearing or watching about bad news; unbearable to see sick children in hospital. Life is so brutal. [lac-leo][hrn2] Sensitive mood. [plat][a1] I am supersensitive to everything going on in the world. Getting very apocalyptic. Feel we are doomed. [vacuum][es-vac] There is a tendency to go to extremes: overstimulation, intense, almost maniacal ability to react, as well, more often, a depressive oversensitivity." [Whitmont] [visc][vml3] (*See Touch XII-5*)

This sensitivity can be to the weather or environment. Acute sensitivity to changes of the weather. [anh][jl1] Car exhausts seem a thousand times worse than normal. [haliae-lc][srj5] Oversensitivity to environmental influences. [mdma][hmd1] Feeling of clearly perceiving the aggressive nature of the city. All the stimulus, the noise, the exhaust fume stench, the ambulances and people's lack of consideration, like an increased sensitivity. [ozone][sde2]

Or to sensations. Extreme nervous hypersensitiveness. [ambr][vml4] All his feelings of pleasure and pain seem exalted. [cann-i][a1] Very sensitive to external impressions. [pip-m][c1]

But, perhaps linked to lack of confidence (*See Lack of Confidence XI-1*), the greatest sensitivity is to criticism or perceived criticism. A slight offence makes him excessively angry, breaking out in personal violence. [anac][a1] Discouragement; dissatisfaction with his situation; he does not bear a joke; slight offences fill him with bitterness. [ang][a1] Angustura has Bitterness as one theme running through its picture. It is one of the most physically bitter substances known to us. On a mental and emotional level there is bitterness not only from past offences but also in the present i.e. taking things in bad part and being easily offended.

Personal offence from slightest wrong. [ang][vml3] Angustura individuals are overly excitable, overly vivacious people whose strong emotions border on hysteria. Their entire nervous system seems to be in a state of uncontrollable oversensitiveness and excitability. Their will appears to be paralysed; they are unable to bring it to bear to control this exaggerated excitability, an excitability which is especially provoked by the slightest offence or trifle. Offences which would leave anyone else unaffected aggravate these people tremendously. They lose all control if anyone offends or criticizes them. [ang][vh1] Crying at the slightest provocation. [ars][a1] Excessive irritability, and quarrelsome inclination. [ars][a1] Felt rejected and oversensitive. [choc][srj3] Easily led by others' opinions, and provoked. Sensitive to others attempts at restricting me. Feel like a teenager, but I don't dare to protest. I just feel it inside. [germ-met][srj5] I feel tetchy, sensitive to anyone prying or being inquisitive about me. [heroin][sdj-h] Feels incredibly emotional. All heart stuff. Sensitivity and can not stop crying, no reason. [agath-a][nl2] I am oversensitive and easily offended. [lac-leo][sk4] Touchy-cannot even look at her the wrong way. [carneg-g][rwt1] Sensitivity to criticism. [tax-br][oss1] Irritability with great over sensitivity and aversion to company. [sej-birds]

The clarity of the senses (*See Clarity I-6*) sometimes has a tendency to go too far and become oversensitivity.

It is perhaps most often found in the sense of hearing. Music and impressions stay longer in mind. [adam][srj5] Incredibly sensitive to noise, can't bear it. [androc][srj5] Hypersensitivity to noise. [anh][jl1] Cannot bear the slightest noise. [ars][a1] The sensitiveness to noise is extreme; can hear a whisper in adjoining room and is irritated thereby. [cann-i][c1] Hearing painfully acute, during evening. [coca][a1] Sadness, tears, hypersensitive to noise. [conv-s][jl1] Comatose sleep, or he sleeps with his eyes open, and hears the noise made about him. [cur][a1] Hardness of hearing, with great sensitiveness to noise. [cur][a1] I have found that voices are sounding really loud. I have turned the television down again, as I wish I could turn the children down and off. [irid-met][srj5] Irritated by the least noise. [pip-m][a1] Increased sensitivity to noise at night. [lac-del][hrn2] Increased sensitivity to noise. Radio bothered me, preferred quiet. [lac-lup][hrn2] Feeling irritable today at times, especially when there's lots of noise and people talking loudly. [latex][nl-latex] I had a really bizarre acuteness to sound – I felt it physically. someone moved her feet and it was as though – I could feel it, I felt that here. Then someone coughed and I felt that and actually wanted to shy away from it. It was as though something had touched me and I wanted to shy away from it. [lsd][nl-lsd] Hearing ultra acute – baby coughed and I jumped – cough felt like a shock that went right through my system. [lsd][nl-lsd] Over-sensitiveness of hearing. [nux-m][c1] Increased sensitivity to noise. [ozone][sde2] Sensitive to small sharp noises. The click of the car door opening made me jump. [positr][nl2] Senses still more acute – hearing odd – either very acute or can't hear background noise at all. [positr][nl2] Irritable and intolerant of noise. [ptel][a1] During the day would be startled at slight unusual sounds. [ptel][a1] Great sensitiveness to noise. [visc][vml3] Sensitive to noise: humming of the fridge gets on my nerves makes jaw feel tight. [tung-met][bdx1] Involuntary starting on someone's opening the door; noise very troublesome to me. [phos][a1]

But it is found also in vision. Great sensitiveness of the eyes to the light. [anac][a1] Great sensitiveness to the impulse of light all day. [cere-b][a1] Most leeches are photophobic, although this reaction is not evident when they are hungry. [hir][vml3] Tendency in retina to retain the impression of objects, esp. of colours; or somewhat of the object last looked at is projected into the next. [lac-c][c1] Everything was unbearably bright, hurting my eyes. [plut-n][srj7] Eyesight extremely poor today, and a strong sensitivity to light. [positr][nl2] When changing long sight into short sight and vice versa; it requires a few seconds for the images to become clear. [meph][vml3] The lights were too bright tonight. [galeoc-c-h][gms1]

And in the sense of smell. Went round Tesco's tonight, had to get away from the meat counter because something smelt so strong. It was a disgusting smell – just had a whiff – it could have made me feel sick, was really strong. [falco-pe][nl2] Noticed I'm really sensitive to smell. [falco-pe][nl2] Strong reaction to smell of perfume, had to move outside after 45 minutes so that I could breathe the fresh air. [lac-del][hrn2] On the way home senses seem very acute. Noticed a smell of burning much faster than other person in car with me. A good 5 minutes later we passed smoke on the road. Not sure how I managed to smell this from such a distance. [latex][nl-latex] Disgust at odour of coffee and tobacco. [osm][vml3] Oversensitive to odours. [osm][vml3] Sensitive to smell. [ozone][sde2] Very sensitive to the smells of last night's cooking; not my cooking, not my smells, I don't like it. [sanguis-s][hrn2] Smells evoke the most emotional response I'm aware of. That and the irritability with noise. One smell is sickening and irritating – another smell is so pleasant and familiar can't get enough of it, e.g. can't stand the smell of cooking food; love the smell on my hands, like linseed oil; can smell my husband's genitals from six feet away. [sanguis-s][hrn2] Sensitive to smells, earth smells are strong, odor of plant and herbs, familiar, sort of comforting. Man-made smells are awful. [sanguis-s][hrn2] Smells a repulsive odour, like garlic. [sel][jl1]

Sometimes it is a combination of several senses. Hyperaesthesia of the senses. [anh][jl1] All senses heightened. Light too bright. Noises too loud. [heroin][sdj-h] All day hyper-acute senses. [galla-q-r][nl2] Sense perceptions of noise and smell are still very much enhanced. [latex][nl-latex] Hyperaesthesia of all the senses, especially of hearing and smell. [phos][a1] The patient is exceedingly susceptible to external impressions. He can bear neither light, sounds nor odors; he is very sensitive to touch. [phos][fr1]

V-3 Childishness

Childishness is a theme that runs through contemporary disease and through the new remedies. It can be a fairly positive expression of innocence. (*See Youth, Beauty, Peace & Love I-8*) It is most perhaps powerfully expressed in a sense of vulnerability. (*See Vulnerability IX-1*)

However, it also encompasses the feeling of instability and sensitivity. This expresses itself as a sense of fun and playfulness. Dolphins are famous for their love of play. In captivity as well as in the wild, dolphins love to play. They chase one another, race from a defined starting point, and use anything they can get their snouts on for a toy. A male will even use his erect penis to pull toys around the tank. They love to leap in and out of the water, soaring as high as possible for no practical purpose other than sheer pleasure. [lac-del][hrn2] Increase in joking, joviality, jesting, silliness, and an increase in laughing. A lot of playfulness during the week. [lac-del][hrn2] But many other animals also enjoy play, wolves in particular. Play is a big part of the life of the wolf. Making body contact, chasing, bumping, teasing, rolling, kissing, biting are everyday activities in a healthy wolf pack. [lac-lup][hrn2]

Playfulness and a childlike feeling extends to most of the AIDS Miasm remedies. There was a sense of frivolity of fun, of wanting to play. [aids][nl2] She ran about the yard, romped with the children, threw them down, even hit them. [agar][a1] I had a feeling of being childlike. [falco-pe][nl2] I felt myself really getting into my yoga and exploring new positions. At one point, I ended up playing with my toes like a baby. [hydrog][srj2] Felt child-like, innocent, happy as though seeing things from a child's perspective. Sat watching a milk tanker, it looks just like a child's toy. Felt like I could pick it up and brrrm brrrm it up the lane. [irid-met][srj5] Felt light and young, found things fun and amusing. [irid-met][srj5] It started with a sense of youthfulness, feeling like I was 21 again, playing 70's music, but not out of nostalgia – I had a real sense of being there, actually of that age. [lsd][nl-lsd] From time to time I speak in a little girl's voice. [vacuum][es-vac] Laughing a lot.

Very playful. [vacuum][es-vac]

As does a feeling of gaiety and excitement. Appears as if newly born, self-confident and humourous. [ozone][sde2] Gay humour, with disposition to laugh and sing. [anan][a1] Mind energetic and fresh, inclined to gaiety. [ars][a1] Very excited; he began dancing about the room; frequently laughing; talked nonsense, but could not stop without an effort of the will, which he did not care to make. [cann-i][a1] Wild fun dressing up. [cygn-b][sle-swan] I was in a jovial state. I noticed a manic energy to it. I wasn't hurried. A pressure to have fun. Pleasant. [maias-l][hrn2] I have felt far more humourous and mischievous than usual and have laughed a lot more than usual. [positr][nl2] Great excitement; she sang, laughed, and afterwards fell asleep. [phos][a1]

In Kava kava there is a keynote that play and amusement ameliorate the symptoms. Have felt satisfied and hilarious. [pip-m][a1] Amel. when amused. [pip-m][c1]

There is, in several remedies, an unwillingness to be serious, Feel like being flippant and I am. [lac-h][htj1] Having difficulty being serious, wants to be light-hearted all the time. [tung-met][bdx1] or to take responsibility. Indecision; no longer wants to think or act for herself. [cur][vml3] Though in Convolvulus the reverse occurs. Restlessness in character; desire to be occupied during the day; prefer to read, to study, the computer. No desire to play with toys; like to be an adult. Precocious; curious. [Mangialavori] [jal][vml3]

The overall appearance is often of silliness or foolishness. A peculiarity of the delirium is to make verses and prophesy; also silly merriness, and incoherent talk, with mania; kisses companions. [agar][c1] Young girls with this Ambra feeling, in their embarrassment can talk in a flitting, flighty manner. They can also become mischievous and play pranks that are very much in keeping with this theme of shame and shamelessness. [ambr][sk7] Manners awkward, silly. [anac][c1] Foolish joy and absurd complacency, with himself and his labour; internal complacency, with smiles. [anan][a1] It causes foolishness. [nux-m][a1] During this he looked foolish and childish, like an idiot. [nux-m][a1] Talkative, repeats the same idea over and over, because words fail to express the delightful sensation, afterwards is sober, but feels foolish. [cocain][a1]

The most common expression of this is in giggling which is found in most new remedies. I feel like giggling and am giggling more easily than usual. [adam][srj5] Felt very peaceful, giggly, silly, adolescent, content, stroppy, confident. [falco-pe][nl2] It struck me that the conversations held between the six female provers became more raucous from week to week and regularly ended in giggling and silly goings-on. [Schindler] [meph][vml3] Perpetual giggling. [cann-i][a1] Feeling giggly.

[choc][srj3] Giggling at seeing the confusion around. [coca-c][sk4] Arrive at tutor's house, one of the other provers is there, as soon as our eyes meet there is an instant bond and we laugh and giggle. I sense that she is relaxed and laid back. We are on the same wave length throughout the evening. Giggling at sexual innuendoes. I'm enjoying any banter that I can engage in, not everyone can play the game as well as the two of us. Felt challenging towards tutor, mischievous, cheeky (like a teenager). [heroin][sdj-h] Things seem ridiculous and amusing, ordinary things like birds. Laughing at them. Everything seemed so absurd or futile. [hydrog][srj2] Laughter wicked and voice seemed low. [hydrog][srj2] I was really giggly, childish. Giggling at night kept me awake. [irid-met][srj5] I made a joke, it was the funniest thing ever heard. I was the funniest person in the world. [agath-a][nl2] Three of us got into hysterics about nothing, and there was laughing tears coming out. [agath-a][nl2] Giggling – absurdity. [galla-q-r][nl2] Immediately on taking the remedy, as if on ecstasy – everything looks yellow; feel giggly. [phasco-ci][rbp2] Felt very giggly, wanted to giggle at silly things to tearfulness – from happy giggling! [latex][nl-latex] Got very giggly, laughing at silly things. [latex][nl-latex] Went to bed and burst into giggles. [lsd][nl-lsd] Giggly, childish, grinning. [neon][srj5] Everything provokes laughter, quite contrary to habit; this was especially noticeable on going into the open air. [nux-m][a1] Giggling fit. tears and laughter about nothing. [positr][nl2] Wanting to laugh for no reason. [sal-fr][sle1]

V-4 Splitting

The most important outcome of instability is splitting. This often appears as a duality or as a state of doubleness. Delusion that he is double. [anac][c1] Impression that the self is double. [anh][jl1] Had a feeling of duality. One of his minds would be thinking of something, while the other would laugh at it. Quick transition of the ideas of one mind to the other. [cann-i][a1] He was conscious of two distinct conditions of being in the same moment, of which neither conflicted with the other. His enjoyment of the visions was complete and absolute, undisturbed by the faintest doubts of their reality; while, in some other chamber of his brain, reason sat coolly watching them, and heaping the liveliest ridicule on their fantastic features. [cann-i][a1] I had two beings, and there were two distinct, yet concurrent trains of ideas. [cann-i][a1] A feeling of intoxication with double sensations. Colours are stronger and hearing is sharpened but at the same time feel absent and removed. [choc][srj3] While relating to another person I can't coincide our two different view points. [haliae-lc][srj5] Aware of being pulled in two different directions, as if being pulled by two elephants, two strong forces. [haliae-lc][srj5] This ability to look two ways, gives to Hydrogen an almost Janus-like feel, as this Roman deity was represented by a face looking two ways. [hydrog][srj2] It dawned on me that it was as if there was a shift in the universe. [hydrog][srj2] Trees, especially if they grow by water, are liable to split down the middle in storms. They will continue to grow, even if split right down the middle, and sometimes other saplings will take root in the split. [sal-fr][sle1] This duality can be in resistance to a tendency to merge into oneness. Partner wants all my time and attention. We have a fundamental disagreement, he thinks we're one, I think we're two. [falco-pe][nl2]

There are dreams of duality and splitting. Dream of a car split in half passing houses. [hydrog][srj2] Dream: A structure or building falling apart as if an earthquake had split the building. [lac-e][hrn2] Dream: I was married to two wives; when one found out she asks me to leave. [urol-h][rwt3]

It can also appear as specific doubleness or delusions that certain parts are double. Double vision. [anh][jl1] A woman who ate several nutmegs with the idea of bringing on abortion had the hallucination that she had two heads. [nux-m][c1] Sees two objects instead of one. [nux-m][c1]

The split is often one of a division between two wills. This is a well known symptom of Anacardium. State as if there were two wills, one of which rejects what the other requires. [anac][c1] He has a sensation as though he had two wills – one commanding him to do what the other forbids. [anac][c1] and of Lac caninum. Lac caninum presents an internal contradiction, they are patients whose body does the contrary of their heart. This is typical of the abused situation. The patient Lac caninum lives between two desires just as the dog lives a conflict between civilisation and instinct. [lac-c][lrp1]

But it is found in many new remedies. Conflict between what I am doing and what I am supposed to do. [polys][sk4] Lots of things about being torn apart, between two opposing people/elements have been coming up for me. [positr][nl2] Felt there was a war going on inside me. [rhus-g][tmo3] Feel like there are two people in me, one living the life that is seen and one living a secret life which is not compatible with the other. I want both. [sal-fr][sle1] Feels as if split. [ara-mac][sej7] Tension between he sense of self and the need for expression. Expression of what is really oneself vs being an integral part of family and society. [ara-maca][sej-birds]

The duality between good and evil is a feature of Anacardium but it is also found in Positronium. Strange dream involving good and bad spirits who kept interchanging roles. They were able to fly, as I was. Set in a very large building with animals in it. Like an aviary. [positr][nl2] And in Fire. Good and Evil seem to me two paths of choices. It is important to strive for the light and shun the dark. [ignis-alc][es2]

The butterfly has the unusual quality of being two very different creatures. One, the caterpillar, is ugly and despised; the other, the butterfly itself, is beautiful and admired. While young, it takes the grotesque form, with ferocious appearance, besides could be extremely poisonous as it is the case of the lipidoptera saturniidae, and after the metamorphosis and evolution to its adult form it enchants with its delicate and soft appearance. [lepd-s][rsi1] Dream: This is strongest dream I ever had. In the dream I am a man wrestling with another man. I have dark hair, the other guy is blonde. Duality. At some point the other guy plays unfair, he does something that totally offends me (maybe this was done before we fight), so I attack this person. So graphic, I dig the nails of my left hand under the skin of his neck as hard as I can. I can feel the skin break and his blood. I lay into him hard. I am fighting for my life. It is totally graphic. I am enraged, impassioned and wild. [limen-b-c][hrn2]

The most important split is between the mind and the body. He thinks he is double. This comes from a vague consciousness that there is a difference between the external and internal will, a consciousness that one will is the body and another is the mind. [anac][k2] I feel a little separated from myself as if there's a gap between my thoughts and my body. Felt like I was not reacting fast enough or like I was missing depth perception. I am unaware. [corv-cor][bdg1] Felt ethereal, disconnected from body but mind is very together and alert and conscious. Felt like my body not there, like I was dying, and I was leaving my body and didn't mind. I was too weak and disconnected. [lac-lup][hrn2] Another general keynote is the alternation of mental and physical symptoms: as physical symptoms disappear mental symptoms appear, and vice versa. [plat][c1] My mind or my head feels separated from my body. [plut-n][srj7] Constant strange feeling of being in a trance, as if my mind and body were separated or as if I wasn't in touch with things around me or with myself. [polys][sk4] Felt an unclear bridge between body and mind. [tung-met][bdx1]

This can be manifest as a split between the head and the body or sometimes between the lower body and the upper. In the body a lot of splits. Lower lumbar, felt a definite line. Same split with my vision, a break. We were having a lot of earthquakes, the huge earthquake in Kobe the day the proving started. I am very connected to Japan, having lived there. Felt a shift, along a fault line, along the spine. Split was at the waist lower back. Vision was split on horizon. [haliae-lc][srj5] Body much smaller than my head. [falco-pe][nl2] Feels like my head is separate from my body. It's like my body is doing one thing and my head is doing another. Felt disassociated, not connected to my body. [lac-lup][hrn2]

On closing eyes to relieve a bad headache, sensation that top of head and headache seemed to rise as I and the rest of my body sank, like a horizontal separation. [neon][srj5] When consciousness first returned kept hands to her head "to prevent it falling off"; was obliged to move her head with her hands, "it being too large and heavy for her body." [nux-m][c1] I have an out of body feeling in my head. [plut-n][srj7] My feet feel far away from my head, while sitting. [plut-n][srj7] Delusion upper part of body is floating in air. [visc][vml3] Excited, as if intoxicated, in the evening in bed, and a feeling as if the head were floating in the air. [jug-r][a1] Had a few times during proving: felt as if cut in half at waist line between top and bottom. [tung-met][bdx1] I feel as though I'm not connected from the waist to the knees. [vacuum][es-vac] In Swan there is split between the back, which is cold and the front which is hot. This happens when the subject is lying down making it another form of upper/lower split.

Or a separation of the spirit from the body. The soul seemed to be separated from the body, and to look down upon it, and view all the motions of the vital processes, and to be able to pass and repass through the solid walls of the room, and to view the landscape beyond. [cann-i][a1] While standing felt my spirit step backwards. [germ-met][srj5] Seems to be able to go out of herself for a short distance, to walk round and return into her body. [pyrus][c1]

Or a split between the conscious and the unconscious. The keynote of this remedy is schizophrenia between the conscious and unconscious life of the patient. [anh][sp1] This happens also in Heroin where the things suppressed in waking find expression in the dream life.

In Lac humanum the split tends to be between dwelling in the material world or in the spiritual one. Constant dilemma of being highly spiritual and God fearing, against bouts of being unreligious and sinful – a turmoil. [lac-h][sk4] Persistent thoughts about how to improve my work, while at the same time the idea kept coming to me of being in a five-star hotel, and just watching movies on television. [lac-h][sk4]

The separated spirit or mind is often an observer of the physical self. In the midst of my complicated hallucination, I could perceive that I had a dual existence. One portion of me was whirled unresistingly along the track of this tremendous experience, the other sat looking down from a height upon its double, observing, reasoning, and serenely weighing all the phenomena. This calmer being suffered with the other by sympathy, but did not lose its self-possession. [cann-i][a1] (*See The Observer II-5)*

There is also a split between the left and the right side. However this is often a leftsidedness that seems to have much to do with the issues of gender and feminization. Feeling as if right side bigger than the left. [adam][srj5] Her usual sensation of left right body split has been much more defined. [choc][srj3] I had a fleeting image of being split down the middle (left and right sides split). [neon][srj5] Half of me ripped away. [lsd][nl-lsd] Feeling as if made up of two body halves which don't belong together properly. The left is wider and blurred, the right is narrower and has a clear structure. [ozone][sde2] The entire left half of the body became numb, the left half of the head being sharply divided in sensation from the other half. [xan][c1] (*See Left Sidedness VIII-2*)

V-5 Chaos & Order

The ultimate and original form of instability is chaos. This chaos and the corresponding need for order are a big issue in Vacuum. The concept of the void, chaos and creation, and the constant repetition of this cycle would appear to be an inherent theme of the remedy. [vacuum][es-vac] The earth was without form and void and darkness was upon the face of the earth. [vacuum][es-vac] From the union darkness and chaos came day, night, Erebus and the air. [vacuum][es-vac] Throughout history, the battle has raged between chaos and order with man desiring to believe in a perfectly ordered universe. [vacuum][es-vac]

Chaos manifests within. Chaotic day! Could not find anything in the house that I needed, everything seems a mess. There is no method to my work, no structure. [limen-b-c][hrn2] It was hard to be disciplined, to do mundane tasks, it was awful to deal with office work, it pulled me down, kept me submerged. [limen-b-c][hrn2] Cannot feel pleasure or sorrow. Everything is Chaos. Cannot restore my energy. Totally meaningless. Feels like an empty battery. [germ-met][srj5] Couldn't get it together, not able to keep things organized. Papers everywhere. Losing my mind feeling. Father is getting more disorganized. And I saw myself going down the same track. [lac-e][hrn2] Dullness and chaotic feeling. [lac-f][wza1] Dream: I felt like I had a lot of work to do. Felt a little messy and confused. [lac-lup][hrn2]

And without. Much more untidy. The house was a mess and it didn't bother her. Made ineffectual efforts to tidy up and then lost interest. [androc][srj5] Everywhere in kitchen is such a mess, untidy, papers lying about, stuff abandoned half done. Can't seem to sort it out. [heroin][sdj-h] Feeling harassed – time is moving too fast and very tired. I cannot stand the mess around me – I must tidy it up. [lsd][nl-lsd]

It causes inordinate concern and even despair. Other people do pleasant things. All my energy I use to keep an intense rage distant so that I won't hurt myself or the kids. Everything was heavy and felt impossible without meaning. Terrible anger. Bad conscience and crying afterwards. Could not do what I had planned to do, because I felt so terrible and everything was chaos. [germ-met][srj5] I feel careless and slovenly about doing the diary. But I also resent the mess around me. [lsd][nl-lsd] Despair in the morning upon awakening, despair over chaos. [ozone][sde2] Dream: The house was a disaster and felt despair that I would never be able to clean it up; when woke up felt like my house was terribly messy. [carneg-g][rwt1]

A feeling that is already well known in Arsenicum. People who are compulsively fastidious, obsessed by the need for order and cleanliness to the point of expending inordinate energy, constantly cleaning and straightening. He cannot overlook an error or inadequacy in his work, no matter how insignificant; he is compelled to continue working until he is satisfied with the results. It is this inner drive for perfectionism that leads him to be very critical, very censorious of others. He readily criticizes anything done by anyone else, and his keen perception readily brings any existing imperfection to light. He is exhaustively fault-finding.[ars][vh1] Arsenicum patients are greatly aggravated both psychologically and physically by the disorderliness of a messy room. [ars][vh1]

The reaction to chaos is a desire for order and an industriousness that is found through a great number of remedies. Dreamt twice that he was in charge of a large meeting which was very chaotic, but he was able to bring order into it. [aids][nl2] Great desire to get my affairs in order. [adam][srj5] Dreams of organizing, finding order, putting in place. [adam][srj5] I wake up in the morning and feel panicky about all the things I have to do that day – as if I have too much to juggle with. Increased willpower to do jobs normally boring to me. [choc][srj3] Industrious, mania for work. [coca][sk7] While doing all the day-to-day things, I thought surely there could be more interesting or more useful things to do, rather than daily drudgery. [coca-c][sk4] Enjoyed doing the dishes, making dinner, doing laundry. Felt like a luxury to be doing simple tasks. [haliae-lc][srj5] Feel very industrious. Organizing things, cleaning out my room. Organizing stuff to give away to charity. [haliae-lc][srj5] Organized, I feel if I could get things neat and organized the world would be perfect, but I can never get to that point, because there will be a flow. [haliae-lc][srj5] Do things around house. House starts to look really good, mostly because son is home, so I am home. [helodr-cal][knl2] Did some chores unusually easily and readily. [falco-pe][nl2] I notice that I'm doing more household chores, without it being a chore. [falco-pe][nl2] Went to a meeting. Asked a lot of questions to make things clear. I wanted things done and simple and was very impatient with complexities. Spent a lot of time cleaning up things that had been said at a previous meeting. [ignis-alc][es2 Feeling the need to get things done and accomplished. [helo-s][rwt2] Spent the afternoon clearing and sorting cupboards and drawers. Three provers said that they could not stop cleaning until everything was in its place and this was definitely a new symptom. [musca-d][stew+] [hydrog][srj2] Fastidiousness – wanting to put women's collars and hair into proper "order". [galla-q-r][nl2] I became obsessive about cleaning and tidying up. [heroin][sdj-h] Decided to clean and polish the house to put things in order and calm the mind. [heroin][sdj-h] Feel organised and ordered, house tidy and clean. [heroin][sdj-h] Felt better after manic cleaning. [heroin][sdj-h] Lots of energy, been busy around house, get it tidied up. [heroin][sdj-h] Much neater than usual, keeping things cleaner, more organized. [lac-e][hrn2] Felt the need to organize; bothered by clutter and mess. [lac-e][hrn2] Morbid conscientiousness. [lac-f][c1] Desire for cleanness, orderliness, only fastidious when decompensated. [lac-f][wza1] A need to put the world close to home in order. Untidiness aggravates. [lac-h][vml3] A need to be orderly. Am I nesting? [lac-h][htj1] Spring cleaning. [lac-h][htj1] Want to dress up so as not to look untidy going to the pub. Much more formal dress than usual. [lac-h][htj1] Feeling very organized or think I am, therefore feel calm. [lac-lup][hrn2] Clearing up old mess and enjoying the creation of new space. [latex][nl-latex] Clutter in house today driving me to distraction but done nothing about it. Just want stillness and quiet and smooth and calm inside and out. [latex][nl-latex] Felt an intense desire to be busy. [opun-v][a1] Feel as if I do a lot of household chores with zest. [ozone][sde2] I am more motivated and more organized: I seem more efficient and controlled. [plut-n][srj7] I've been very industrious. [plut-n][srj7] Dream I was doing boring, repetitive household chores. [plut-n][srj7] Fastidious. Urge to put things in order. [plut-n][vml3] In the evenings, a desire to keep things clean and in their proper place, and to have everything in a good appearance. [polys][sk4] Had the feeling that I should be more organized and methodical in work, make things function in a better way, otherwise everything will be haywire. [polys][sk4] Desire to do a lot of cleaning in the house which I normally postpone. [polys][sk4] Concerned about personal cleanliness – rare! Wanted to be clean and well-presented. [positr][nl2] Feel motivated to get things done, but not mechanically or obsessively. A sense of order and proportion in things. [positr][nl2] The key thing for me today is that I want to be very organised. I want to sort everything out. [positr][nl2] Am organizing lots of stuff around course, life, etc., but still not able to settle down to any work. [positr][nl2] When I got home, I just blitzed my house, I cleaned it from top to bottom. [positr][nl2] Feeling very practical. (desire to clear up). [positr][nl2] Urge to clean everything. It was a great feeling to get the place in order. [rhus-g][tmo3] I was also very determined and efficient.

[sanguis-s][hrn2] Need to organize. [carneg-g][rwt1] Dream: Cleaning out drawers in dresser. [urol-h][rwt3] I've done a lot of gardening – cutting back and tidying up. This is unusual, as I like the garden to look a bit wild. I've also done lots of painting on the house. [vacuum][es-vac]

V-6 Structure

Like the desire for order a sense of structure is an important balance to the sense of instability.

Some of the remedies are made from substances that are involved in viewing and understanding structure. They are used medically in Positron Emission Tomography, which is probably the most accurate and detailed method of looking inside a living body. [positr][nl2] Tungsten is used in the production of filaments for electric lamps, X-ray tubes and radio tubes. [tung-met][bdx1]

There are also dreams of the structure of things. Dream: Underneath the house it looked as if there was something to do with mechanics. There were all these pipes and things like the mechanics for a swimming pool. [aids][nl2] Dream: I am on a ladder that goes into the rafters of a building, into the attic – you can also see over the walls into other apartments. I can see the whole internal structure. [positr][nl2]

There can be a simple awareness of structure. Its taken me beyond my limits, structure and form. I feel expanded out through and beyond my form, but my form remains. [lsd][nl-lsd] I'm aware of my body, my breasts going up and down with my breath. I'm relaxed and sleepy. [haliae-lc][srj5] I had a peculiar sensation of more than one set of eyelids closing, as if I were closing down further and further, going deeper and deeper and the light kept getting darker and darker and I went in. All I got was a sensation of completeness and very much aware of the structure of things. [positr][nl2] This has made me even more acutely aware of the insides of people and things. [positr][nl2] I began to feel a sense of "completeness". Inner structure, not bones but lines of tension (not stress) from my periphery to my centre. [positr][nl2]

Or a feeling that the subject can actually see the inner structure of people and things. Material objects appear to lack substance. I see molecules. [adam][srj5] After waking, pattern on walls became fluid in movement, in air. The wall lost solidity; could easily move through it. [adam][srj5] Impression that objects and his own body are transparent: sees his own internal organs. [anh][jl1] I could trace the circulation of the blood along each inch of its progress. I knew when every valve opened and shut. The beating of my heart was so clearly audible that I wondered it was not heard by others. [cann-i][a1] Can feel my legs from the inside distinctly. [helodr-cal][knl2] After meditating I put my left hand over my face and I could see a skeleton of light, my bones glowing. [plut-n][srj7] Can see into herself; thinks the blood dark blue. [pyrus][a1] The feeling of my body tingling removed from itself, outside itself, beside itself was intense, subtle. I felt differently extended, solid but unstable. This alternated with feeling my bones, my structure, quite firmly. [galeoc-c-h][gms1] The other day in town I saw a woman with an extremely thin face. I got a flash of what her skull looked like behind this thin veil of skin. I saw everyone's skull around me. I knew what they would be like, regardless of the amount of flesh on their faces. [vac-uum][es-vac]

A manifestation of the importance of structure is the idea of black and white without intervening shades of colour. Things are very black and white for me. [adam][srj5] All or nothing. [androc][vml3] Things seem more black and white, less gray. Not comfortable in the gray zone. [lac-e][hrn2] Think in extremes, black and white, especially on the emotional level when "attacked". [lac-f][wza1] Black and white dreams. [lsd][nl-lsd] Dream: White candle wax drips onto my black trousers. [ozone][sde2] (*See Clarity I-6*)

Truth without gradations of ambiguity is a common expression of this. This truth needs to be expressed, to be revealed, The remedy seems to be really about communication and saying what you feel, not selling yourself short. [falco-pe][nl2] Less tolerant of ambiguity. [lac-e][hrn2] Feeling like my truth is readily available, speaking what is true saying it like it is, with no affectations. [lsd][nl-lsd] Clear head and the feeling of having to be direct, to tell everyone the truth. [ozone][sde2] I experience great, eternal truth, depth. [ozone][sde2] I feel as if I speak only when it is important to speak. No wastage. [positr][nl2] I can acutely sense the truth, even if what is said is something different. [positr][nl2] This is a symptom very strong in Chocolate. A friend visited and I felt I wanted to tell her the truth. [choc][srj3] I wanted to ring a few friends and tell them what I really thought about them. [choc][srj3]

This tendency is often linked to insensitivity and can become cruelty. I'm ready to speak my mind – I don't care if people cease to like me. [choc][srj3] The issue at the center for me now has a lot to do with talking and telling people what I think, especially in the stressful situation when I am seeing things they don't want to talk about. [haliae-lc][srj5] Heightened feeling of honesty in expression. Fearless in relationships. Being able to say things I normally wouldn't. A feeling that thoughts which I may well suppress must now be expressed. [lsd][nl-lsd] (*See Lack of Emotion III-4 and Cruelty III-6*)

There is in some remedies, especially Moschus and Lac caninum, the other side of this in a difficulty with telling the truth. However much they pretend to be honest and truthful their reported sensations are untrustworthy. [mosch][k2] They not only have volumes of real and imaginary symptoms, but they become adepts at producing at will a kaleidoscopic complex of symptoms, increasing in quantity and intensity until all their own desires are attained. [mosch][k2] Is impressed with the idea that all she says is a lie; that all her symptoms are unreal, and the result of a diseased imagination; it seems to be very difficult to speak the truth, but continually distrusts things; when reading anything she rapidly changes the meaning, omitting or adding things. [lac-c][c1]

Focus, a concentration on the detail of things, is an important way of finding stability and order. When focused, subjects are sharp and clear but when not things become fuzzy and chaotic. Very sharp today, got heaps of work done. [aids][nl2] There was another experience which totally contradicts the sharpness, and the only way I can think of to describe it is like using a camera lens. You can zoom in on fine detail, or you can pan out to a wider angle, missing the fine detail in the center of the picture but still seeing the picture. For example, looking in the cupboard under the sink, seeing what was there, but not being able to identify the washing-up liquid sitting in the center. Or on the other hand, neatly setting the table for dinner, and not seeing that I had done it completely wrong. [adam][srj5] Able to complete things at work. Almost withdrawing from people in order to concentrate. [dream-p][sdj1] My clarity and focus is much better. Not so many things distracting me. Life is much simpler, much clearer. [haliae-lc][srj5] My vision has been a bit funny. If I do not concentrate it goes blurred. Whenever I focus on something different, everything jumps. It is as if I am aware of the process; it's not smooth and flowing. [irid-met][srj5] Forgets all about her pains if amused with anything, but directly she is tired of it she exclaims, 'Oh, my… ! [pip-m][c1] Curious, things have to be interesting, repetition can be boring. [lac-f][wza1] Vision: At distant squint through fuzziness, zoom in with crystal clarity. [lac-loxod-a][hrn2] Enjoying work when I'm in it because of lack of internal distraction. [latex][nl-latex] Eyes, field of vision felt scattered. I was driving home, and I had no central focus. I felt as if I had to stay in inside lane on motorway, did not trust my perception. [lsd][nl-lsd] In the Oak state, one may develop "tunnel vision," ever focused on task completion and on upholding of life's commitments. [querc-r][rcb4] I have noticed that when I am actively doing something, engaged in something, with my mind focused that the apprehension goes away, I don't notice it. [positr][nl2] Basically I have been OK today when I've been doing something and when my mind has been focused on something else other than me; otherwise the tight feeling in chest/apprehension was there. [positr][nl2] More forgetful than before the proving, and, yet, by collecting the thoughts, able to recall things read many years ago; able to supply some additional items to a professional paper, intended to be exhaustive. [ptel][a1]

VI-1 Extremes

There is a tendency in modern society, contemporary disease and the new remedies towards extremes. In an unstable world without boundaries there are no restrictions to temper the progress of any action. Anything, once begun, is likely to continue unimpeded until it reaches an extreme state. Have I gone too far? Is it too extravagant? I have to pull back. [ara-mac][sej7]

Many of the recently proved remedies are in themselves extreme examples of their type. Thus they include the heaviest metals. Iridium is one of the densest and heaviest known metals, being twice as heavy as lead. [irid-met][srj5] Osmium is the heaviest substance known: a piece of osmium as big as a building brick weighs 22.5 kilos. [osm][vml3] Iridium is one of the most resistent metals and Tungsten is used to make alloys whose hardness is only surpassed by Diamond. Diamonds are the hardest mineral (Hardness 10) they are capable of scratching others and can only be scratched by itself. [adam][srj5]

The Whale and the Elephant are the heaviest and largest creatures in the sea and on earth, while the Bald Eagle is The largest species of eagle in the world. [haliae-lc][srj5] The Carnegiea Gigantea is one of the largest cactuses in the world. [carneg-g][rwt1] The fastest creature on Earth is the Falcon. LSD 25 is the most potent psychotropic substance known to us. [lsd][nl-lsd]

There are corresponding extremes in many of the remedies and pathologies. These can involve pathologies that change quickly and sometimes from one extreme to another. (*See Instability V-1*)

Behaviours can also be extreme. These extremes are found throughout the remedies and the themes discussed here.

The tendency to extremes can result in a form of perception that exaggerates everything this is a well know symptom of Agaricus. During intoxication they lift and carry the heaviest loads, take long steps and jump over small objects, as if trunks of trees lay in their way. [agar][a1] But it is also a feature of Dolphin. Exaggerations: Gestures, dreams, big breasts, depths, diving. Every detail exaggerated. Food on huge plate. [lac-del][hrn2]

One of the most extreme remedies is Scorpion and the remedy shows a frightening pattern of symptoms taking an extreme form. They have been found living in extreme conditions and harsh environments. [androc][srj5] Very strong liking and disliking to people. Very intense, ranging from immense sexual attraction to extreme hatred. Spoke with hatred and maliciousness about colleagues. [androc][srj5] Terrible uncontrollable temper. [androc][srj5]

Symptoms and pathologies take extreme forms but so do pleasures. The drug remedies all involve extremely pleasurable or ecstatic experiences of one form or another. These to be balanced by experiences of extreme horror or discontent.

It is possible in the electronic age to reach dizzying heights of creativity, understanding and spirituality. One of the reasons that Bi-Polar Disorder or manic depression as it used to be called can be so hard to treat is that some patients feel that the episodes of depression are a price worth paying for the creativity and spiritual wholeness that they experience during their manic phases.

A similar attitude is often expressed about drug experiences particularly the psychedelics such as LSD and Mescaline. This feeling was expressed by one of the Hydrogen provers. There is a very fine line at this time between enlightenment and insanity – a split consciousness. The dark side is horrendous, but the positive side of the proving has been well worth it. The positive aspects are beautiful. It's a shame we need to come down. I guess the price of going into the heavens is a trip to hell. [hydrog][srj2]

VI-2 Tallness

One of the most common extremes found in these remedies is that of height or tallness.

Sequoia are the tallest trees on earth. [seq-s][vml3] and Kauri are not far behind. Generally trees are the substances that epitomize the principle of height.

The sensation of being taller or larger is well known in Platina. As if everything about her were very small, and all persons physically and mentally inferior, but she herself physically large and superior. [plat][a1] But it is found in several new remedies as well. I feel very tall and large. I am a giant, 12:30 a.m. – powerful feeling. [adam][srj5] Imagines he is gradually swelling, his body becoming larger and larger. [cann-i][a1] Delusion, greatness of his body parts. [coca][sk7] Feeling extremely tall. Feeling as if kitchen table too low. [irid-met][srj5] After a shower, I felt enormous, massive, yet in proportion. [neon][srj5] I was amazed at how huge I was, particularly the legs. [neon][srj5] Feeling very tall as if pulled up through the spine. Felt tall and light. [tung-met][bdx1]

The corresponding sensation that everything else is smaller is also found. Objects perceived are too small, but more often violently bright. [anh][jl1]

The sensation of height can be an aspect of the many symptoms involving floating and flying. Dreams of places located high up. [lars-arg][fkw1] Felt very tall and high off the ground. Looking far down as though looking far down to the ground. Felt very airy, high in the air. In motion, but stillness. [lac-loxod-a][hrn2] Feeling aloof, floating. [tung-met][bdx1] (*See Floating & Flying IV-8*)

It can also be an aspect of being detached from the world and becoming an observer. I have a sense of elongation. I feel as if I'm longer and higher. I can look down from a great height from a still and silent head. [plut-n][srj7] (*See The Observer II-5*)

VI-3 Nobility

The spirit that finds physical expression in tallness finds more emotional expression in the theme of nobility.

Nobility runs through the substances used in the new remedies and is reflected in their symptoms. Sherr has proved most of the Noble Gases, though only Neon has so far been published. Neon is classified as a Noble gas. Sometimes referred to as " inert" because their electrons are full, they don't share readily. [neon][srj5] Just as the substance stands apart from other elements; there is a tendency to stand apart from the common throng. This is an aspect of the theme of detachment. (*See Detachment II-4*)

Another area of the periodic table that is referred to in this way is that containing the Noble Metals which includes Platinum, Osmium and Iridium. A feeling of superiority and haughtiness is one of the keynotes of Platinum. One of the most striking characteristics of this drug is pride and over-estimate of one's self. [plat][k2]

In the animal kingdom the Lion is the King of the Jungle and the feeling of being kingly came through in the proving where it was manifest as arrogance and irritability. Anger, brooding; visit a patient who normally provokes a gentle loving feeling yet I feel anger towards him. I wonder if he is looking angry, but the mood continues after I leave. I feel this underlying arrogance – a sort of broody anger just generally towards almost anyone I think of. [lac-leo][hrn2] Felt very strong and great like a king, and thought of others that they were slow creatures who were in my way. [lac-leo][sk4]

The goat may not be regarded as a noble animal, though it was a goat that was chosen to suckle the infant Zeus, the Lord of Olympus, but the need to establish a superior position as a place of safety was very clear in the remedy. Others noticed that I had become contemptuous and was acting superior. Was deliberately using complicated words which people wouldn't understand, and was getting a lot of satisfaction when they would ask me for an explanation. [lac-cp][sk4] To find a safe place, in this remedy it means to have a high position (No one above you who can spear or pierce you; you are the one who is in control). [lac-cp][lsy+dmk] A high social position is just as safe and you have to keep that up at every price because it is life saving. It is not out of ambition or love of power! [lac-cp][lsy+dmk]

A very similar feeling was evident in Polystyrene. Feel like starting a debate with allopaths, want to show them where they are and where we homoeopaths are. Want that they should agree to our superiority. Hatred towards them. [polys][sk4] Wanted to put people in their proper places, to show them where they are. [polys][sk4]

The Salmon is regarded as the most noble of the fish.

The birds already look down on the rest of the world but some of those that have been proved have a particular association with nobility. The Falcon is known as the Noble Bird, both for its power, speed and courage and for the nobility it bestowed on the men who hunted with them.

Likewise the Eagle is the undisputed King of the Skies. Dream: I feel regal and generous. [haliae-lc][srj5] However, this is deceptive. The Eagle, and in a similar way the Lion, are scavengers happy to appropriate the kills of other animals and only to hunt themselves when they absolutely have to. Primarily a scavenger, the bald eagle hunts only when there is no easier available source of food. The favorite prey among coastal eagles is fish, especially salmon. [haliae-lc][srj5] Their reputation as hunters rather than as the scavengers they primarily are, may come from the fact that they are dominant among carrion-eaters, so they are often the first to be found feeding on the carcass of a dead animal. [haliae-lc][srj5]

Many of the trees that are important in treating contemporary disease have a noble quality. The Sequoia could not be thought of as anything but noble and the Kauri is an antipodean equivalent. When mature they are the largest, among the tallest, and in their towering crowns as well as their huge clean trunks (boles), the broadest trees. It has been written that even in their youth they have a clean upward thrust of trunk that distinguishes them 'as a master race'. They really are the Lords of the Forest. [agath-a][nl2] Likewise the Walnut. From many points of view the walnut-tree is of very great importance, and well deserves its lofty name. The Royal Nut, has a place in medicine which deserves to be better known. [jug-r][c1] The Oak is often referred to as the Royal Oak and Oak Galls were a symbol of the return of royalty to Britain in 1660.

Many other remedies also have symptoms and issues around pride and nobility. Coca is the only drug remedy that "Desires grandeur". It also has delusions of being a great person. [coca][sk7] After a long walk (pushed to limit) felt proud – didn't let others know how proud I felt. [tung-met][bdx1] Delirious fantasies that she was a noble lady. [phos][a1] He imagines that he is a great person surrounded by grand accoutrements, the mania of grandeur it is sometimes termed. [phos][fr1] I have felt a lot more above myself, my life, my situation, just vain, contemptuous. [vacuum][es-vac]

VI-4 Strength & Hardness

Another common expression of the tendency towards extremes is hardness. Diamond is the quintessentially hard substance. Diamonds are the hardest mineral, they are capable of scratching others and can only be scratched by itself. [adam][srj5] A diamond resists acids, can penetrate steel, and has the best thermal conductivity of any material. Modern industry would virtually halt without it. Diamonds are unequaled for etching, grinding, engraving, polishing and sharpening. They form the teeth of drilling bits for oil wells, and the blades of knives used by surgeons to cut cataracts from eyes. [adam][srj5]

Tungsten is probably the next hardest substance. Tungsten is used in the production of alloys of great hardness, the most important being the tungsten steels, which are used for tipping and facing cutting tools. [tung-met][bdx1] With Osmium and Iridium close behind. Because of its resistance to corrosion and its hardness, it is used for pointing fountain pen-nibs, and for electrical contacts subject to severe conditions. [irid-met][srj5] Iridium's resistance to high temperatures means it is the only metal that can be used, unprotected, in air at temperatures up to 2,300°C without undergoing catastrophic failure. [irid-met][srj5] This metal is very hard and difficult to mould or shape. It is the heaviest metal in the periodic system and also the most resistant to pressure. [osm][stj2]

Symptoms of physical hardness are found in Diamond. Feeling alone and tall and capable, like a beacon beaming out rays of light to all and sundry. [adam][srj5] And in other remedies. During intoxication they lift and carry the heaviest loads. [agar][a1] Argument with doctor at work. I held my ground, did not mince my words. This happens very rarely. [lac-loxod-a][hrn2] Walking up a long gradual incline, I felt every stride was covering great distances. I felt I was doing the usual 20 minute walk in seconds. I felt like a titan in 7-league boots, but then I couldn't decide which league boots they were and I wanted an even number. [neon][srj5]

Coca and Arsenic are both used as folk medicines to increase strength and toughness. In certain districts Arsenicum is indulged in as an article of diet. The women take it for the purpose of beautifying the complexion, and the men indulge in it because it enables them to work hard with little or no fatigue. [ars][fr1] Constant desire to undertake vast feats of strength. [cocain][a1]

This strength can give the subject a sense of invulnerability and a lack of fear. This effect is well known in Agaricus, Some run and walk involuntarily in the most dangerous places. [agar][a1] but also appears in other remedies. There is a lack of the panic which one would expect in such states. It is not normal for an individual undergoing such overpowering illusions to remain untouched by fear, as is the case in Anhalonium, and this lack of fear becomes a characteristic of the remedy. [anh][vh1] They leave the calves with the "aunties" (non-pregnant or nursing females) who, while baby-sitting, will form a circle and swim round and round the calves to protect them from danger. Thus, the feeling in the dolphin is that there is calm and safety in the center of the circle, even though there is danger outside. [lac-del][hrn2] Dream: While roaming in a forest I saw wild animals like snakes, lions and panthers roaming about, and felt no fear. [lac-h][sk4] Even though they are fearless they are very peaceful creatures. They move forward slowly and calmly and only spray when there is no other alternative. Being the sympathetic creatures that they are, they always give a warning before they spray. [meph][vml3] I am positive, centred, strong, courageous and protected. [rhus-g][tmo3]

The sense of strength is often delusionary and the resulting fearlessness become dangerous. In two cases this sense of confidence was distinctly immature and potentially dangerous, either to self or to others. A sense of adolescent omnipotence, of invulnerability emerged. [Guess] [androc][vml3]

This is clear in Mescaline and in one way or another applies to all the drug remedies. Consciousness of unusual energy and intellectual power (which, when tested, was found not to actually exist). [anh][c1] Sense of superiority and well-being. Sense of depression and inferiority. [anh][c1]

VI-5 Excess

The lack of boundaries and the tendency towards extremes that are found in the new remedies lead to symptoms of excess in many of them.

Superficially the excess found in the AIDS Miasm is very similar to that found in the other miasms, particularly the Sycotic. However, these patterns actually come from very different places. Sycosis is motivated by a deep seated feeling of inadequacy. This leads to a feeling that you can never have as much as you might need of anything, whether it be money, power, sex or food. At any time whatever you have may not turn out to be enough and so the subject always tries for just a little bit more. In the Syphilitic Miasm the aim is to have more than the enemies that surround you. In the Cancer Miasm the movement towards regimented monoculture marches apace and the next object unless brought into the ordered fold could represent a chaotic danger. The problem is that there is always a next object that will have to be transformed.

The excess in the AIDS is perhaps the simplest. The boundary between having enough and having too much is simply not there. The subject continues accumulating more and more and never realizes that he or she has already come to a point where stopping would be the sensible thing to do.

Extravagance in the Miasm can be a fairly general thing. I wanted to do something naked and extravagant. [aids][nl2] She walks further than she needs to. [ars][a1] Feel like a driver in a car with no brakes. [heroin][sdj-h] There are many examples of young people squandering ridiculous amounts of money on E and only living for their next binge. [mdma][saunders]

Angastura has a particular bitterness that enough can never be achieved. These are people who are always disappointed as soon as they reach their goals and obtain what they wanted. They must learn that bliss is not reached through achievements in the material world, nor in the aggrandizement of the ego, but in fulfilling the true potential of the heart. [ang][ggd1]

Excessive sexual activity is something that was associated with the early picture of AIDS and it allowed the disease's rapid spread. This sexual excess is a feature of many of the remedies. (*See Sexuality VIII-5*) However, it is worth mentioning Anantherum, a remedy in which sexual excess is taken to an extreme. Another aspect of Anantherum is its tendency to invoke a state of self-satisfaction, a kind of narcissism that can be seen quite prominently in some cases of male homosexuals. They seem "satisfied with themselves," as if ready to savor pleasure all the time, lacking a sense of duty, of responsibility. They appear to adopt the attitude that everything is here on earth for their own pleasure. They feel that they are more intelligent than others, more sensitive, more capable in their work, and more well-suited to enjoy sex than anybody else. [anan][vh1] Unrestrained sexuality. [anan][ggd1]

This tendency to keep going without any restriction is a keynote of Rubber and was found in every area of the proving. Feel need to clarify numbness symptom as it is central to my experience of the remedy. Usually on waking, but also sometimes sitting, I have feeling of numbness arising out of the fact that I am lying heavily on one part. There is no tingling or pins and needles, which would be normal for me in the circumstances, and there is definitely no pain, but it does feel bad. I know that I should move but I do not, I stay immobilised. It is not actual paralysis and it is not can't be bothered it is actually there is no volition or impulse to put the thought that I should move into action. The same feeling pervades many different things. I have been taking extremely long baths, it is because I don't get out not because I can't or won't but just because I don't. Sleep is similar I have been sleeping long and deep just because I don't stop and I stay up late because I don't go to bed. Eating I might not start for a long time and then when I start I don't stop. The same feeling is felt mentally and emotionally. About sex and about business affairs. I can feel them in a funny sort of way though the numbing is there I know that they are there but I don't have the volition to do anything. To act in any way. [latex][nl-latex] Dream: Waiting for buses rushing around darting in and out of food shops wanting more and more. I remember eyeing up the man in the bakery. [latex][nl-latex] Once I or we started doing something we were on a mission, driven, on tracks – hard to stop, hard to change direction. At first this was OK but it became somewhat overwhelming and I ended up feeling as depressed and fed up with the monotony of life (if not more so) as I ever have. [latex][nl-latex] Have noticed the last few days that it's increasingly hard to stop working. Once I start I can't seem to stop. Even taking a break is difficult (I'm rebuilding our kitchen). [latex][nl-latex]This feeling is also found in the Dolphin. Enjoyed effort and sweating of exercise and the power of it. Felt I could keep going and going and going. [lac-del][hrn2]

The other major areas of excess are materialism and appetite which have their own sections.

VI-6 Materialism

One of the most memorable dream themes to emerge from the AIDS proving was one of luxury and sumptuousness. There were dreams of beautiful buildings and of great treasures. Dream: There were lots of boxes in this house and very big rooms, but everything was decorated beautifully. There were chandeliers, beautiful furniture, beautiful paintings, antique carpets and there were railings and you just looked down and there was a great feeling of space. [aids][nl2] Dream: In a catholic church, very rich gold paintings, colours, statues. [aids][nl2] Dream: They brought in these crates and opened them up. The crates had false centres that were packed full of treasure. There was gold dripping out and jewels and crowns. They were full of treasures and I was really excited – but I was moving out. I walked to the patio where there was my box which was full of old junk. [aids][nl2]

This theme is found in many of the remedies of the AIDS Miasm. Dreams of sumptuous living, of pleasures and enjoyments. [anan][a1] Out of nowhere a few days ago saw high heeled shoes at the shoe store and wanted to wear heels which I haven't done in 19 years. [carbn-dox][knl3] One cannot deny that chocolate is a very sensuous experience combining the senses of smell, taste and touch. It just melts in your mouth, gradually softening and enveloping the taste buds. No wonder the advertisers of chocolate products use images of seduction and unadulterated pleasure. [choc][srj3] Fondness for luxury and grandeur. [cur][a1] Magnificent Castles; far off places and fantasy. [helodr-cal][knl2] Dreamt about being on a college campus and visiting sororities. Each one in a different setting and huge like castles or giant apartments. [helodr-cal][knl2] Want to shop. Look at things. Try on clothes. Look at beautiful jewellry. [helodr-cal][knl2] Dream of noble setting, opulent surroundings. [irid-met][srj5] Desire to be pampered as opposed to desire to be independent. [lac-f][vml3]

In many of these remedies there is a feeling of becoming more materialistic. Arising from the insecurity is the Arsenicum dependency on other people. For this reason the Arsenicum patient becomes very possessive – possessive of objects, of money, and especially of people who are near, such as a wife or husband. [ars][vh1] The possessive quality of Arsenicum extends to physical possessions as well as people. He is reluctant to give money or material objects away; he is even stingy with his discharges! [ars][vh1] Extravagance in purchases, spends much money. [buteo-j][sej6] The cacao fruit was also used as a monetary system. Tribes conquered by the Aztecs had to pay tribute in beans. Apparently the rich could buy a rabbit for 10 beans and a courtesan for 12 beans. The conquistadors were astonished to find that the cacao beans were valued more than any other substance, even more than gold. [choc][srj3] Involved dreams about money and counting and stashing large quantities of money. [hydrog][srj2] Anxiety about no money; feel everyone ripped me off. [phasco-ci][rbp2] Greed – seems to be tiring me out, not wanting to end the day and go to bed, not satisfied with one drink wanting many, smoking too much etc. [latex][nl-latex] Lost any spiritual connection. Became much more materialistic. Blow all this spiritual stuff. Life would be easier if I could be like my family and go and play golf. [lsd][nl-lsd] Feel gross side gaining and spiritual side receding. [lsd][nl-lsd] When they have been encouraged to resort to crafty cunning, to have every whim gratified from infancy to eighteen years of age they become fit subjects for Mosch. [mosch][k2] Wanted to earn more, have luxuries – a materialistic attitude. Wanted to take up a side-profession simply to earn more. [polys][sk4] Have a desire to spend money and also fear of not having enough. I'm very fixed on material things. [positr][nl2] I feel very cynical with friends. Kind of like 'get with reality'. Not into all this mystical crap. I feel very strong; like I need to assert myself. [vacuum][es-vac] And sometimes of going on spending sprees. Went on a wild spending spree. [falco-pe][nl2] Had a compulsive need to buy things. [musca-d][stew+] I went out and bought myself a new jacket for £95 – I want to look good. I also got my hair cut – I feel like looking good to go with feeling good. [lsd][nl-lsd] I have found myself spending a lot of money. [vacuum][es-vac] I went to the bank, just realised I completely overspent the other day and haven't enough money to cover the rent. [vacuum][es-vac]

This easily becomes something undesirable or something about which the subject feels guilty. Thinking of money all the time. Money, money, money, I want it. Patients = money. Feel guilt about this I am a materialistic money person now. [heroin][sdj-h] The nickname 'leech' is given to persons who attach themselves to other persons for personal gain. [hir][vml3]

There is in some remedies a conflict between the material and the spiritual. The Lizard contains this conflict between greed and guarding the hoard and wisdom and transformation. They share the characteristics of power with the dinosaurs, but also encompass wisdom, greed (guarding the hoard), intelligence and transformation. Lizards have played a role as the guardian of the unconscious. The hero must accost and come to terms with the dragon/lizard before the hero can win through. This is part of the hero's journey. The alchemical journey is filled with dragon symbolism. Jung calls the dragon the instinctual psyche. [helo-s][rwt2]

The same conflict is perhaps more straightforward in Diamond. The image of the diamond has been carefully nourished to symbolize the purest love, but it also arouses the basest greed. [adam][srj5]

In Lac humanum the desire for luxury is also part of the central conflict between being spiritual and being of this world. Persistent thoughts about how to improve my work, while at the same time the idea kept coming to me of being in a five-star hotel, and just watching movies on television. [lac-h][sk4]

There can also be a feeling of despair about the material world as in this Tungsten symptom. The senselessness of modern life. Thought of yesterday feeling lost in the supermarket. "What am I doing in the supermarket". Overwhelmed, disorientated. All the things we have, material things are so useless. [tung-met][bdx1]

Oxygen is an element which Scholten connects to materialism and possessions. Possessions are a problem to the Oxygens, in the sense that they have difficulty finding a balance between giving and taking. They are afraid of losing their possessions and they tend to hold on to them in a rather selfish way. They may even become quite mean and avaricious. They are also very afraid of thieves and robbers. 'An eye for an eye' is an expression that fits into their line of thinking. [oxyg][stj2]

As Carbon is also tied closely to the physical world and material things it is not surprising that Carbon Dioxide contains much about money. Dream: With myself and a friend and a few other people, I didn't know she was trying to sort out a money situation – who owed what. I was a little annoyed and thought it humourous – what was the big deal, everything had to be even as far as each person. [carbn-dox][knl3] Dream: A cheque is flying in the air coming to my hands and I catch it. My attitude is one of a bit of doubt maybe it won't be enough. [carbn-dox][knl3] This afternoon I found out I had $5K less in my bank account than I thought. Opened to possibilities. Fired my bookkeeper and hired a new one. Fairly unemotional about it though. Nothing personal. [carbn-dox][knl3] Realized missing $3000 in checking account. [carbn-dox][knl3] Very big anxiety about money – sadness, forlorn, no one with any sense looks after me. [carbn-dox][knl3]

VI-7 Appetite

Eating disorders are undoubtedly some of the defining forms of illness in the modern developed world. The clinical rubrics Anorexia and Bulimia do not contain anywhere near the number of new remedies that they should. However a few are already there including: Agath-a, Carneg, Positr, Lac-f, Germ along with older ones that have a relationship to the AIDS Miasm: Ars, Op, Anac, Agar, Plat, Cann-i.

There is found in many of the remedies of the AIDS Miasm a straightforward great appetite. The adjective canine is used to describe an excessive appetite which is found in Lac caninum. Very hungry, cannot eat enough to satisfy; as hungry after eating as before. [lac-c][al2]

Birds need to eat a great deal to sustain their metabolism and appetite is found in bird remedies. Warmer and eat more. If a person ate like a bird he would eat 100 hamburgers a day. [sej-birds] Hunger – voracious or can't eat. [sej-birds] Hungry at night before bed, but the hunger couldn't be satisfied. Maybe chocolate would have done it. Hunger like a stomach anxiety. [haliae-lc][srj5] especially Raven, Each prover basically told his/her story of how their appetites had greatly increased during the proving – one prover had even developed the habit of standing in front of his open refrigerator, methodically eating his way through it's contents, unable to stop until the last kernel of leftover rice casserole was gone. She felt she was not really belonging to her body. [corv-cor][bdg1] and Seagull: Hunger, hunger, 'attacks of eating'. [lars-arg][fkw1] For some time I have no brakes concerning eating, I could eat constantly, regardless what kind of food. [lars-arg][fkw1]

The drug remedies are also associated with hunger. The 'munchies' is a well known side effect of cannabis. Ravenous hunger, which is not decreased by eating enormously; he ceases eating only from fear of injuring himself. [cann-i][a1] Though the reverse is also found. Loss of appetite. [cann-i][a1] Great appetite is found in Agaricus. Ravenous appetite, with bolting of food. [agar][c1] Even Ecstasy which is related to slimming pills, Dry mouth and loss of appetite are almost universal. [mdma][saunders] Loss of appetite; anorexia. [mdma][hmd1] can have the reverse effect. Another subject's appetite increased and they gained weight. [mdma][saunders]

Coca is used to suppress hunger by the Andean Indians allowing them to work harder with less food. Great diminution of the usually vigorous appetite; chewing the leaves suspended the sensation of hunger. [coca][a1] Though eating one-half less than usual, his weight did not diminish, nor the capacity to endure labour. [coca][a1] Great satiety, without longing for nourishment, for a long time. [coca][a1] but it can also have great appetite. Appetite extremely irregular, for the aversion to all food is often suddenly followed by an insatiable craving, especially for animal food. [coca][a1] Indians, after chewing all day, not eating any food, ate at night like hungry men, and sometimes at a single meal swallowed as much as would serve others two days. [coca][a1]

Milk is very much a part of the most basic nurturing and nutrition and all the Lacs tend to have appetite issues. Eating disorders and huge fluctuations in body weight. [lac-h][vml3]

In the Elephant and Swan there is a particular fear of famine, or perhaps a sense of impending famine. I felt a sudden need to eat – not because my stomach was growling or I wanted to taste something I like – but because I had a physical sensation in my body of being unwell from not having eaten for a while. This was not my usual irritability or mild nausea feeling. It was deeper, like hunger of the cells of my body. It is hard to explain. [lac-loxod-a][hrn2] Dream: Eating takeout and there was not enough food. [lac-loxod-a][hrn2] Dreams of starvation, not enough food to go around. [cygn-b][sle-swan]

Several other remedies have a voracious appetite. Dream of food. [adam][srj5] In this connection may be mentioned the effects on the crew of the ship Zion, which carried arsenic as a portion of its cargo. This was exposed somewhat to the sun's rays, and the crew noticed a peculiar smell. Soon they all began to notice themselves growing stout, and on reaching Philadelphia from England they had all gained much, one to the extent of two stones in weight. [ars][c1] During some of the proving, noticeably a day or two previous and succeeding to the ninth day, took in food with a sort of ravenous haste; no taste of food, but a ravenousness would have impelled me to swallow anything with an abnormal avidity. [pip-m][a1] Desire for every kind of food. [propl][vml3] Voracious appetite. [seq-s][vml3] Strong desire for whatever is available. [seq-s][vml3] I gained two pounds in the last six weeks. [galeoc-c-h][gms1] There were chocolate wrappers and chocolate everywhere; not one of the six seemed to be worried about their figure." [Schindler] [meph][vml3]

Often the appetite comes out of a loss of control. It lacks real pleasure or satisfaction and is often linked to a sense of shame. Less control to stop eating. Eating without relish. [limen-b-c][hrn2] She's eating a lot although she doesn't have an appetite. She's disgusted with how much she's eating, losing control of what she eats. [corv-cor][bdg1] Don't have as much self-control. Usually very disciplined, especially with diet. Chocolate, started eating it for first time in 17 years! Didn't care, not a big deal. The eating chocolate wasn't as much about chocolate as it was about an attitude: "This isn't part of my diet," lessening. [lac-del][hrn2] Embarrassed and hiding, thinking what others would say about him when he could not control his urge to eat much and frequently. [lac-h][sk4] Then came the increasing paranoia over food and exercise. [lsd][nl-lsd] (*See Shame & Humiliation XI-3*)

The most important appetite symptoms indicate a discrepancy between the appetite and what is really needed. Her desire exceeds her need; she eats and drinks more than is good for her. [ars][a1] Very difficult to decide what to eat. [haliae-lc][srj5] Not hungry until I eat – then I am hungry. [falco-pe][nl2] Can't think what to eat, but very hungry. [irid-met][srj5] Lack of appetite but ravenous after starting to eat. [latex][nl-latex] Didn't feel hungry but I thought I ought to eat. [latex][nl-latex] The lack of appetite has also been significant and I have lost 10lb over the course of the proving. It may possibly have been more, but when I have eaten it has been fast food because I have had no interest in preparing or taking care over what I have eaten. I have probably not eaten so badly ever. I have, most days, only eaten one meal of rubbish. I have not been able to eat a normal size meal so on the days that I have felt hungrier I have snacked on odd bits and pieces but bread has felt too heavy, as has pasta, rice and potatoes. [latex][nl-latex] Voracious rapidity in eating, with a disposition to find fault with everything (to detest everything around himself). [plat][c1] Appetite: very hungry, but eat a few mouthfuls. [polys][sk4] I didn't have a day appetite today but I just kept eating – not continuously but every few hours I wanted something else. It was like a comfort eating but I didn't feel anxious. [positr][nl2] Appetite is not at usual times, normally eat at 6 p.m. and haven't; Feel appetite is being mucked around. [positr][nl2] I have bought really salty things at least three times in the last week, only to eat a little bit, and then, finding myself revolted by them, throwing them out. [vacuum][es-vac] The Shark can eat and store the food until it is needed. There are no digestive fluids in a shark's stomach. When the shark needs energy food is moved to the intestines for digestion. [galeoc-c-h][gms1]

Often there is hunger but the stomach is not up to the task of eating. Hunger, with sensation of fullness in the stomach; even the little he eats causes clenching of the teeth and contraction of the throat. [anan][a1] There is a feeling of fullness in the stomach as if too much had been eaten. [castm][c1] Appetite good, he would eat more if there were more room, the abdomen being filled with water. [conv-a][ll1] Very hungry, but not able to eat much. [pip-m][a1] Thinks the stomach very weak, as if it would digest nothing; thinks it is dry and wrinkled. [pyrus][a1]

The opposite effect, a lack of appetite is also common, as is an alternation between the two. Haven't felt like eating today. [choc][srj3] Absence of appetite. [lac-f][c1] No desire for food – seems unnecessary, energy available from other sources. Woke very early and felt that I didn't need any more sleep. [latex][nl-latex] Loss of appetite, anorexia. [rhus-g][a1] Diminished appetite. [urol-h][rwt3] I have been quite disinterested in eating, went for a thirty six hour period without eating. [vacuum][es-vac]

Lack of appetite can become an active aversion or disgust with food. Aversion to all foods, despite strong salivation and hunger. [anh][jl1] Repugnance to food and constant nausea. [castm][MP4] Averse food. I don't want to eat and no desire to swallow. [choc][srj3] Anorexia, aversion to fatty foods, meat and milk. [conv-s][jl1] Senses too acute to eat. [latex][nl-latex] I did not want anything anywhere inside of me, especially cold things, while normally I like cold drinks. This was a general feeling of not wanting any, which was not restricted to food and drink. I felt totally unneedy. [neon][srj5] Anorexia, could eat but a few mouthfuls at breakfast, and could only drink half a cup of coffee, which was vomited soon afterwards. [xan][a1]

There can be a powerful appetite for meat which is discussed in the section on transgenic confusion. (*See Transgenic Confusion VII-5*)

The attitude towards food reflects similar symptoms to other attitudes, particularly the carnal. The venereal appetite is increased by every attempt to satisfy it, until it drives him to onanism and madness. [anan][a1] (*See Sexuality VIII-5*)

VII-1 Confusion

Instability, chaos and a lack of order lead inexorably to confusion, the principal intellectual symptom of many of the new remedies and certainly of the AIDS Miasm.

There can be general confusion. I felt "out of phase," out of focus and dizzy, sort of spaced out and slightly uncoordinated. [irid-met][srj5] I made major mistakes with people, e.g. there was a patient in the waiting room, and I could not figure out who it was. Called a classmate by another classmate's name: confusions with names, used phrases differently, twisting numbers around. I am feeling like "I am not my mind or body". [lac-e][hrn2] I can experience joy and pain at the same time. [lars-arg][fkw1] One of our visitors had gone out to buy a newspaper. When he came back I could not recognize him, although I've known him for 12 years. It took 30 seconds or more, not just a flash, thinking he was a total stranger. [neon][srj5] Dullness. The mind is slow to learn, disorganized easily, poor memory, fuzzy and foggy. [tax-br][oss1] Confusion and making mistakes in things I know how to do. [urol-h][rwt3]

The most common manifestation of this confusion is an inability to concentrate. Without boundaries and containment thoughts continually disperse and become mixed. I felt dispersed, it was hard to concentrate, [adam][srj5] Concentration poor, inability to focus. [buteo-j][sej6] Mind scattered, thoughts all over the place, difficult time focusing. [lac-lup][hrn2] My concentration on my work was not very good. My mind was all over the place. [sal-fr][sle1]

This leads to an overall lack of concentration. Inability to formulate thoughts and words properly. [aids][nl2] Extreme absence of mind; he is unable to recollect things; for instance in playing cards, which he was fond of and knew well, he did not know what card he was to play, or what he was to do at all. [agn][a1] He finds reading difficult; he has to read several things twice; he is unable to fix his attention. [agn][a1] he has to read everything three or four times, and, after all, he does not seize the meaning of what he reads. [ambr][a1] Aversion to concentration of thought upon any one thing. [coca][a1] Absent-minded – drove through red light. [dream-p][sdj1] Difficulty concentrating on one thing for very long. [germ-met][srj5] More absent minded than usual. [germ-met][srj5] Poor concentration. [gink-b][mp4] Unable to confine his mind to any object. [helo-s][rwt2] Slightly disconnected. Unable to focus. Sound very vague and speech is very slow. [heroin][sdj-h] Weary, with heavy head, and difficulty in concentrating. [hir][jl1] I was just reading and it wasn't actually reaching anywhere in my head. I felt a bit sort of scrambled. General confusion of mind. [musca-d][stew+] [agath-a][nl2] Cannot concentrate the mind to read or study. [lac-c][al2] Not able to pay attention to remedy, not recording symptoms. Not very concerned. Just no ability to do it. [lac-e][hrn2] Complaints and lamentations on account of excessive sufferings, with inability to indicate the part affected; when questioned, patient complains still more urgently, but without saying where he suffers. [mosch][c1] Complains without knowing what ails him; complains much, but of nothing in particular. [mosch][fr1] Thinking is slow, concentration difficult. [ozone][sde2] Confused as to whether to drive through traffic lights when they are on red or green. [ozone][sde2] Concentration difficult, can only concentrate on one thing at a time. [plac][Biggs+] Absent-minded, she hears a conversation, but after it is finished knows nothing of it. [plat][a1] Very absentminded. [plut-n][srj7] Difficult concentration. [seq-s][vml3] Mind somewhat dull not sharp. No edge to mental function, which I usually have. [galeoc-c-h][gms1] Some confusion of thought. Lack of mental clarity in writing out cheques and getting cheque numbers correct. [galeoc-c-h][gms1] Cloudiness in thinking. Better walking. [galeoc-c-h][gms1] Impaired concentration, especially when people are speaking in a group and can't understand what others are saying. [tax-br][oss1] Could not concentrate on what my head was doing. [urol-h][rwt3] Lack of ability to focus and think deeply. [tung-met][bdx1] My mind is fuzzy can't think straight. [vacuum][es-vac] I'm not recognising people I know in the streets. [vacuum][es-vac]

There are also no boundaries to keep thoughts ordered and at bay. Thoughts pop into the head and drive one another out and about. And so he jumps about from one topic to another. It can hardly be said to be confusion, it is a dreamy state of mind, a state of senility. [ambr][k2] He cannot decide, especially in an action of good or evil. [anac][k2] He hears voices commanding him to do this or that, and seems to be between a good and an evil will. [anac][k2] One moment it is a delusion and next moment it is an illusion. [anac][k2] Hundreds of thoughts pop in and out of my brain, thoughts of 'why are we here?', deep philosophical issues. [androc][srj5] Great distraction; when he occupies himself with something serious, other things immediately come into his head. [ang][h1] Ideas crowd upon him, he is too weak to repel them in order to dwell upon one idea alone. [ars][a1] At one moment the intellect is obscure, and loses itself in forgetfulness of the past; then it returns clear, and is able to form a judgment for a moment, and disapprove of any acts it may have before sanctioned, but only to be again involved in that state of automatic folly which is so peculiar a phenomenon during Hashish intoxication. [cann-i][a1] Finding it difficult to concentrate. Hurriedly pottering about, although I feel tired and clumsy. [choc][srj3] Keep making silly mistakes, as if I haven't slept at all. [choc][srj3] Sudden complete lapse of concentration. I walked right into the middle of a crowded ladies' toilet. It took me a few seconds to notice that the 'men' were wearing skirts and looking at me in disbelief. [choc][srj3] I am vague and it is hard to entertain thoughts for too long. [rhus-g][tmo3] It makes women violently hysterical, and causes all sorts of strange and apparently impossible symptoms. [lac-c][k2] Impatient and hurried. Too many thoughts came to mind; could not hold on to any thought for long and could not concentrate for long. [lac-h][sk4] Unfitness for intellectual labour, caused by too lively an imagination. [meph][c1] Rush of ideas that were difficult for her to put in order. [phos][a1]

An effort to counteract this tendency by concentrating on one thing leads to all others being excluded. There is no sense of flow and continuity. Fuzzy, woolly feeling in head. Mind blank when concentrating. Unable to think of more than one thing at a time. The current thought excludes all others. I often forget what I am doing and am easily sidetracked. [androc][srj5] When thinking of the one, or of any business, he forgets everything else, and on account of this he neglects much that is necessary. [tell][a1] Feel lost, fragmented, confused, over focused on one thing. [urol-h][rwt3]

However, without this intense concentration it is almost impossible for the subject to compose his or her thoughts. Often a patient asks me one question after another, never waiting to have the first one answered, a flitting, flighty talker, who does not seem to realize that I have not answered his questions, that patient, I say to myself, needs Ambra grisea. That state of mind belongs to modern society women in such great frequency that you will be astonished to note it on all hands. [ambr][k2] Confusion of ideas, with sensation as if in a constant delirium. [cur][a1] The thoughts are disconnected and unfixed. [cur][a1]

A sequential train of thought is not possible in the modern, electronic world, it is a mode of thinking adapted to the industrial age and it is an issue in contemporary disease. He was not able to reflect upon anything properly; he feels stupid. [ambr][a1] Every kind of intellectual labour is difficult for him, like a kind of absent-mindedness. [anac][a1] Anhalonium seems to paralyze the logical mind, the individual's ability to think in a logical manner, and to create vivid visions of new dimensions in time and space. It appears as if its initial effect is to break down the usual concept of time and space, replacing it with an entirely novel experience. Time seems prolonged, space disintegrated. The patient mistakes localities, makes mistakes in space and time; he loses his conception of time, the present seeming to merge with eternity. [anh][vh1] Talking nonsense while asleep at night; on a waking, he talks unconnectedly. [cact][a1] My left brain seems to have gone on holiday. [lsd][nl-lsd] Only after having answered does she reflect whether the answer was suitable. [plat][a1] Dullness of mind, unable to appreciate things, lack precision. [polys][sk4]

If a train of thought is difficult then a conclusion often becomes impossible. I've noticed that my memory is confused. I don't seem to come to the point. I forget what certain things are called. It's frustrating. [adam][srj5] The ability to make conclusions is lost. [anh][sp1] Difficult to make a decision. [germ-met][srj5] It is difficult to describe the symptoms. Want to correct myself all the time. [germ-met][srj5] Inability to solve mental tasks. [gink-b][mp4] Is impressed with the idea that all she says is a lie; that all her symptoms are unreal, and the result of a diseased imagination; it seems to be very difficult to speak the truth, but continually distrusts things; when reading anything she rapidly changes the meaning, omitting or adding things. [lac-c][c1] Difficulty making decisions. Had to go back and forth, going somewhere and not sure what to wear. Went out the door with two different shoes on. I could not decide; forgot I was making the decision and realized I had two different shoes on. Normal, everyday, simple decisions were hard. [lac-lup][hrn2] I have no answers any more. All is soft and unformed. No plans and no ultimatums. [positr][nl2] Can't judge state – nothing to gauge it by. [positr][nl2]

VII-2 Confusion of the Senses

The confusion is found in the senses which become unreliable. Hallucinations are found not just in the psychedelic drug remedies such as Mescaline and LSD. Audio-visual hallucinations. [anh][jl1] Optical hallucinations: at one moment perception of all objects, and then only of certain objects. [anh][jl1] The chief feature of the drug's action is the production of coloured visions of most over-powering brilliancy, associated with moving shapes of fantastic design, the motion being regulated somewhat in time by music. [anh][c1] But in many others as well. Distorted images, grimaces, diabolical faces crowd upon his fancy; he cannot get rid of them. [ambr][a1] On going upstairs, all colours seemed incredibly bright and the walls were pulsating in towards him and out again. This felt similar to an LSD experience years ago. [androc][srj5] Delirium with hallucinations, excitability, mumbling. [conv-s][jl1] Feel on the verge of hallucinating, of things disintegrating but not scared. [falco-pe][nl2] Illusions of vision: objects appear too distant, too large, or too small. [nux-m][c1] Sees two objects instead of one. [nux-m][c1] One characteristic symptom, either when found alone or in association with other conditions, has led to many cures with Plat. – lost sense of proportion in both ocular and mental vision. [plat][c1]

Likewise there is confusion about what is being sensed and which quality and sense organs are involved. Again synaesthesia is a feature of the drug remedies, Noises and touch are perceived through coloured vision. [anh][jl1] A unique symptom was green experienced as a metallic taste; also, two dimensional objects appear multidimensional. [anh][sp1] Heard the noise of colours, green, red, blue, and yellow sounds coming to him in perfectly distinct waves, the sensations it produced were those, physically, of exquisite lightness and airiness. [cann-i][a1] See the colours of people speaking. [lsd][nl-lsd] Then I started to taste the colours. [lsd][nl-lsd] It was a doorway into places I am certain I dreamt about in my childhood, crystal dimensions, where I could taste colours and touch sounds and smells with my hands from the very first trip on. [lsd][nl-lsd] But is also found in others. Strong sense of smell. And liked it, a way of connecting. Could almost take the place of ideas. [limen-b-c][hrn2] The fly is capable of tasting with its legs as it walks over the surface of potential food. [musca-d][stew+] I see sound waves from speakers. I feel them in my head like a bat, especially in the bones of my face. [plut-n][srj7]

VII-3 Vanishing of Thoughts

Just as there are problems sorting and making sense of thoughts in an unbounded world; there is nothing to contain thoughts and they have tendency to just vanish. Now, when this man undertakes to meditate upon something his ideas are whisked away. [ambr][k2] The mind is much confused, as if a cold were coming on. Thoughts vanish. [anac][a1] Thoughts followed one another through my head in most rapid succession; they were very vivid, but were forgotten immediately, at their very beginning. [cann-i][a1] He wished to write down his symptoms, but he had to give up the attend on account of the wandering of his thoughts. [cann-i][a1] Racing thoughts – difficulty in holding concentration. [mdma][hmd1] Loss of concentration. Lost my thoughts while driving, nearly causing two accidents. [germ-met][srj5] Blank mind on waking, no idea of what there is to do today. Woke up disorientated. [heroin][sdj-h] All day my mind felt absent. When people spoke to me I thought I understood them but my replies indicated to them that I hadn't, but I was replying to what I thought I had heard. [latex][nl-latex] Sudden loss of his senses. [mosch][a1] She goes about the house performing her duties, but if interrupted, forgets what she has been doing, forgets that she was all day in conversation with her son; she has no recollection of past events. [nux-m][k2] Difficulty in holding thoughts together, overall view gets lost. [ozone][sde2] She is constantly absent-minded, without knowing where her thoughts are. [plat][a1] I was thickheaded; kept forgetting what I wanted to say just before I said it. [plut-n][srj7] Loss of thought; it seems as though he were thinking, yet he has no thoughts. [rhus-t][a1] Loss of senses, as if he could not grasp any thought, with headache. [phos][a1] I kept finding myself/my thoughts wandering and coming back again to find I wasn't quite sure what the teacher was talking about. [vacuum][es-vac]

As in many areas, water metaphors are used. Concentration comes and goes. "Like water," I said thinking of waves. [irid-met][srj5] (*See Water IV-3*)

This description from one of the Neon provers is particularly apt. A phrase from a Lewis Carroll poem repeated itself over and over in my mind: "Come tell me aged man he cried, come tell me how you live. / And his answer trickled through my brain like water through a sieve." I felt this was about dissolving, which related to my feeling in the proving. [neon][srj5]

Flying and air metaphors are also used. Lack of concentration. Thoughts fly. [choc][srj3] (*See Floating & Flying IV-8*)

And in LSD water and air metaphors become mixed. My mind feels like it's freewheeling – spinning with thoughts which I can't stop from buzzing through my mind – feels as if there's no resistance. Thoughts just pour through so – feels like my mind could just fly off into outer space. [lsd][nl-lsd]

VII-4 Forgetfulness

General forgetfulness is a major symptom of most of the new remedies. Could not perform her daily routines. Could not remember her appointments. [androc][srj5] Diminished memory. [ars][a1] From having had a remarkably good memory, she lost her memory completely. [ars][a1] Loss of memory of what had been saying previously. [berlin-w][evans] Forgetfulness and must write things down. [carbn-dox][knl3] On three separate occasions today, I put something down and then couldn't find it. [choc][srj3] Loss of memory and prostration. [conv-s][jl1] Forgot my glasses at home, which I have never done before. [haliae-lc][srj5] Forget where I put things. Forget to take things with me. Don't remember whether I have locked the car or not. [germ-met][srj5] Absent-minded and forgetful. [gink-b][mp4] Loss of memory. [gink-b][mp4] Forgot what I was going to do. Forgetting what I had gone into a room to get. [irid-met][srj5] Real problems with memory; forgot I had already been given the case I'd asked for. Forgot I was supposed to be looking after a friend's baby. [irid-met][srj5] Very forgetful, absent-minded; makes purchases and walks away without them. [lac-c][al2] Left purse at restaurant, very unusual. [lac-lup][hrn2] Forgetful all day.

[latex][nl-latex] The preserved nuts, if eaten too frequently, destroy the memory. [nux-m][a1] Difficult memory, can't remember names or what she was going to say. [oncor-t][srj-case] Forget a lot; can't memorize the simplest things. [ozone][sde2] Forgetful, could not recollect what had happened in the morning, whether I had eaten breakfast or not. [polys][sk4] Marked forgetfulness, with increase of the headache (after eight hours); more marked (second day); more forgetful than before the proving, [ptel][a1] Oh yeah, I completely forgot an appointment; I was going to meet someone and I just didn't go, which is very unlike me, although I have to say that recently I'm forgetting more than I used to, and that's very disconcerting. [sanguis-s][hrn2] Memory is very dull; he can with difficulty recall things and names. [rhus-t][a1] Forgetful, forgot where I put my keys, my glasses. [sal-fr][sle1] Lost two important pieces of paper. No idea where I put them. [sal-fr][sle1] Forgetful of everything: what I am about to do, write, what I just thought of. [galeoc-c-h][gms1] I can't remember simple things from yesterday. [vacuum][es-vac]

In the AIDS Nosode the feeling that the subject has forgotten something is perhaps more important than the reality. Lethargy and confusion – feels that she has forgotten something, or to do something. [aids][nl2] Continually sensing that I have forgotten something or forgotten to do something. [aids][nl2] This is also found in Vacuum. A feeling like I've forgotten something, haven't grasped the full picture. [vacuum][es-vac]

The usual term for such a symptom is "loss" of memory, but in several remedies it was put more strongly, that memory was "gone" or "non-existent". My memory feels totally non-existent, I can't remember things from second to second, let alone from day to day. [falco-pe][nl2] My memory has gone. I can't remember a phone number. [irid-met][srj5] My memory is totally gone. [agath-a][nl2]

Although it is only explicitly described in Scorpion, Memory very poor for recent events. Long-term memory unaffected. [androc][srj5] the memory that is affected is usually for recent events rather than for the long term. This is similarly the most common symptom in some modern diseases such as Alzheimer's.

Selenium has the peculiar symptom that what is forgotten in the day is remembered in the evening or in dreams. Very forgetful, especially about business, but when lying half asleep everything recurs to him. [sel][a1]

Often such forgetfulness makes the subject feel foolish or stupid. Unable to remember things; feel foolish. [coca-c][sk4] Forgetful and stupid, so that he did something quite different from what he wished. [phos][a1]

VII-5 Confusion of Identity

The most fundamental of all forms of confusion must be as to who we are, and this is perhaps the most frightening feature of the AIDS Miasm. Lost all sense of identity – didn't know who I was, found this experience very frightening, I burst into tears. [aids][nl2]

It is a feature of the hallucinogenic drugs, and the one that most often causes terror in both Mescaline and LSD. Depersonalization – does not know his identity. [anh][jl1] Loss of egocentricity. [anh][sp1] I feel lost, I've lost myself. [lsd][nl-lsd] My sense of self is slipping through my fingers. I feel lonely and isolated within and without. [lsd][nl-lsd]

It is also found in Agnus castus where it causes despair. He sometimes feels as if he were nobody, and would rather be dead than have that feeling. [agn][a1]

In Anacardium the feeling is externalized and it is the identity of family members that becomes confused. Delusion her husband is not her husband, her child is not hers. [anac][c1] One moment she sees it is her child and another that it is not. [anac][k2]

In Lac caninum the feelings of self loathing lead to delusions of identity. Imagines she is not herself and her properties not her own. [lac-c][k2] Delusion he is someone else. [lac-c][lrp1] Mistakes his own identity. [lac-c][lrp1] The Chinese link the nose to issues of social status, which perhaps explains the peculiar symptom: Imagines he wears someone else's nose. [lac-c][c1]

Wolf's milk also has concerns about identity but they are not as strong as in its domesticated cousin. Dream: Standing waist-high in clear water, with another man, my wallet had dropped to bottom of pool. I was freaked out that I lost my wallet – not sure if it was about the loss of money or the loss of my identity – but then I found it and picked it up and started to dry it. Felt detached and didn't care that it was wet. [lac-lup][hrn2]

The issue of personal identity is particularly strong in Eagle where it is manifest in several ways. As well as general confusion, Am I hot or cold? I don't know, I think it's kind of warm heat I'm feeling. Who is writing this anyway? [haliae-lc][srj5] there is fragmentation of the personality. The remedy worked very directly on my will. Fragmentation is the denial of will. Integration is the use of will. All separate states under a unified country. [haliae-lc][srj5] There can also be a loss of the boundaries between the subject and other people which results in the subject identifying with whoever he happens to be with. Unconsciously, I have taken on the characteristics of the speech of a guy I work with; an actual copying of a certain vernacular.

When he talks, he stretches a word. I don't do it consciously, but when it happens, I'm aware I've adopted a small part of that personality. The way he gestures, the way he uses his teeth – enunciates – the gestures of his language. I feel I'm malleable. I don't like it. It feels like I don't have my own personality, no true identity. In fact I might even believe that. I'm more outward with actual copying. It's something I like in him, so when I do it, it makes me feel good about myself. I realize it then try to combat it. I don't want to be like a piece of clay that can be pressed this way and that way. [haliae-lc][srj5] When I was alone in my apartment with the lights on, I manifested many fragmented personalities, probably around five or six. Never did before like this. What was different was nobody was in the room to make a chain reaction. I was alone. Needed no provocation to make a change, or experience a change. I talk out loud, and talk to the person in a number of different ways. Fearful Joe, Vindictive Joe, One That's Just Like Someone Else Joe – each will act out in a number of different ways. [haliae-lc][srj5]

This effect is also seen in Plutonium The prover felt clearly that he changed identity depending on where he was and whom he was with. [plut-n][vml3] (*See Empathy & Clairvoyance I-5*)

Confusion of identity can be non specific. Concerned I am not myself. [adam][srj5] Dreamt about clothes – people changing their clothes/identity. [latex][nl-latex] Confusion as to his identity. [pyrus][vml4] Confusion of identity. [plac][Biggs+] Do not feel integrated into myself – as if I am a blurred image of myself. [sal-fr][sle1] Dream: As long as I keep answering the phone, "Hello, this is me." I will find out what I want to know. I will find my identity. All the different identities will be exposed. Identities are sides of myself. The feeling is that I would be exposed to different sides of myself. [galeoc-c-h][gms1] I have almost felt as if my values were so strangely shifted out of kilter. It is as if a liar has set up shop at my house. [vacuum][es-vac]

There is often a feeling that the subject is not himself. His voice seems strange, as if not his own. [cann-i][a1] When I look in the mirror, I don't recognise myself. I look different, especially around and over the eyes – my face doesn't seem familiar. [choc][srj3] Had a feeling when walking into a friend's house that it wasn't me in my body – it was someone I didn't know – didn't feel familiar somehow. [ignis-alc][es2] Eyes looked as if didn't belong to her, almost as if there wasn't anybody there. [irid-met][srj5] Feel I looked weird but when I looked in the mirror I looked normal. [lac-h][htj1] My stomach seems almost unreal, as if it's not really mine. I look at it and it looks alien to me, as if it's someone else's. [plut-n][srj7] Feels strange and singular in his whole body, but cannot describe the sensation. [tell][a1] I feel next to myself –

not really me. [tung-met][bdx1]

But it can also be related to other features of the Miasm, such as separation. **I feel as if I am separated from myself. [ozone][sde2] I have felt a certain isolation from the realities of my actions, like looking at what I am doing from this detached place of non responsibility. It has wreaked havoc on my sense of self. [vacuum][es-vac]** *(See Detachment II-4)*

Or splitting. **Nux m. is one of the most profoundly active of psychical remedies in the Materia Medica, producing states of exaltation resembling hysteria, and the mesmeric state with exalted senses and consciousness of double personality. [nux-m][c1]** *(See Splitting V-4)*

In Hydrogen the most important identity confusion is sexual. **Confusion of identity (especially concerning sex and homosexuality) and became more religious. [hydrog][srj2]** This is also a major issue in the Housefly. **There was confusion of sexual identity. [musca-d][stew+]** *(See Sexual Confusion VIII-4)*

Jealousy is a feature of several new remedies. **Ungovernable jealousy, everything causes jealousy. [anan][a1] I am fidgety and angry and very jealous of people. [adam][srj5] It was a custom for rejected lovers to wear willow in their hats, to attract new love to them and to protect them from jealous thoughts about their lost love. [sal-fr][sle1]**

Jealousy is of course a feature of many other remedies, however, in the AIDS Miasm it does seem to come from a different place. In the Hydrophobic Miasm, as exemplified by Hyoscymus, the fear is that the person you have will be lost to you, that someone else will take him or her, the consequences are much less important than the immediate feeling of loss and betrayal. In the Sycotic Miasm the feeling is similar but goes a little further because the consequences are recognized. In, say Pulsatilla, there is jealousy because the loss of love would not only represent the loss of the loved one but also the loss of security and material benefit that he or she provided. In the snake remedies, where jealousy is best known, the feeling is that the loss would not be of just the person, or even of the security and benefits, but the loss would represent a victory for someone else and so a defeat in the competition that is life. The pain of being beaten is almost more important than the physical loss. In the AIDS Miasm the boundary between what is mine and what is not becomes tenuous, resulting in an equally tenuous hold on the things that are ours. There is a deep insecurity that they may drift out of our possession. Even more terrifying is the feeling that this tenuous hold applies even to our selves and our identities. At anytime someone might appear who will take not just what we have but in the process might also take our very identities.

There is in the LSD proving a story that illustrates this form of jealousy particularly well. Feeling intolerant of a friend who has come to stay, feel she's dishonest because she is so nice. This is bothering me a lot more than it ever has done before. This friend is due to arrive tomorrow. When ever I think of her arrival I am convinced that she will want to borrow a favourite dress of mine which is purple. I get madder and madder at the thought of it, especially as she is seven months pregnant and it will not fit her. I decide to ring her up and remind her that one of the evenings we will be circle dancing and suggest that she brings a dress! I go and meet my friend from the station, she has had her luggage stolen! This means that for the entire visit of 5 days I have to lend her my clothes, even my knickers! I don't lend her my purple dress! I also have to lend her paper, pens, a bag, toiletries etc. I start to wonder who has manifested what? I decide that I haven't created the theft of her bag, rather that I tuned into the theft unconsciously and it filtered through me as I'm not lending her that... Of course, I could be entirely mistaken. Feel that I need to watch my thoughts. My friend comes into the kitchen dressed in my clothes and says to my partner 'There seem to be two Genevieves now'. I am really pissed off with her, think she is making a direct suggestion that she could replace me. [lsd][nl-lsd]

VII-6 Transgenic Confusion

In the electronic age even the boundaries between species have started to dissolve. AIDS itself seems to have originated in a transgenic leap from African primates. The great apes have been shown to be virtually identical to ourselves with barely one percent DNA difference between humans and some species. This leads us to question the difference between us and them. The once unfathomable gulf between humans and animals has almost vanished.

Genetic engineering itself is one of the new sciences of the electronic age. It has allowed the transfer of features freely from one species to another.

HIV is a retrovirus that employs the host's genetic process to do the work of reproducing it. In HIV infection the virus enters T4 cells in the blood. Once inside the cell the virus releases an enzyme, reverse transcriptase, which causes small pieces of RNA in the virus to produce a relatively short length of DNA. This piece of DNA becomes part of the infected cell's genome and starts producing RNA which will in turn become part of a new virus. In this process the host T4 cell, a leukocyte which has an important role in the working of the immune system, is destroyed and the whole system is severely compromised. [aids][nl2]

Retroviruses are also the mechanism used by genetic engineers to splice the new gene into the chromosome of the host.

Two of the new remedies, the Raven and the Wolf, have an extraordinary ability to communicate. Lawrence further discusses another special feature of wolf vocalizing, which involves the wolf's distinctive relationship with the raven. The raven's caw alerts the wolf that there is a herd or weak animal nearby. The wolf then makes the kill, and the raven comes in for his share of the meat. In mutual celebration, both raven and wolf sing together in a song that Lawrence calls haunting, spiritual, and primitive. [hrn2]

Man also often feels that he can communicate with certain animals, particularly the Horse, the Dog, the Dolphin and the Falcon. Dreamt of a dog speaking to me about his problems. [aids][nl2] Humans and dolphins have an ancient connection. From stories such as those about the mystery temple at Delphi – Greek for "dolphin" – where the oracle gave people spiritual messages, to the mariner legends of the "singing mermaids" – thought to be dolphins – who lured and enchanted sailors, we continue to be intrigued by this winsome creature with the smiling face. [lac-del][hrn2]

These same animals are often regarded as the bridge to the other world. (*See Portals XII-6*)

Several remedies have transgenic or half human half animal dreams. Half animal half human in dreams. [helodr-cal][knl2] They can have dreams about half animals-half humans, the upper half being like a dog, the lower half being a fish. They dream about creatures that emerge from the water and then disappear down into the water again. We might associate these with mythological figures like mermaids or centaurs. But it also reminds us of the possible results of genetic manipulation. [plut-n][vml3] Dream: Sleeping in a forest with a man who becomes a raccoon who is playful with me. [urol-h][rwt3]

One of the strongest features of many remedies is an increased desire for meat. This is undoubtedly partly connected to the fact that many of the remedy substances are at the top of the food chain: the Eagle, the Falcon, the Lion, the Dolphin, the Shark and the Rat. I look at rabbits and birds in a different light. Wondering how a rabbit would taste raw. What would the fur taste like? [haliae-lc][srj5] I had raw food for a few days, because when I cook I burn things. I don't want to cook really anyway. [haliae-lc][srj5] Dream: I gave a small animal to a man to eat, it was still alive. Then I wished I had not as the man was so cruel to it. [falco-pe][nl2] Started craving meat, haven't done that in years. [sanguis-s][hrn2]

However, this symptom is found in other remedies. Strong desire for rare meat. [adam][srj5] Desire for meat. [ara-mac][sej7] Eating more meat and feeling OK about it, previously had been vegetarian for health and moral reasons. [choc][srj3] I ate chicken. I'm a vegetarian and usually averse to chicken. First time in six years that I had meat other than fish! [maias-l][hrn2] Desire for raw meat. [plut-n][srj7] Dream: I'm eating meat and enjoying it. [rhus-g][tmo3]

Arsenicum seems to fill a need that is usually met by eating meat. According to Teste Arsenicum "acts much more powerfully on vegetable-eating animals than on carnivora. [ars][c1] It strengthens the muscles," an old indulger in the habit is reported to have said, "helps to digest our coarse bread and potatoes, and allows us to breathe freely and easily. [ars][c1] Meat-eaters have no need for such a thing, but with us it is a necessity". [ars][c1]

There is also the polar aversion to meat. Averse meat. [helo-s][rwt2] Husband wanting Sunday lunch. I felt a strong aversion to eating meat. [sal-fr][sle1]

There can be a disgust at eating meat which is expressed in dreams of eating disgusting things. This ties in with the other symptoms about dirt and disgust. Dream of a picnic with lots of traditional food that was seen as a joke, cleared away and the real food brought on – a corpse and other revolting edibles instead. I was revolted but not totally surprised. [falco-pe][nl2] Went round Tesco's tonight, had to get away from the meat counter because something smelt so strong. It was a disgusting smell – just had a whiff – it could have made me feel sick, was really strong. [falco-pe][nl2] Revolting dream of ordering crepes with baby rabbits and kittens inside. The tiny animals were whole and live in tomato sauce, but only moving a little. I managed to finish my plateful as it tasted good, but it revolted me and I was relieved to finish, but my horror returned when my friend came in with a plate of the same which I had to help her eat. My revulsion became worse when one of the kittens clung to my hand. This dream occurred after feeling self-conscious about eating meat-filled crepes the previous night. [hydrog][srj2] Dreamt of disgusting meat, offal and brains. [plut-n][srj7] (*See Dirt X-3*)

Sherr attributes this feature in Chocolate to the fact that it contains a significant proportion of cockroach parts. I wanted to eat beetles, big black ones, this morning. Desired the crunch as when you eat celery. It surprised me. [choc][srj3] Wanted to eat slugs and grasshoppers. I could feel how they would be in my mouth while they were still alive and wriggling. (Has been vegetarian for twenty years). [choc][srj3]

However, it is found in many more remedies and Shore's explanation would seem to be more widely applicable. The predator and prey are one. Most animals don't kill unnecessarily as it is so painful for them. [sej-birds] It ties in with the guilt that often accompanies the desire for meat. Guilty conscience on slaughtering a ram. I have a pitch black conscience that I am having the animal slaughtered. [ozone][sde2]

BSE/CJD is another supposedly transgenic disease and though it, and Alzheimer's, may be part of another miasm, it is certainly connected to the AIDS Miasm. Horrific dream about sick cows wasting away with a sort of "cattle aids". I had an awful, sinking, helpless, end-of-the-world feeling. [hydrog][srj2] The description of calves fed with chocolate indicate that it might be an important remedy for these diseases. Chocolate Poisoning. The feeding of waste chocolate bars to cattle has led to fatal poisoning in calves in the UK. The animals showed excitement, stared about in all directions, walked with exaggerated strides, and had convulsions. [choc][srj3]

VII-7 Confusion about Time

One of the most significant features of the electronic age is the alteration in our perception of time. Electronic things happen instantaneously. The instant, the present, becomes disconnected from other instants, from the past and from the future. Just as sequential, rational thought is no longer applicable in the electronic age, so a sequential approach to time can no longer be taken for granted.

This is very clearly expressed in the Eagle. Had no sensation of how much time went by, five minutes or an hour. [haliae-lc][srj5] Time is very slowed down. I'm in the moment. [haliae-lc][srj5] In retrospect, over the last few days, it seems as if the past and the future have collapsed into the present. The past was unimportant, and I don't concern myself over the future. [haliae-lc][srj5] It feels like it's been at least two weeks since starting proving. (It's only been 10 days.) [haliae-lc][srj5] Sitting down watching things pass you by. Time is a factor. You only have a certain amount of time to get there. After a certain time you've blocked yourself from the opportunity to have made a move. [haliae-lc][srj5] AlsoHydrogen. Time sense seems warped. [hydrog][srj2] I looked at the clock. I think it was about an hour clock time. Time is different on this level, its moving very quickly. [hydrog][srj2] My whole time scale has changed since taking the remedy, I've lost a lot of boundaries on time. Don't hurry, just do things in my own time. [hydrog][srj2] It seems as if all the days became one. [hydrog][srj2]

In other remedies there is an awareness of a fundamental shift or distortion in time. Change in perception of time. [ara-mac][sej7] Time seems interminable, space illimitable. [cann-i][c1] Feeling that the time isn't right. [choc][srj3] Time either goes fast or slow, it feels a bit warped. [irid-met][srj5] Everything is changed; distortion of time. [phasco-ci][rbp2] The main feeling of the last two weeks has been one of being intermittently spaced out. It is neither pleasant nor unpleasant. It is kind of like being in a time warp because my perception of time changes, slows down incredibly. [lac-loxod-a][hrn2] Sense of time seems altered. [lsd][nl-lsd] Sense of time still feels very distorted. I don't really have any idea what time it is – nor do I really care. [lsd][nl-lsd] Time distortion – The day is endless and timeless, no structure. [lsd][nl-lsd] I had a sense of timelessness and wanted to find the clock but could not. I had no reference points and thought that if I could find the time, it would be a reference point in the void. [neon][srj5] Distortion of sensation of time. [ozone][sde2] The positron is mathematically best described as an electron moving backwards through time. Although this concept is fundamental to Feynman's Quantum Electro Dynamics, it is something that even quantum physicists have trouble getting their heads around. [positr][nl2] Confusion of time, missed meeting. [plac][Biggs+] I have a time machine and can travel through time. [rhus-g][tmo3] The feeling that they are running out of time (dreams of a time bomb in his room), there is a need to hurry, and distortions of time sense. [rhus-g][tmo3] Confusion around time. Like an alien abduction you go off the time space continuum and lose no time during the experience. [galeoc-c-h][gms1] Thought it was morning, I was waiting to rise. Time seems slow. Did the clock stop? Not wanting to believe the clock. [galeoc-c-h][gms1] Notice that time seems meaningless. Realise that 30 years ago, I couldn't imagine being where I am now or my life now. But now I am here and the rest is irrelevant. Its like everything is happening now. [vacuum][es-vac]

The most common symptom is that time passes too fast or too slowly. This is very common in the drug remedies. Loss of sense of time. [anh][jl1] Time seems long; intervals between words and sentences seem inordinately long. [anh][c1] There is an exaggeration of time – it passes too slowly. [anh][vh1] Extreme exaggerations of the duration of time and extent of space – a few second seem ages – the utterance of a word seems as long as a whole drama, and a few rods are a distance which can never be passed, it is so great. [cann-i][a1] Attention principally occupied by an hallucination that time was indefinitely prolonged. [cann-i][a1] Minutes seem to be days. [cann-i][a1] The most commonly noted effects included losing track of time, [mdma][saunders] 90% experienced altered time perception (speeded up or slowed down) [Leister][mdma][saunders] Loss of sense of time. [lsd][nl-lsd] Time feels like it's slowed down – I keep expecting it to be hours later in the day than it is. [lsd][nl-lsd]

And is found in many others as well. Time has gone very quickly. [aids][nl2] Feeling of time passing slowly. I kept thinking it was earlier than it was. [adam][srj5] Great difference between the thought of how long it will take and actuality. Thought much longer than actuality. [adam][srj5] Time seemed to go slowly. [androc][srj5] Time passed very slowly. [cere-b][a1] Sensation of time passing too slowly. 15 minutes feels more like an hour. [corian-s][knl6] My sense of time is slightly confused in that I can't quite tell whether it's morning or evening. [corv-cor][bdg1] Sensation that time is passing quite slowly. [dream-p][sdj1] Arrived for appointment one hour early. [germ-met][srj5] Ten minutes seemed like an hour. Time seemed to pass slowly. [germ-met][srj5] Time goes too fast. I'm late for tutorial by half an hour, not like me. [irid-met][srj5] Am realizing that time is passing very quickly. Thursday now, and Monday seems only yesterday. [irid-met][srj5] All afternoon it felt as if time was spinning by. [irid-met][srj5] I feel slow and down and far away. [irid-met][srj5] Time seems to have gone extremely slowly; it feels like weeks have passed since proving started. [irid-met][srj5] Time seemed to have flown. [latex][nl-latex] Time seems to pass very slowly. [latex][nl-latex] Disturbances of time – feeling of slowness. [galla-q-r][nl2] Things go too slowly. [galla-q-r][nl2] Time – dragging or rushing. [galla-q-r][nl2] Time passes too quickly. [polys][sk4] Sense of time is weird, the days seem long. I feel like it's so long ago since yesterday. [rhus-g][tmo3] I want to hurry up as if I have no time and a lot to do. [rhus-g][tmo3] When I got to the car, I had only been there for about ten minutes. I thought I had been there for at least a half hour. [sanguis-s][hrn2] Time, passes too quickly, appears shorter [visc][vml3] Aware of time, usually very hurried, has slowed down. [tung-met][bdx1]

The new understanding of time can be liberating. I do seem much slower than my usual pace. I feel like I've more time. [aids][nl2] Should have gone to work today but thought it was tomorrow. Didn't care much. [sal-fr][sle1]

However, it can cause feelings of panic, Woke up disoriented. Mad panic about time thought I was late for work. [sal-fr][sle1] obsession, Obsessed with how long everything would take, even things where this wasn't really appropriate at all. Someone might do a doodle or write a list of things to do and I'd ask how long it took to do it. [falco-pe][nl2] or frustration. Felt quick and was frustrated at the slowness of others. [irid-met][srj5]

VII-8 Confusion about Position

In an unbounded world it is difficult to define position accurately. One place merges into the next without demarcation and so it becomes impossible to say exactly where you are. This was particularly strong in Neon. Shortly after taking the remedy, I was confused about where I was. [neon][srj5] I'm not here, miles away. [neon][srj5] Three incidences of a miscalculation of where I was in space. I tripped twice going upstairs and once fell over from a standing position on cross-country skis. I don't quite seem to know where my body is in space. [neon][srj5]

The expansion of immediate space so that it encompasses all space and its corollary that all space is immediate space is a common feature of the remedies, particularly the hallucinogens LSD, Mescaline and Cannabis. Decomposition of shapes [anh][sp1] Decomposition of space [anh][sp1] Deformation of all objects. [anh][sp1] Extreme exaggerations of the duration of time and extent of space – a few second seem ages – the utterance of a word seems as long as a whole drama, and a few rods are a distance which can never be passed, it is so great. [cann-i][a1] The room expands, and those around the centre-table near recede to vast distances, and the ceiling is raised, and he is in a vast hall. [cann-i][a1] Time seems interminable, space illimitable. [cann-i][c1]

Confusion as to the left and the right sides of the subject is common. The left and right sides have definite gender identification and their confusion is inextricably linked to gender confusion. Confused between left and right in recording symptoms. [germ-met][srj5] Confuses left and right. [hydrog][srj2] I am confusing my left and right sides. I was describing the pain in my eye cavity and said that it was my left. [agath-a][nl2] Whilst talking to my supervisor, I was getting my left and right sides confused. [plut-n][srj7] For the first time ever I do not have any confusion about the sides of my body. [vacuum][es-vac] (*See Gender Confusion VIII-4*)

There is also confusion as to up and down. When I close my eyes, don't know which direction I'm facing, or even whether up or down, didn't know where I was. [irid-met][srj5] Seconds of complete disorientation. Like being spun upside-down and round and round. Not sure which way is up just for a few seconds at a time. Lasted about 30 mins on and off. [latex][nl-latex] I feel as if perhaps I am the wrong way up. [plut-n][srj7]

In Anacardium the symptom: He imagines he hears his name called by the voice of his far-distant mother and sister. [anac][a1] reflects how the feeling of being able to connect with people has the effect of distorting space. (*See Communication I-4*)

In the electronic age the rules of cause and effect and sequential connection break down. The same thing is not necessarily the same in different circumstances. This effect is most commonly seen across different places in time, but it can also appear across different places in space. Different species in different areas can vary in toxicity. For example Buthus Occitanus gives a fatal sting in North Africa but is quite harmless in France. [androc][srj5] A similar effect may lie behind the confusion between the different types of Gila Monster (suspectum and horridum).

It has been shown that susceptibility to Heroin is dependent on the familiarity of the place where it is taken. In mice that are habituated to receiving heroin in a particular environment the normal dose becomes fatal when given in an unfamiliar setting. Many fatal overdoses in addicts occur when they take the drug away from the place that they are used to taking it.

The confusion of the senses can also result in a changed perception of space and time as is apparent in this Diamond symptom. Dream: By listening rather than looking I could tell where I was going. My hearing seemed enhanced for spatial things. [adam][srj5]

One of the main manifestations of confusion about where the subject is in space is a general clumsiness and a tendency to bump into things. A bit clumsy, tendency to drop things, bump into things. [neon][srj5] I nearly killed us twice driving which is not really like me. I can be a bit day dreamy and vague but I am not normally that stupid whilst driving. I was misjudging distance and speed. [sal-fr][sle1] Clumsy. Knocked over three cups of tea. [androc][srj5] Started to feel the floor moving, undulating, disorienting under my feet. Almost fell because of this. [coca-c][sk4] Have found myself becoming extremely clumsy. I am constantly walking into things and dropping things. [falco-pe][nl2] Accident prone at work because of not thinking about what I am doing. [germ-met][srj5] Clumsy awkward, knocked over tea. [germ-met][srj5] Notice I'm dropping things at school. Piles of paper, walking into things and kids. [heroin][sdj-h] Was so clumsy dropping and breaking things. [ara-mac][sej7] Full of nervous energy. Lots of clumsy accidents today. [latex][nl-latex] When dancing I made lots of mistakes with steps, couldn't get into the rhythm of the music. All seemed like too much hard work. Couldn't connect. Glad when we finished. [latex][nl-latex] There was an awkwardness in the extremities. [musca-d][stew+] Clumsy and knocked things over more than usual. [hydrog][srj2] Have noticed a difference in my spatial awareness. Am misjudging distances when driving not to a dangerous degree. Keep bumping into things and people in the house and street. [irid-met][srj5] I'm clumsy, I knocked over two cups of tea today. [agath-a][nl2] She became very awkward. Fell three times in 15 minutes for no reason. Stumbles. She was dropping things that she picked up, and stumbling. [lac-del][hrn2] Awkward, broke a pot in a store. Clumsy, lost contact lens down the drain. [lac-leo][hrn2] Clumsy and have noticed that I am having a hard time doing more than one thing at a time. [lac-loxod-a][hrn2] Klutzy, tripping over things, dropping things. Dropped baking soda into garlic, broke Christmas ornament. [lac-lup][hrn2] Awkward; dropping, toppling, breaking things. [polys][sk4] Very clumsy (even more than usual!) – stood on people, walked into things, etc. [positr][nl2] Coordination bad – keep walking into things. [positr][nl2] Walking around I could not judge distances. The floor seemed too far away. I felt like I would not have been able to walk successfully through a shop full of china and glass without knocking them over. [sal-fr][sle1]

This sensation can be associated with lightness. Felt light, I don't quite seem to know where my body is in space, tripping and falling. [neon][srj5] *(See Floating & Flying IV-8)*

It can even come across in dreams. Dreams of clumsiness and mishaps. [ozone][sde2]

There is also a lack of understanding as to exactly where the body is and how the different parts of the body relate to each other. I'm ripping all my clothes. I'm so much fatter that I'm not aware of my width, and I'm catching on things. [haliae-lc][srj5]

The effect of this is a lack of coordination. Motor incoordination. [anh][c1] Had noticeable ill-luck in performing accurately when he undertook anything requiring precision. [cact][a1] My hands feel more powerful, but less co-ordinated, especially for fine work. [choc][srj3] Incoordinated, feel heavy and slow – almost like flu. Feel feverish, but no fever. [choc][srj3] Movements diminished from want of co-ordination. [cocain][a1] Knocked a cup of tea off the side unit in a pretty sudden and surprising way! [latex][nl-latex] Have noticed that all day whilst using computer I keep pressing the wrong keys, misspelling words. Feel uncoordinated. [lsd][nl-lsd]

Also a tendency to drop things. In handling things she drops them. [agar][k2] When lifting anything, fear lest I should let it fall. [coca][a1] I was in a store and dropped something and couldn't quite get the jelly beans out of the container with the scoop. Paid for them and realized I was still holding the scoop. I felt very "spacey" and my head kind of heavy. Afraid that I will make a foolish mistake that could hurt someone. [corian-s][knl6] Clumsy, dropping things, spilling my lunch on my blouse several times. [haliae-lc][srj5] I've been clumsy tonight, dropping things, they just seem to slip through my fingers. Remember I kept knocking into people today. [heroin][sdj-h] Dropping things all morning, coffee, money, pens. [latex][nl-latex] Fear of dropping things. [plut-n][srj7] I kept dropping things, like part of the dinner I had just cooked. [sal-fr][sle1] Felt bubbly and excited, giggly, dropped the kettle, lack of coordination. [tung-met][bdx1]

In a wider context the effect of the confusion is to feel lost.

Confusion as to which side (of the street) I'm on. [limen-b-c][hrn2] Rode on the wrong train, and then disappointed in myself for making such a stupid mistake; felt like crying. [coca-c][sk4] Feel like I've lost my way. [corian-s][knl6] I drive home (usually I ask him to drive because I don't like driving). The first roundabout we come to I ask "which way do I go round it?" I really couldn't think for a few seconds which way I should go. I've never done that before – not even when I was learning. [falco-pe][nl2] Got lost, my unerring sense of direction went. I'm not focused. I have to keep pulling my attention back. It's a concerted effort to focus myself. [irid-met][srj5] Being outside of home – particularly outside, walking the streets, I have felt directionless and lost and this has been connected I think to constantly taking wrong turnings, though this has been more in the car. [latex][nl-latex] I feel lost, I've lost myself. [lsd][nl-lsd] Lose orientation on the underground. [ozone][sde2] I felt really lost. I opened my eyes a couple of times and just didn't know where I was. [positr][nl2] Feeling lost. [urol-h][rwt3] Feeling of being lost, helpless and out of control. [urol-h][rwt3] Was in a dream/daze, turned left instead of right, and walked 200m before realized it was wrong direction. [sal-fr][sle1] Immediately after taking remedy felt 'spacey'. Aware that motorway exit is approaching, but just drive right past it – not with it at all. [sal-fr][sle1]

Even the familiar becomes confusing. Repeatedly have I wandered past doors and houses which, in my ordinary condition, were as well known as my own, and have at last given up the search for them in utter hopelessness, recognizing not the faintest familiar trace in their aspect. [cann-i][a1] Did not know which way to go on a well known route. [germ-met][srj5] Went past turning on well known route. [latex][nl-latex] On a journey I know well I took wrong turnings twice I just couldn't pull myself together to concentrate on where I was and where I was going. [latex][nl-latex]

There are also dreams of being lost. Dreams – being lost, trying to get somewhere and not succeeding. [adam][srj5] Dream: I was alone in a tall building. I was scared to enter the lift because there was no one around, so I took the stairs. While coming down I found myself lost, could not find my way. [lac-h][sk4]

A common feature of being lost is going round in circles. Got lost going home; went around and around. [coca-c][sk4] On the drive back from the party we kept going round and round the same roundabouts etc. and taking or nearly taking wrong turnings. It was ridiculous. [falco-pe][nl2] Got lost and was going in circles. [urol-h][rwt3] (*See Waves, Circles & Cycles IV-4*)

In the gases such as Hydrogen, as in the drugs, there is a tendency for personal space to become limitless and the sensation of being lost in this limitless space is overwhelming. The general impression is that the prover entered a larger totality/dimension in terms of space and time, whereupon all previous or smaller totalities became trivial and alien. A conflict of understanding and behaviour arose. I feel I have moved into a different state of consciousness and there aren't any guiding posts or means of navigation – a bit like being lost in space. [hydrog][srj2]

Homesickness is a particular spatial manifestation of the sense of isolation common in these remedies. Want desperately to be at home. [adam][srj5] All I wanted to do was to be at home, miserable feeling that I didn't want to be out, I wanted to be home. I felt vulnerable, needed to be home. [agath-a][nl2] Homesickness for the first time in my life. [galla-q-r][nl2] Felt lonely. Was missing my family. Wanted to go home. Felt like weeping and weeping. [lac-cp][sk4] During the proving I was told unexpectedly by my landlords that I would have to leave my flat. [sal-fr][sle1] Dream: Returning home from a trip. There was a feeling of homesickness in this dream. [galeoc-c-h][gms1] (*See Isolation II-8*)

In the Eagle the homesickness is described as being particularly for the wilderness and the mountains. Dream of traveling and making choice of which home to return to. [haliae-lc][srj5] Pictures of the mountains make me homesick. Deeper than homesick. Feeling low, remembering the freedom of going to them. Missing mountains and the outdoors. [haliae-lc][srj5]

VII-9 Confusion about Words

The development and use of language can be seen as a key indicator in the stages of progress and each stage of this development (speech, writing and printing) can be linked to the major miasmatic states. It is not therefore surprising that language and writing should cause problems in the electronic age, and that when these artefacts of the earlier worlds are integrated into the electronic world they should cause confusion.

Just as thoughts are hard to find and hold on to and tend to vanish (*See Vanishing of Thoughts VII-3*) so are words. Also finding I lose words. Know what I want to say but the odd word just vanishes. [aids][nl2] Cannot find the right word, with difficulty of enunciation. [anh][c1] Slow in finding the words to express himself at times. [coca][a1] Brain feels so muddled that he cannot read French journals understandingly; must look in dictionary for words usually familiar to him. [coca][a1] Could not get the right words to describe something. [falco-pe][nl2] When talking I had to search for the right word or expression. I stop in the middle of a sentence without finishing it because I can't find the right word. [neon][srj5] Difficult to connect words and thoughts and get out what I want to say. [positr][nl2] Memory weaker, can't think of words, spelling, forgetting to do things. [tung-met][bdx1] Provers were constantly heard to say, "I can't find the word for..." or they frequently used wrong words. [vacuum][es-vac]

Speech can be difficult, slow or confused. I see a sign for two towns that I have known for years. The sign reads, "Allston-Brighton". I read it out loud to myself, "Allton-Blighton". Knowing that sounds wrong, I try out loud again and again, "Allton-Blighton". After three wrong pronunciations, I am finally able to say it correctly. [corian-s][knl6] She is not completing sentences; talks slowly. [haliae-lc][srj5] Difficult reading out loud. Tongue wouldn't work quite right. [helodr-cal][knl2] It is difficult to describe the symptoms. Want to correct myself all the time. [germ-met][srj5] Dream of not being able to decipher people's speech. [plac][Biggs+] I feel I'm not pronouncing my words properly. I keep tripping over them. [vacuum][es-vac] Problems formulating words, I feel verbally clumsy. [vacuum][es-vac]

Or even backwards. Spoke backwards again paper get car drive. [corian-s][knl6] Said words back to front, "healing of feet," instead of, "feeling of heat." [germ-met][srj5]

The most common manifestation is a confusion of words or a tendency to use the wrong words. Mixing up words calling things by other names: "My hoover is broken" instead of "My washing machine is broken." [falco-pe][nl2] Having some problems with my speech very aware of how badly I speak, leaving ends off words, being aware of it is making my vocabulary very restricted. I feel I sound stupid. [falco-pe][nl2] I said, "Well that's not soon, is it," instead of saying," Well that's not long, is it." [germ-met][srj5] Said nerve underneath sciatica instead of underneath thigh. [germ-met][srj5] Friends have been saying that I talk in clichés and make spelling mistakes— 'currant' for 'current' and "iiritability' for 'irritability.' 'Aso' for 'Also,' and I'm repeating phrases. [germ-met][srj5] Notice I keep mixing up names, especially eldest son! He remarks, you can't even remember my name now. Call him all the other male names I know – so strange, like I can't concentrate or something. [heroin][sdj-h] Use of opposites, mixing words up, e.g., slight – masses; melancholia – euphoria; microscopic – enormous [irid-met][srj5] I've been using the wrong words – 'a bar of garlic; he's a lesbian'. [agath-a][nl2] Using wrong words. [galla-q-r][nl2] I noticed that when writing I am making mistakes, also in speech. I wrote the number "3" backwards and could not figure out for a second what was wrong with it. In speaking I noticed I was using a word and I was going to say "further" in a sentence early on, and therefore out of context. Or I used a word I had already spoken again but out of context. [lac-loxod-a][hrn2] Misplaces words in the same phrase. [osm][a1] I make mistakes, saying light instead of heat. [plut-n][srj7] Very difficult to speak – words wrong way round. Also typing wrong words (normally a good typist!). [positr][nl2] Forgetfulness, writing one familiar word for another of similar sound. [ptel][a1] A kind of stammering; he uses syllables of words in wrong connections, therefore pronounces some words incorrectly. [sel][c1]

In both Lac caninum and Neon there is a confusion between what is seen and what is thought which leads to the wrong word being used. When speaking, substitutes the name of the object seen for that which is thought. [lac-c][c1] Examples of the kind of mistakes made were: 'left' for 'right' and looking at a table and wanting to say 'chair' but saying 'table' instead. The visual stimulus affected my ability to say the right word. [neon][srj5] (*See Confusion of the Senses VII-2*)

In Mare's milk these problems are applied to numbers rather than words. Secretary said I was making mistakes adding numbers; couldn't add simple figures. [lac-e][hrn2] Increased trouble picking up phone numbers correctly from voice-mail messages; reversing numbers. [lac-e][hrn2]

However, it is the written word that is most threatened in the electronic age. Just as speech was subsumed into writing and writing into the printed word, so the printed word is being subsumed into electronic media. In each case the previous format is unsuited to the new medium and is forced to change.

Orthography and spelling can be individualized and fluid in the written word. In the printed medium they are forced to become fixed and regulated. In the electronic world there is a conflict between the two important issues of precision and fluidity. There is a tendency in modern society towards recapturing the contractions and abbreviations of the written word which is being expressed in text messaging. There is also a recognition of the importance of precise language which is termed, both positively and negatively, as Political Correctness. This is particularly so in the politics of HIV and AIDS, both of which terms have enormous value judgments associated with them and whose usage becomes very important.

This conflict is expressed in confused spelling. In writing, omitting the first letter, transposing first and second letters of words. [adam][srj5] Mistakes in writing and spelling. [androc][srj5] Writes one word for another. [cann-i][a1] Difficulty spelling. [carbn-dox][knl3] Mistakes in writing – writing word twice and missing out letters of words. [choc][srj3] Am rewriting some notes and realize that I don't seem to be able to spell at all. I'm usually a good speller, I always had a knack for it. [corian-s][knl6] Can't spell – have to keep checking with people. [dream-p][sdj1] Spelling is weird on this remedy. [helodr-cal][knl2] Mistakes in spelling. It worries me. Also say wrong word quite often. [germ-met][srj5] Difficulty in remembering the spelling of simple words. [helo-s][rwt2] Mistakes in writing; leaving letters out, confusing letters etc. [hydrog][srj2] Transposing "e" and "l" when writing. "Slef" instead of "self." [irid-met][srj5] Making mistakes in writing, writing y instead of i; leaving out e. [galla-q-r][nl2] Having to think about spelling which suddenly feels difficult. [lac-h][htj1] Making the same mistakes writing and typing words with the vowel sounds the wrong way round always the middle of the word, probably rushing, need to slow down, feeling pressure of time ticking away. Very aware of time. [latex][nl-latex] I seem to be having difficulty spelling simple words. I have to concentrate to get it right and add the letters afterwards if I've missed any out. [lsd][nl-lsd] I have been making spelling mistakes. I couldn't spell "biscuits" today. [neon][srj5] Omits the first letter of a word in writing, transposes the first and second letters. [opun-v][a1] Difficulty in writing. Just doesn't know how she should write words, writes oce instead of once. [ozone][sde2] Concentration difficult, getting words back to front. [plac][Biggs+] Making spelling mistakes that wouldn't normally make. [sal-fr][sle1] Noticed I made a lot of spelling mistakes at the ends of words. [tung-met][bdx1] In the notes supplied by the provers, the spelling of words was atrocious. [vacuum][es-vac]

Mistakes are especially common when there is a contradiction between the spelling and the sound of a word. Spelling mistakes – Writing is very untidy. Wrote "ull" instead of "dull," "speach" instead of "speech." [adam][srj5] Wrote "knawing" for "gnawing." [neon][srj5]

As in speech the wrong word can be used. In writing, uses too many words or not the right ones; omits final letter or letters in a word. [lac-c][al2] Mistakes in writing – wrote December instead of February for the date. [neon][srj5] Or things can be written backwards. For the last 2 days I have been writing things backwards and getting all mixed up instead of writing 52 I would write 25. [agath-a][nl2] I'm writing numbers backwards, i.e. the 6 before the 1 when writing 16. [lsd][nl-lsd] Typing numbers backwards. [vacuum][es-vac]

Even the wrong alphabet can be used. While writing he omitted letters, wrote in different alphabets against his will, and changed from one subject to another. [nux-m][a1] The name 'Sequoia' is derived from Sequoiah, the inventor of the Cherokee alphabet. [seq-s][vml3] Sequoyah (George Guest) was an illiterate Arkansas Cherokee with a withered leg. About 1809 he started working on a means of writing the Cherokee language. In 12 years he worked through the path followed by many civilizations over millennia, starting with pictographs, through ideographs and in 1821 he devised a phonetic alphabet that could use Greek and Latin letters making printing easy, but with no reference to how the letters were used in any other language. In 1825, just four years after its invention, it was in widespread use and the majority of Cherokee adults were literate, a far higher proportion than was then to be found in the United States or other developed nations.

There is also an inability to write properly. Couldn't write properly, the letters wouldn't form, different size and untidy. [germ-met][srj5] Her writing seemed messy to her. [hydrog][srj2] My handwriting is so bad at the moment and I keep getting my words round the wrong way – tongue twisted/tied. [lsd][nl-lsd]

Or to type. Typing still feels very strange. I can do it if I don't think about it, but when I think about what I am doing I get lost in looking at the keys rather than typing and make loads of mistakes. [lsd][nl-lsd]

Iridium: because of its resistance to corrosion and its hardness, it is used for pointing fountain pen-nibs, and for electrical contacts subject to severe conditions. [irid-met][srj5] This leads to the interesting writing symptom. Borrowed a pen, fountain pen, really got into the smoothness of how the nib flowed, kept on borrowing it. Went to buy a pen, didn't know whether to by Platignum or Osmoroid, so didn't buy one. Came home and found a really nice one. [irid-met][srj5]

Other particular symptoms to do with literacy are: Unable to register things I had read. [polys][sk4] This reflects the important insulating pattern in Polystyrene; and Dreamt I was proof reading, comparing one set of proofs with another. [plut-n][srj7] , which reflects the Plutonium feature of comparing two different views of reality.

Dyslexia is one of the defining disorders of the modern ages. In some ways it can be seen as an inability to work with the written word, but as the old printed word is being superseded, Dyslexia might be the result of trying to work with an industrial age medium in a mind that has already adjusted to the Electronic Age and which works in a new way, through pattern thinking rather than sequential, rational thought.

Whatever the case may be, Dyslexia is extremely important in the AIDS Miasm. Dyslexia, dyspraxia, learning difficulties. [lumbr-t][evans] Having decided on Camphor he proceeded to read at length about it. This is unusual for him. He usually asks someone else to read due to his dyslexia, but this time he read for a good while without hesitation. [falco-pe][nl2] Dyslexia. [gink-b][mp4] And particularly in Germanium. Wrote dylexist instead of dyslexic. [germ-met][srj5]

VIII-1 Feminization

Many aspects of the electronic age are feminine in nature, just as the industrial age was predominantly masculine. Multitasking and communication are seen as feminine strengths whereas rationality and focus are considered to be the province of men.

In many of the recent provings there has been a tendency towards feminization and an appreciation of the power of the feminine.

This was particularly true in Diamond in which the feminine power of the night and of the Moon is exceptionally strong, Excited by the power of night. [adam][srj5] Enjoy the powerful night force. I can fly in the dark. [adam][srj5] Dream I had a lover, my skin was smooth, eyes blue. Desire to wear blues and silvery grey. I swam with seals and felt truly connected. Sexual love felt too gross and unnecessary. Woke feeling beautiful and receptive, like the moon. [adam][srj5] Attracted to dark night skies. Stars seem more visible. [adam][srj5] And feelings of being more feminine, voluptuous and attractive. Feel bright, free and beautiful, more feminine, more fertile and voluptuous. [adam][srj5] Males finding me attractive. I'm finding others more attractive. [adam][srj5] Skin is paler. Feels more feminine, round and soft. [adam][srj5]

The power of the night is also important in Neon and Tungsten. Dream having a quality of darkness or night time. [neon][srj5] Walking in the garden in the dark – the darkness seemed magical. [tung-met][bdx1]

The Moon was related to symptoms in other remedies. Worse from the full moon. [lac-h][htj1] Ailments from moonlight. [meph][vml3] Anger at the time of the full moon, throwing things. [cygn-b][sle-swan] Worse at full moon. [plac][Biggs+]

The theme of primordial chaos is relevant in many remedies, but especially in Vacuum. This chaos is identified with the feminine principle. Chaos was also associated with female expression as order was with the male. [vacuum][es-vac] (*See Chaos & Order V-5*)

The dinosaur species that was chosen for the proving is the only dinosaur to receive a feminine name using an "a" at the end instead of an "us," such as in "Albertosaurus." [maias-l][hrn2]

Other remedies are taken from species in which the female is dominant. Thus although the substance of the Falcon was taken from a Tiercel (male); the species shows extreme reverse sexual size dimorphism with the male up to a third smaller. [falco-pe][nl2]

The Horse, the Dolphin, the Whale and the Elephant and even the Lion all live in groups that are based around and often run by the females. The dolphins' main social grouping is the pod, which, similar to the elephant, is comprised of adult females and their offspring in groups of two to fifteen. [lac-del][hrn2] The basic family unit of the elephant is the cow-calf group led by the elder matriarch, plus her grown female daughters and their young. [lac-loxod-a][hrn2] As with dolphins and lions, the horse family is basically run by the females. [lac-e][hrn2]

The most important aspect of the feminine domination of the recent remedies is the importance of the Milks. The earlier mammal remedies were generally made from anal and preputial gland secretions, often those of the male (Musk, Beaver, etc.) or from other sarcodes such as Ambra grisea. The modern mammal remedies have all been from milks with the exception of Koala and the Rat. That the latter was not a milk was forced on the proving by circumstance as milk could not be obtained and blood was used instead. Even so the feminine energy still came through. I felt very feminine today, more so than usual. I felt more aware of being a woman. I enjoyed being a mom, being womanly. I felt blessed. [sanguis-s][hrn2]

Ecstasy has a powerful feminizing effect, It seems that a universal effect of the drug is to remove male sexual aggression, or, as one woman put it, "to bring out the feminine qualities in men". [mdma][saunders] which empowers women and giving them more confidence. Women feel truly liberated; they can let go and enjoy themselves without fear of being taken advantage of by aggressive men, and this allows them to approach men who they don't know. [mdma][saunders] The atmosphere inspires confidence and independence so that girls don't feel the need to be under the protection of a boyfriend. [mdma][saunders]

Iridium is particularly associated with boundaries and the skin as a boundary, (*See Skin XII-4*) and symptoms of smoothness, softness and curves, especially of the skin, are strong in the remedy. Desire to touch backs of hands on face. Enjoy touch on skin. Old memories of gentleness, delightfully feminine. Wearing bright pink (unusual!) and stroking my legs. Enjoying my skin, touching bottom, stroking it. Dancing erotically at 8.00 a.m. [irid-met][srj5] Delight at seeing my own female form in mirror, desire to shave legs so they would be smooth. Highly sexual, more refined, dressed in best clothes today. [irid-met][srj5] Thought that the feminine form is rounded and curved due to magnetism; arcs due to magnetic forces. [irid-met][srj5]

This softness and feminine quality are apparent in other remedies. I feel softer and round within and maybe more feminine. [dream-p][sdj1] My skin on my face feels softer, not so dry. [falco-pe][nl2] Today I felt almost a sexual, ecstatic feeling in me, I am very sensitive. My breasts are very sensitive. I am a very, very woman. I think, whatever the substance, it made me feel very aware of my sexuality today. [heroin][sdj-h] She has a softer appearance. [ozone][sde2]

As was a desire to be more feminine and attractive. On waking put on make up – unusual! felt more feminine – more girlie. [positr][nl2] In Germanium this is described as: I feel an intense yearning for the feminine. [germ-met][srj5]

There is an understanding and sympathy with woman's lot. I think I'm being really conscious of women's suffering, more so; feel like I see it in a new light. I feel ages of women, felt the pain of Othello's wife in the video, felt so sad and emotionally charged by her death, by all women's death by men. [lac-lup][hrn2] I feel how conditioned I have been by the stereotypes of women, good socially acceptable women – wives and mothers. It has almost felt like I don't have a right to a life of my own, but must give up to everyone else's needs, must endure patiently and accept this. [positr][nl2]

And a feeling of support and understanding from contact with women. Need the support of other women, feel more attracted to them. [ozone][sde2] Feel much better for talking to Mum, better for consolation, better for female emotional support. [sal-fr][sle1]

In the extreme this becomes a hatred or revulsion towards men. Anger with men. [cygn-b][sle-swan] I am repulsed by males; I want to flee from them to avoid being dominated. [plut-n][srj7] I feel a strong revulsion towards men; feel we should never rely on men. [plut-n][srj7] This feeling can also lead to a fear of men as in the many dreams of rape. (*See Rape, Child Abuse & Incest IX-4*)

There can also be a reaction to this overpowering female energy, particularly from the few male provers participating in modern provings. Felt too much surrounded by women. [galla-q-r][nl2] Dream: Women were in control of everything. [urol-h][rwt3]

There is also a general connection with female functions. (*See Motherhood & Pregnancy VIII-3*) This is to be expected in the milks, but it is also obvious in Chocolate, The need for Chocolate often appeared in connection with menses. [choc][srj3] which, like Stingray and Diamond, must join Sepia, Pulsatilla and Lachesis as major "female" remedies.

VIII-2 Left Sidedness

There is a strong correlation between the sides of the body and gender. The left side, which includes the heart, and the corresponding right brain are considered feminine; while the right side, which includes the liver, and the left, rational side of the brain are considered masculine.

This is often reflected in remedies where left sidedness, as in Lachesis, indicates feminine qualities; while right sidedness as in Lycopodium, is more masculine.

The AIDS Nosode is very left sided and one prover even became more left handed. Noticed that, when I was playing football, I was kicking with my left foot which I never would have done usually. [aids][nl2]

On the whole the new remedies and the remedies of the AIDS Miasm are strongly left sided. It is a left sided remedy. [cere-b][a1] Symptoms worse on left side. [choc][srj3] Laterality left side, but not exclusively. [hir][jl1] The majority of symptoms appeared on the left side. [irid-met][c1] Left-sided headache. Left-sided sore throat, Left knee aggravated. [lac-del][hrn2] Bleeding from the left nostril (before taking the drug, he bled from the right nostril). [del][a1] The hardness felt in the right side of the abdomen has passed to the left side. [del][a1] Left-sided headaches were strong in the proving, and this was a good confirmation because they were also strong in the old Lac felinum (milk of the cat) proving. [lac-leo][hrn2] The left side of her face is more open and free. [ozone][sde2] All symptoms left-sided. [plat][a1] More symptoms appear on the left than on the right side. [tell][c1] My hair is falling out – mainly on the left side. [sal-fr][sle1]

Or they have the sensation that the right side is paralyzed, missing or doesn't belong to the subject. Vivid dream of being paralyzed down the right side of my body. (Right hemiplegia [c1])[irid-met][srj5] Feeling as if my right and left were equal, previously feeling as if my right side bigger. [irid-met][srj5] Feeling of not having a right side – no sensations. [galla-q-r][nl2] Feel as if my right arm doesn't belong to me. [ozone][sde2]I feel tilted to left, as if I only have the left half of my brain, so I am unevenly balanced. [positr][nl2]

In Vacuum there is confusion around the issue of left-right sidedness that is expressed in terms of mirrors and mirror images. Driving home, I realised that I feel like a mirror image of myself. I looked in the mirror and realised that my hair was parted on the wrong side again. I realised that now I can see myself the way others see me. [vacuum][es-vac] A lot of stuff with mirror images. Seeing my reflection in the mirror. The mood of reflection looks different from the way I am feeling. [vacuum][es-vac] The feeling of being a mirror image has persisted. I've been doing strange things like constantly going to the wrong side of doors in my house for the handle. [vacuum][es-vac]

This is not exclusively so and there are remedies of the Miasm that are predominantly right sided. Arsenic is predominantly right-sided. [ars][c1] I sat down thinking I should write up what had occurred, picked up the pen in my right hand and started to write (I am left handed). [latex][nl-latex] Or have left sided paralysis. The entire left half of the body became numb, the left half of the head being sharply divided in sensation from the other half. [xan][c1]

VIII-3 Motherhood & Pregnancy

The ultimate expressions of femininity and the female function are pregnancy and motherhood and they are major themes in many of the new remedies.

There is a general concern for babies, children and animals that can be an expression of the "maternal instinct". I still have the protective thing, a sort of mothering, I just want to make sure that everyone's OK. [falco-pe][nl2] Dream of the beauty of mother love as opposed to other kinds of love and their different qualities. [plac][Biggs+] *(See Babies, Children & Animals IX-2)*

However, there are many symptoms that relate directly to pregnancy and childbirth. Dreams of being pregnant are common. Had another dream last night that I was pregnant. [corian-s][knl6] Dream: I'm pregnant, my belly is big. I have a feeling of satisfaction. [galla-q-r][nl2] Dreaming of being pregnant having a scan being told by the doctors that the baby is disabled or deformed in some way. I had to make a decision whether or not to keep it. I decided to go and see some children with disabilities to help me decide. Remember feeling very protective not wanting to get rid of it. I was wearing a skirt that was too tight and I was worried about harming the baby. [latex][nl-latex] Dreamt pregnant with around fifteen babies. [plac][Biggs+] Dream of two pregnant women, very, very large. Aware the pressure she would be feeling on the uterus, had to stand to relive downward pressure like contraction. [latex][nl-latex] Dreamt I was pregnant, worried about my figure, don't want it to show. [neon][srj5] Dreamt that I was pregnant. [plut-n][srj7] Dream that I was talking to my husband and I realised that he was six months pregnant. [plut-n][srj7] Dream: I was pregnant nearly 9 months. I never new about it. [rhus-g][tmo3]

As is the delusion that the subject is pregnant. Delusion she is pregnant. [gink-b][vml3] Almost the impression that I am pregnant – many old sensations and emotions from previous pregnancies recurred. Like having another person inside of me. All physical symptoms of pregnancy. Went for a test. [hydrog][srj2] Looking in the mirror I felt my gaze fixed on my breasts and my stomach – thought I was pregnant. [galla-q-r][nl2] Did a pregnancy test today the result is negative, I can hardly believe the result. [lsd][nl-lsd] Strong feeling of pregnancy, as if baby moving around in belly and sensation of breasts filling up with milk. [plac][Biggs+] I am convinced that I am pregnant but don't want to admit it to anyone. [sal-fr][sle1] Felt like I had symptoms of pregnancy; issues of motherliness and motherhood; concern and care taking feelings; felt pregnant but no emotion going with it. [urol-h][rwt3]

In Crack Willow a substantial number of those involved became pregnant. Fertility: One of the supervisors was pregnant when the proving began, two of the women provers became unexpectedly pregnant shortly after the proving, and one of the provers felt as if she was pregnant. [sal-fr][sle1]

These dreams of pregnancy can contain an element of doubt or shame. Dreamed I was pregnant. Mixed feelings – felt ashamed to tell my family. [hydrog][srj2] Dream: Pregnant, but not sure if I was, and feeling of responsibility, and not wanting to take on that responsibility. [lac-del][hrn2]

There are also dreams of childbirth. Dream: Of having a baby and delivering myself. [lac-leo][hrn2] Dreams of birth. [ozone][sde2] Dream: Birthing babies. [urol-h][rwt3]

Sometimes with a nightmarish element. Horrible dream; I had a baby (great) but after it was born it got smaller and smaller until it was only an inch big, then it disappeared. [aids][nl2] Dream: My sister was having a baby, she was in labour, and holding my hand. Her nails were really long and kept digging in. I was asking her how quick the contractions were, but she was in a lot of pain and couldn`t answer. Her nails kept digging in, and I was trying to rearrange her grip so that they wouldn`t dig into her or me. [falco-pe][nl2]

The breasts are an important focus for symptoms. Sometimes they are sexual objects. Breasts are a very prominent theme in the sexuality. [lac-cp][lsy+dmk] Dreams: Running naked with breasts exposed. [lac-e][hrn2] Dreamed a dying man was suckling my breast and I was sexually excited by that. [sal-fr][sle1]

But more often the symptoms are concerned with the breasts in their nurturing role. Feelings concerning the texture, smoothness, warmth and 'melting in the mouth' qualities were most venerated. These feelings were often associated with breast feeding and motherly love. [choc][srj3] When hearing talk of babies, breasts aching with a sensation as if filling up with milk. [choc][srj3] An image came to me where I found myself suckling young hairy babies, sometimes animals, especially hedgehogs. [choc][srj3] Breasts sensitive and swollen, big, rounder than usual. [dream-p][sdj1] My breasts are swollen and heavy. [agath-a][nl2] Dreams: Same, two nights in a row during proving, none like this before or since. Strong feeling of having and nursing a baby. Strong feeling of my breast. Strong feeling of fulfillment. [lac-del][hrn2] Delusion that breasts are swollen as if pregnant. [plac][Biggs+] Dreamt breasts full of milk, leaking, proud of them, jutting them out. [plac][Biggs+] Breast is full and heavy. Sensation as if breast separated from me. [plut-n][srj7] Dream of expressing milk from my right breast. [positr][nl2] Dreams or feelings for Mother, not so specifically my mother but some sense of Mother as universal, my Mother, I am Mother, Everything is Mother. [sanguis-s][hrn2] The rays are ovoviviparous – the lining of the uterus exudes milk during pregnancy to aid in nourishing the developing embryo. [urol-h][rwt3] Milk let down reflex in breasts like when nursing. [urol-h][rwt3] Breasts enlarged and heavy. [sal-fr][sle1] Dream: Told boyfriend that I was going off to conceive a child. [tung-met][bdx1] Breasts have got bigger (outgrown my bra). [vacuum][es-vac]

VIII-4 Gender Confusion

Confusion is a keynote of the AIDS Miasm and the tendency towards feminization and the tendency for women to find empowerment leads to many forms of gender confusion.

Some of the substances used in the new remedies are in some way hermaphroditic. Even though they have organs of both sexes they still reproduce with two worms. [helodr-cal][knl2] Leeches are hermaphrodite. Each individual produces both eggs and sperm; however, this does not occur simultaneously, so that self-fertilisation is avoided. As a rule, a leech first functions as a male and then as a female. [hir][vml3] The wasps of the Cynipidae have an unusual life cycle in that alternate generations take two, often very different forms. One generation, the one that lives through the summer months, consists of both males and females and reproduces sexually. The alternate generation which develops through the winter and hatches in the spring is entirely female and reproduces asexually. Its form may be quite different from that of its mother and daughters. [galla-q-r][nl2]

The names of some substances are associated with ambiguous gender or change of gender. Andropogon, an alternate name for the remedy, is a Greek word indicating an androgynous person with a beard simultaneously suggesting bisexuality and an excess of male hormones. [anan][vh1] In Romania and Yugoslavia, the rainbow is associated with change of sex. [irid-met][srj5]

In many remedies there was a feeling of being more masculine or harder. A guy called me 'mate,' and then said he only usually says that to guys. [haliae-lc][srj5] The joining with this energy was as if a male energy joined with me sexually, but with no desire, pleasure or pain involved. This unification with the male energy lasted quite a few days – I'm not used to seeing myself as a man. [hydrog][srj2] Feelings of vulnerability and anxiety about being masculine, both in looks and in behaviour/roles.

Hope it doesn't get more. To counteract this, I have been stressing the feminine. I spent lots of money on silk clothing and spent a lot of time making myself up, curling hair, etc. People comment that I look softer, but I feel harder inside. I feel confused about my sexual identity. This is in contrast to my previous proving of the remedy, when people commented that my moustache disappeared and breasts grew. [hydrog][srj2] Thinking a lot about the saints – particularly St. Joan of Arc. Imagining myself dressed as a man – at the head of an army for a good purpose. [ignis-alc][es2] I have been thinking a lot about the way in which men treat women. I have always felt that a women's role was to act submissive and fragile so that the man will feel strong and dominant. Recently I have felt like playing men at their own game, I feel strong in myself and not so caught up in how I appear, people (men) can take me as I come. It is funny because I don't know if I have ever acted in that way with past relationships but there is this fear of losing my femininity. [latex][nl-latex] Predominant feeling today and yesterday is of feeling ugly. I tried on a couple of dresses and looked at my hair which is so fine, and I feel masculine, ugly I don't feel feminine. I do feel that I look like a man. [lsd][nl-lsd] Imbalance of feminine and masculine qualities. (Too much masculine energy) [querc-r][evans] Burping and farting loudly. I'm turning into a man! [vacuum][es-vac]

This was very strong in Plutonium. My legs are more male, hairy and thrust forward. [plut-n][srj7] I feel more male – strong perspiration, skin coarser, my shoulders hunched forwards, my brow greatly enlarged, great strength in my arms and hands, my feet prehensile. I want to eat with my hands, eat raw meat. [plut-n][srj7] Feeling masculine today. I wouldn't be surprised if I looked in the mirror to see a man. I feel like a man in a woman's body. [plut-n][srj7]

One of the most common expressions of this feeling in provers is the sensation that the voice is getting deeper or louder. My voice has dropped what feels like octaves. [adam][srj5] Shouted and it came out louder than usual. Voice seemed quieter than usual. [dream-p][sdj1] Voice is deeper in pitch. [haliae-lc][srj5] I had a note played on the piano for me to sing, and I sang the right note but an octave higher or lower. [germ-met][srj5] Laughter wicked and voice seemed low. [hydrog][srj2] Voice sounded deeper. My immediate reaction, "Oh God, I'm turning into a man." [irid-met][srj5] My voice has gone husky and deep. [lsd][nl-lsd] Slight huskiness, hoarse voice. [ozone][sde2] Couldn't sing soprano at church. [sal-fr][sle1]

The occurence of the reverse feeling (male to female) is much less but that could be the result of the lack of male provers in many recent provings. For example it came up in the Vacuum proving in spite of the fact that only one of the 20 provers was male. Questioning what it is to be a man. [vacuum][es-vac]

The main expression of gender confusion is in the dreams. Dreams of toilets are common (*See Shit & Toilets X-4*) but a particular variant of this is entering public toilets of the other gender. Sudden complete lapse of concentration. I walked right into the middle of a crowded ladies' toilet. It took me a few seconds to notice that the 'men' were wearing skirts and looking at me in disbelief. [choc][srj3] Dream: I was in a hostel by the sea playing cards. The blokes were washing in the girls' bathroom and the girls were in the blokes. I had to tell people there was confusion coming. [heroin][sdj-h] Dream: Toilet – women's – man with us, he goes in as well. [tung-met][bdx1]

There are dreams of women who are masculine or have beards. Dream: Female genitals that are enlarged, and starting to look like male genitals. [coca-c][sk4] Dream: I was in the gym with a friend when a big, macho man came over and was being quite obnoxious. I told him he had a small penis, and that put him in his place. Then I was suddenly prompted to do many push-ups, even with one hand. I was sweating hard and breathing fast, with accelerated pulse rate – a feeling of omnipotence and power as though I was more male, though I felt powerful as a female. [coca-c][sk4] Dream: In a bed with my partner on one side and another man on the other side. Got up to go to the toilet and got into bed with mum. There was something strange; she had a penis. Couldn't work out what was wrong with that. [rhus-g][tmo3] Dreamt last night about a woman with a beard it was beige, and looked soft. She shaved it off and had stubble on her face, I found it quite freaky. [positr][nl2] Dream about a short haired, thin, blond woman, no curves. Looked like a boy dressed in winter underwear, off-white and ribbed. She is sitting curled up, arms around her knees. [galeoc-c-h][gms1] Dream: Woman had been disguised as a man during a war. Even though the war is over it still has to be a secret. [tung-met][bdx1] Dream: Working in an office with an older woman and a girl I used to know, who'd just come back after long unexplained absence. Then I had to shave either this woman's beard off or my own with electric razor. [tung-met][bdx1] Dream a nurse with a full bristly man's moustache. It was grey and I knew she had chosen to grow it. [vacuum][es-vac]

There are also dreams of men with breasts, Dream: Being lectured by a man with breasts. [irid-met][srj5] particularly in the Koala bear. Dream: Being chatted up by a woman with large breasts in a car. She is a truck driver; we talk about trucks. [phasco-ci][rbp2] Dreams about men with breasts. [phasco-ci][rbp2] 'The best dream of my life'. In meditation with my Guru (a male) and other people. (First time in my dreams that I am there and others there also.) I started to go into shocks and moans – a kind of chorea – from the spiritual energy in my body. My guru leant over and uncovered his breast (a female breast) and fed me milk from it. I felt nurtured to my soul by God. [phasco-ci][rbp2]

Of effeminate men. Dream: A beautiful, dark, slender, young man with soft, curly hair; delicate, gorgeous, feminine. [coca-c][sk4] Dream: I also notice that all the people are men dressed as women; one in a black lace negligee; some are dressed like men or women but are very effeminate so they look like women though they are very big and bald. [urol-h][rwt3]

And more general dreams of gender confusion. Dreamed of confused sexuality; not sure if I was a man or a woman in the dream. [irid-met][srj5] Me [male] and my family are living on an island kingdom with a castle. I am the mother. Dream: Of a man dissatisfied with his gender, and being described as being old for his gender at age 42. [tung-met][bdx1] Dream: Mother looking after man who was having a sex change operation. Also looking after another woman who was donating her uterus. [tung-met][bdx1]

These dreams often have and erotic quality. Dream: This is strongest dream I ever had. In the dream I am a man wrestling with another man. I have dark hair, the other guy is blonde. Duality. At some point the other guy plays unfair, he does something that totally offends me (maybe this was done before we fight), so I attack this person. So graphic, I dig the nails of my left hand under the skin of his neck as hard as I can. I can feel the skin break and his blood. I lay into him hard. I am fighting for my life. It is totally graphic. I am enraged, impassioned and wild. [limen-b-c][hrn2] Had a dream that I had a penis and a close female friend of mine also had a penis and we are having sex face to face. Wake up pondering the strangeness of the dreams and the logistics of such a sexual act. [corian-s][knl6] Erotic dream: two women making love; it turns into a man and woman; one woman tall, becoming Rafael like – atmosphere of lush pleasure, leisurely pace. [urol-h][rwt3]

Homosexuality has been associated with AIDS since its first appearance. The appearance of opportunistic infections in apparently healthy young men was called Gay Related Immune Deficiency, GRID. [aids][nl2]

This is not to say that homosexuality should be regarded as a symptom. There are many homosexual men and women who are at home with their lifestyle and for whom it does not form any part of their pathology.

Dreams of homosexuality, even where the dreamer is a participant do not necessarily indicative of latent desires in the dreamer but should be taken at face value, particularly when confusion is such an important feature of the modern situation. I had a sexual dream. Embraced a woman, a known lesbian, who succumbed to my embraces. I seduced her and professed my love. It felt wonderful, but afterwards I felt guilty because I knew I couldn't remain with her and be faithful to her, because I had equal devotion to my husband and children. I felt guilty because I had led her on. I told her all this. she was not at all upset or fazed; completely accepting. Then I got defensive and started saying that she didn't exactly discourage me. It felt like very male behaviour. [agath-a][nl2] Dream: Two women are getting married. Everything is very beautiful, the dream is really about these sensory impressions: peoples' clothes, flowers everywhere, the wedding takes place out in the front yard. Everything is very beautiful. Inside the house there is lots of food, dishes, much abundance. The feeling is of lots of beauty and abundance. [corian-s][knl6] Dreams about homosexuality. [plut-n][srj7] I dreamt that Mary Tyler Moore's last show was about her sleeping with another woman. [urol-h][rwt3] Dream: Encountered a female lover. It was temporary. Attracted to her physically. No real inner connection. (Female prover)[vacuum][es-vac]

There is also in the modern world and in the new remedies an acceptance of homosexuality that was anathema in industrial society and which would not be expected in a Syphilitic remedy. Another social effect of Ecstasy is to break down barriers between homosexuals and heterosexuals. Women are free to hug one another without being thought of as lesbian, and gays are as likely to be hugged by women as men. [mdma][saunders] Tried to examine, out of curiosity, how sexual perversions arise in people, right from the embryonic stage, and why homosexuality is commoner amongst males. Felt it is quite normal or natural to have perverted ideas and homosexuality should not be treated as a taboo or looked down upon. [polys][sk4]

Probably the most important pathological feature of homosexuality in the AIDS Miasm is feelings of confusion and an inability to clearly express sexuality. This was well demonstrated in one of the early AIDS Nosode cases. At parties he often used to be approached by men. He had always hated this. Since the proving this has stopped. Now he finds that women are attracted to him, which he is much happier about. [aids][nl2]

This feeling is also very strong in the Housefly. The most reliable prover had strong feelings of lurking homosexuality. He felt men were watching him, touching him, and were attracted to him. He admitted to a homophobic reaction, one that he believed was an entirely new symptom. [musca-d][stew+] Which, like Hydrogen, has strong issues of gender confusion. Three provers had recurring dreams of gay men or homosexual issues. [musca-d][stew+] The proclivity of a specific gender seemed to be quite ambiguous. A common theme throughout was homosexuality and pornography. [musca-d][stew+] There was confusion of sexual identity. A toddler child of two provers began calling his mother "Daddy" and the father "Mommy". [musca-d][stew+]

It is in Hydrogen, which is the only element that is equally a taker and a giver of electrons, that gender confusion is greatest, and in which serious symptoms around homosexuality and the confusion of sexual identity are found. Sexual desire for men (in a man). Developed an aversion to the idea of sex – confused about sexual issues and identity. Became aware of being bi-sexual or homosexual (in a man). "I want to find out who I am. I should know at 23. I used to know. What am I sexually?" Very confused. This led to suicidal depression. [hydrog][srj2] Confusion of identity (especially concerning sex and homosexuality) and became more religious. [hydrog][srj2] I've been looking at other men in a sexual light. [hydrog][srj2]

VIII-5 Sexuality

Sex is about as close as our physical and emotional experience can get to dissolving the boundary. Since the myth of AIDS as well as its 'discovery' is bound up with the gay community in San Francisco we will home into this: casual sex with multiple partners is attempting an impossible union, too much thinning of the boundary, and certainly has resulted in frequent venereal infections and associated allopathic treatments as well as providing the pathway of infection. This hunger for intimacy expressing as its perversion in superficial unions may be associated with a low self opinion (and its compensations in arrogance) and isolation feelings. [aids][nl2]

We live in an openly sexualized world that would have been unimaginable before the revolutions of the 1960s. It is therefore not surprising that sexuality and issues of sexuality are important in contemporary disease and in almost all the remedies of the AIDS Miasm. Many of the remedies are animal remedies in which, as a group, sexuality is an important general theme.

There is in many remedies an increased sexuality that can be unrestrained, undirected and overpowering. Unrestrained sexuality. [anan][ggd1] Felt as if he would explode with sexuality. [Sherr] [androc][vml3] Dream: There was a large orgy, not tender, more animal-like. [limen-b-c][hrn2] The sexual thrill is very much prolonged, with more than a dozen ejaculations of semen. [cann-i][a1] Went to Buddhist meeting in London for the day. Had great difficulty concentrating on the speaker, on what he was talking about. Having sexual fantasies instead. This is unusual – these meetings are normally very precious to me. [heroin][sdj-h] Many provers experienced an increased libido. [musca-d][stew+] More amorousness during the primary part of the proving than for years. [pip-m][a1] Desire for a young man. [irid-met][srj5] While watching TV felt feelings of attraction to older men. I would not normally be attracted to older men. [irid-met][srj5] I've never felt so desirous, I've never felt so desired. I've felt great. I've felt like a teenager out on the razzle. I can flirt. I feel like a fourteen year old looking at every man, totally ace. [agath-a][nl2] Sexual desire quite marked. [lac-c][c1] Dolphins are by far the most sexually exploratory and freewheeling creatures in the animal kingdom. To put it simply, they will have sex at any age, any time, anywhere, with anything: young and old, male and female, mother, father, daughter, son, toy or human – they are ready and willing. The female often lures the male. They chase and caress and nuzzle and rake each other with their teeth. They even knock their heads together. It is all done in a spirit of fun and play and lasts for hours. Most scars found on an adult dolphin are, in fact, created by the enthusiastic sexual activity of adolescence. [lac-del][hrn2] Very violent erections, with strong sexual desire. [del][a1] Dreams, all of sex, again in another big house. It was of desire and lust, no act, but very very strong sexual tension. [lsd][nl-lsd] Go to town looking for sexy underwear. Feel womanly. Want to flaunt it. [heroin][sdj-h] At night dream of women. [opun-v][c1] Lust to be sexually together with my husband. I enjoy the longing. [lars-arg][fkw1] My body is full of sexual emotions. [lars-arg][fkw1] She has many thoughts about sex. Constant dwelling on sex. Highly sexual as a teenager and had many short affairs with quite a few men. Dreams are usually sexual. [oncor-t][srj-case] Priapism, with lascivious desire. [opun-v][c1] I felt sexually aroused. [plut-n][srj7] Feeling extremely lustful, so made love with partner. [positr][nl2] I want sex, I want it right now. Thinking about sex all day. [positr][nl2] Sexual desire increased. Men seem more attractive. [choc][srj3] Sexual energy high. [lac-leo][hrn2] I make love with my partner at lunchtime! I'm not interested in foreplay only intercourse. [lsd][nl-lsd] Sexual desire is much excited in both sexes, even in the aged. [mosch][c1] Sexual dream of flirting with a young punk. [plac][Biggs+] Nymphomania agg. in puerperal state. [plat][c1] I am feeling very sexual, a very overpowering feeling. [plut-n][srj7] Ogling at women. [plut-n][srj7] Increased sex drive. [urol-h][rwt3] Sexual excitement is great in both sexes, going to the extent of satyriasis and nymphomania. [phos][c1] Frequent erections in men, and sexual thoughts entirely beyond the patient's control. [phos][c1] This is particularly noticeable in the Shark. Embarrassed about increased sexual thoughts. [galeoc-c-h][gms1] I had sexual desire anytime I was not focused on anything else. Constant thoughts of desiring sex. I was frustrated because it was often impractical to have sex. [galeoc-c-h][gms1] Increased sexual desires. Obsession. Wanted to antidote the remedy, the thoughts were so constant and pervasive. All I could think about. Very tense, uncomfortable, uncontrollable. [galeoc-c-h][gms1]

Sexual desire becomes something that seems never to be satisfied. The venereal appetite is increased by every attempt to satisfy it, until it drives him to onanism and madness. [anan][a1] Anantherum is a remedy that stimulates the lower passions of man, most specifically the sexual passions, to such excess that an individual so affected may be driven mad by the sheer force of his desire. It creates an insatiable desire to satisfy the sexual urge, driving the person to repeated sexual contacts. If this urge cannot be satisfied, he is driven to masturbation. The desire is pathological, indicative of an organism completely out of check, impulsively driven to actions which could very well lead to its rapid self-destruction. [anan][vh1] That compulsion of my instinct, sincerely with a lot of frequency it is disturbing me the rest, with an increased disposition the masturbation, at least to satiate some pulses that don't allow to fall asleep, I don't also feel in the right of tormenting somebody to my side, a dear wife that in many moments he/she is entitled the full of being resting and it should not be a simple one servile to my pleasure. The problem is that there I don't get to sleep, with sexual fantasies in the head, with excitement, that becomes inevitable the masturbation. I don't know as explaining. [lepd-s][rsi1] Sex drive increased – couldn't be satisfied and was bothered by it. [carbn-dox][knl3] Dream of constant endless sexual arousal and activity, a burning never satisfied. [haliae-lc][srj5] Sexual dreams, but not fulfilled. Strong sexual tension between me and men – none I know. Fumbling, etc., but more looks and glances, flirtatious and me trying to take it further. Not happening, frustration! No completion, powerful desire with no act. [lsd][nl-lsd] Greatly excited sexual desire in both sexes, with intolerable tickling. [mosch][a1]

There is a tendency to talk about sex but it is generally in a crude or superficial way. Boasting about sexual performance, alternating with self-reproach and the feeling he has achieved nothing. [agn][vml3] Start on the wine. As evening progressed lots of talk around sex. I've noticed that I make a lot of references to sex, or there are sexual innuendoes. [heroin][sdj-h] Sexual talk – crudeness. [galla-q-r][nl2]

In the Rat there is a peculiar desire to be stared at, to be sexually attractive in a very basic way. I wanted men to stare at me. It was the weirdest thing. I would be driving and looking for men to stare at me. [sanguis-s][hrn2]

The sexuality can be described as purely physical. The erection was accompanied with a kind of amorous rage, without any desire for emission; he gnashed his teeth from an excess of voluptuous sensation for half an hour in the morning, when rising. [agn][a1] Increased sexual desire which is purely physical, rising from irritation of genitals. Desire returns soon after intercourse. [androc][srj5] Complete absence of sexual desire, in spite of violent erections. [cur][a1] Hard erections; often after midnight, always on waking in morning, later they last longer, even after rising, desire moderate. [osm][a1] Constant erections, at night, without emissions or lascivious dreams. [plat][a1] Erections while riding, walking, and also while sitting still; not caused by amorous thoughts. [cann-i][a1] In the evening while by his wife no erections, but the next morning on lying awake in bed erections, without sexual desire or voluptuous sensation. [sel][a1] He had erections all night, a thing which had never before happened to him. [tell][a1]

And it can be easily aroused. After an embrace he has an involuntary emission the same night, and a long-continued erection. [agn][a1] Unusually violent erections without cause and without any amorous thoughts. [agn][a1] Seminal emissions with great excitability. [castm][mp4] Sexual desire, with furor uterinus, heat, itching, and burning of the vulva. [cur][a1] Sexual organs extremely excited; very much agg. from the slightest touch, as putting the hand on the breast, or from the pressure on vulva when sitting, or the slight friction caused by walking. [lac-c][c1] Sexual desire increased, easily excited by clothes and pressure. [lac-h][htj1] Priapism in presence of the opposite sex (third day). [cere-b][a1] While dancing with a slightly known acquaintance felt sexually aroused; unusual for me. [neon][srj5]

The arousal can be so great that sexual activity becomes painful. This is especially so in Platina. The sensitiveness of the external genitals is often so great as to make coition impossible. [plat][c1] Unnatural increase of sexual desire, with painful sensibility and voluptuous tingling from genitals up into abdomen. [plat][c1]

Lac caprinum is a remedy that embodies this unrestrained animal sexuality which takes the intellectual aspects of the self completely by surprise. An important theme in lac caprinum is sexuality (goat=lecher) but in a very special way: It also jumps at you. It is a sexuality which takes you by surprise, leaps at you like a beast of prey. And this beast makes you leap at your "victim" without any control, without any distinction. From the waist downward, that is the only thing that counts. [lac-cp][lsy+dmk] In Greek mythology, satyrs are forest demons as mischievous as they are bothersome. They are half man, half animal, shaggy-haired, with goats legs, horns and a tail. They are descendants of

Dionysus and personify the rough sensual side of life. Drinking, playing and pestering nymphs were their favourite pastimes. In the iconography, they are usually depicted in sensual and sometimes obscene scenes. The nature of these forest demons is still reflected in words such as satire and satyriasis. Pan, a satyr with divine status and discoverer of the Pan flute, could give unsuspecting passers-by a nasty scare [panic]. Carousals he organised often ended in Pandemonium. [lac-cp][vml3]

In some remedies symptoms are improved by sexual activity. All symptoms were improved by sex. [lac-h][htj1] Though this is often short lived and they can be worse afterwards. All the symptoms of Agaricus are also aggravated after sexual intercourse. [agar][k2] During coitus, all his sufferings cease, only to reappear afterwards with increased severity. [anan][a1] Great desire for coition, and after satisfaction, nausea and vomiting. [mosch][a1]

One of the most important group of symptoms relate to a sense of detachment during sex. I felt detached during coition. [adam][srj5] I feel detached and not sexual. I could bite my partner as a signal I loved her, not in a loving or hungry way. My partner said, "He is looking at me like a piece of steak, he wants to eat me. He looks like a cave man. He wants to nibble me." [adam][srj5] I had sex for first time since I took the proving remedy. It didn't feel the same, I felt detached. [adam][srj5] Enjoying sex. It flowed better. More detached from husband. [germ-met][srj5] Detached when making love. [lac-h][htj1] (*See Detachment II-4*)

Sex has a tendency to become separate from the usual concomitants of love and affection. Dreamt I was about to embark on an affair with a married, middle aged businessman, just for the sex. We didn't do it though because the night passed in carousing with friends. [aids][nl2] Dream: Went to bed with a guy that used to like me. Then he was calling me to see me again and I didn't want to see him. I told him we just had sex. I didn't want to see him. [haliae-lc][srj5] I let myself have sex with a new guy – I didn't want to – I didn't feel anything, but did it anyway. [phasco-ci][rbp2]

This is extreme in Agnus castus where subjects of both genders found sexual excitement outside of a relationship but none within. A woman who indulged extensively in secret vice, found after marriage that she had no sexual thrill, was cured by this remedy. [agn][k2] His young and beautiful wife excites no erection, though only recently he had clandestine success. [agn][k2] Women may also need Agnus castus, but to a lesser degree than men. In such cases the women are very lascivious, almost hysterical in their desire for sex. Incapable of being satisfied by normal relationships, they resort to their fancies and excessive masturbation. And, interestingly, if they eventually marry, they become depressed and frigid, completely lacking in sexual interest. [agn][vh1]

Sexual activity can become routine without any feeling or passion. Desire for sex with strong erection which remained long after emission, allowing further intercourse. In spite of this, enjoyment was diminished and the act performed without any inspiration in an almost routine way. [germ-met][srj5] Appetite suppressed, the conjugal act done by act of volition, and the usual thrill in ejaculation absent. [osm][a1] Coition, with very little satisfaction, and very short. [plat][a1] Extreme excitement during an embrace, without stronger desire or any repetition of the act. [tax][a1] Dream: Awoke with feeling of crude sexuality without any feelings or emotions attached to it. [polys][sk4] Went to bed and clung to husband, needed him to hold me (due to depression). We made love out of need rather than passion. [irid-met][srj5]

In Rat there was indifference to that which might be expected to arouse jealousy. Dream: My husband and I were at a party. He was flirting with a friend of mine. Lots of sexual innuendoes going on between the two of them. [sanguis-s][hrn2]

Likewise there are erotic dreams that do not arouse or excite. Lewd fancies, even when dreaming; the mind and the sexual organs, however, do not feel excited by them. [ambr][a1] I dreamt of an orgy in which I was the observer. The participants were very energetic and anxious to get it all over quickly and get on with other things. [heroin][sdj-h] Dreamt I was with a group of adults, staying together in one room. The bed in which I slept was adjacent to another bed, in which a woman was masturbating – she must have thought everyone else was asleep. I was curious but not aroused. [neon][srj5] Dreams of cuddles with smaller men, non sexual. [plac][Biggs+] Sexual dream of feeling a vulva with bristly pubic hair; there is no face or identity to the woman. Wake up without feeling sexual. [plut-n][srj7]

There is a strong desire for touch and for nakedness (*See The Skin XII-4 and Touch XII-5*) but they are often divorced from the expected sexual content. A guy told me I was hugging him like a nun. I didn't want my genitals to touch his. I feel like a sexual nun. [haliae-lc][srj5] Dream: I had a lover, my skin was smooth, eyes blue. Desire to wear blues and silvery grey. I swam with seals and felt truly connected. Sexual love felt too gross and unnecessary. Woke feeling beautiful and receptive, like the moon. [adam][srj5] Night – laying in bed with my wife felt warm and cuddly, still no sexual physical desires that are strong enough to act – but somehow its OK with me. She's not too OK with it. [carbn-dox][knl3] Interesting; warm and cozy and cuddly thing sufficing instead of animal grasping thing! [carbn-dox][knl3] Constant need for cuddles without sexual desire. [germ-met][srj5] I imagined being naked, not having sex, with female houseguest. (Male prover) [irid-met][srj5] Still want to touch husband. Not wild desire but more like a pet dog. Affection rather than desire. Getting him cups of tea, stroking him. [irid-met][srj5] Sexual drive seems decreased in the last couple of days, affection and intimacy desired, though. [lac-lup][hrn2] Dream: There was a big hall where boys were making friends with girls; there was no sexual intention, there were just being friends. [polys][sk4] I want affection but I don't want to be touched anywhere very erogenous. [sal-fr][sle1] A sexual feeling, diffuse throughout entire body especially in hands. Sexual feeling increased when sitting still, decreased when doing things. When still, became more aware of it. Pleasant, really nice feeling, like being turned on but not like I have to have sex. Feeling warm, not crude, sensitive, definitely sexual. No urge to do anything with it. [tung-met][bdx1] Dream of being in the bath, with 2 male friends, open and friendly, not self conscious, not sexual. [tung-met][bdx1] Feeling very tender towards my boyfriend these last couple of days. Not a sexual feeling, just a humane, gentle, caring kind of love. [vacuum][es-vac]

This is especially true of Ecstasy which is extremely sensual yet it does not arouse, and usually suppresses the desire and the ability to have sex. On Ecstasy, "thoughts about sex are not always matched by desire". [mdma][saunders] Sexual longings are sometimes expressed, but not the immediate desire for sex. [mdma][saunders] The attraction of raves for women derives from being in a pleasurable group setting, from which the pressure towards an emphasis on sex from men has been removed, in contrast to alcohol-based night life. [mdma][saunders] The pleasure of dancing with expression and empathy pushes sex into the background. [mdma][saunders] Girls sometimes enjoy kissing at raves because it feels good but is 'safe', i.e. is not going to involve sex. [mdma][saunders] MDMA is a curious drug in that it can increase emotional closeness and enhance sexual activity, yet it does not increase the desire to initiate sex. [mdma][saunders] Couples who have had sex on E say that it is unusually nice even without orgasm; they feel more loving than passionate and unusually sensitive to each other. [mdma][saunders] People on Ecstasy tend to become more sensual and less lustful. [mdma][saunders]

There is a lack of understanding as to what sex is all about. Dream of three men with whom I have some kind of intimate relationship. [aids][nl2] This was most noticeable in Positronium. Sex seems strange, not wanting it. Feeling like a child who doesn't know what it's all about, what to do, what will happen. Apprehensive, shy and innocent in this area. [positr][nl2] Strange symptoms around sex and libido either a lustful wanting or a fearful avoidance. In the latter state I feel like a child, sex is something unnerving, something I can't quite understand. I'm too young, and it makes me quite nervous. This has been followed later in the day by a strong desire. [positr][nl2] There has felt as if there is no tension within me at all even to the extent that there seems no point in sex. [positr][nl2] Off sex. I cannot imagine what the purpose of this act is. I think I have had sex only once since the proving and that was boring. [positr][nl2]

There can be issues of violence and coercion in sexuality. (*See Rape, Child Abuse & Incest IX-4*)

And of shame. Sexually totally closed when my girlfriend kissed me. I felt as if it was a sin. [hydrog][srj2] Dream of old friend. A few of us in his house. There where we grew up, he was just down the road. My husband is there too. I kept hugging and embracing this friend. We both knew, this is wrong, but it felt so good. Theme: morality versus desire. Waking up, thought; what was that all about? [helodr-cal][knl2] Dream: Giving oral sex to a woman which began to taste bad. [urol-h][rwt3] (*See Shame & HumiliationXI-3*)

The issue of sex with priests came up in both Eagle and Positronium. Date with the local Catholic priest who has a thing for me. I haven't had a date in years and now this – a priest! [haliae-lc][srj5] Dream about having an affair with a vicar, although all that happened was we were seen together walking holding hands. [positr][nl2]

And of secrecy. Dream: Then there was some sexy sex in a sleeping bag. Quick and rough sex. A man was staring at me in the shower through an eyeglass. [maias-l][hrn2] Dream: I was with a man I couldn't have as my own partner because he was married to a conservative woman. We were having a secret affair. [sanguis-s][hrn2] (*See Privacy & Secrecy IX-6*)

The most widespread sexual symptoms are either a lack of interest or a lack of ability in the sexual sphere.

There is a general reduction in libido. Libido is not there. Don't seem to fancy husband sexually. [aids][nl2] Feeble erections without the sexual desire being irritated. [agn][a1] Diminished sexual instinct; after an embrace the body feels easy and light. [agn][a1] The seeds were once held in repute for securing chastity, and the Athenian matrons in the sacred rites of Ceres used to string their couches with the leaves. Ground seeds were used in medieval monasteries as a condiment to suppress libido ["monk's pepper"]. [agn][vml3] Erotic sensitivity dulled. [anh][jl1] Loss of libido. [anh][jl1] Sexual frequency decreased – but satisfied – not urgency. [carbn-dox][knl3] Sex drive decreased to point of none. [carbn-dox][knl3] Complete lack of sexual desire. Even when partner was keen, I really didn't want to – thought 'Oh, do leave me alone' and then 'Oh, get on with it then'. NO feeling at all – SO unlike me. [falco-pe][nl2] Desire absent. No sexual desire, not even when seeing my wife naked. [germ-met][srj5] Diminished libido. [gink-b][jl1] Sex drive (which had been high for several weeks previous to taking the remedy) was depressed. Orgasm delayed. [lac-e][hrn2] Lack of sexual passion. [latex][nl-latex] Absence of sexual desire. [nux-m][c1] No sexual desire. [sanguis-s][hrn2] Did not feel up to having sex with my wife tonight. [tung-met][bdx1] One reason why women are not into sex at raves is that men on Ecstasy have less interest in sex and do not expect sex. [mdma][saunders] The sexual appetite was very much increased for several days, after which there was a total absence of sexual excitement, until the medicine was discontinued. [ptel][a1] Sex drive is low – almost non-existent. [vacuum][es-vac]

This is often expressed as indifference and "can't be bothered". Sex drive very low, really can't be bothered. [aids][nl2] Disinterested in sex and do not have my customary morning erection. [aids][nl2] No desire to touch, make love to husband all week in spite of easy, relaxed week. I feel detached from him, as if this is a problem within me. [irid-met][srj5] Not interested in love making, last night just couldn't be bothered. [irid-met][srj5] No longer frightened to be on my own. I don't need anyone any more. I don't need sex. [phasco-ci][rbp2] (*See Indifference III-1*)

In the Shark there is a peculiar version of this in that the subject is able to think and act sexually at a distance but when her lover is present she loses all sexual feeling. I am excited that a male friend from California is coming for the weekend. What was interesting was that he was flying to see me from California, and I could be sexual with him on the phone but couldn't be sexual with him when he arrived. He courted me from across county but I would not respond to him when he got here. [galeoc-c-h][gms1] A male friend came to visit four times. I had high libido when he wasn't here, but no libido when he arrived. I could sleep with him in the same bed but not be sexual. [galeoc-c-h][gms1] Visit with boyfriend – no libido, no interest. [galeoc-c-h][gms1]

There can also be an active aversion to sexual activity. Disliked being touched and uninterested in any sexual relationship. Began to be repulsed by boyfriend. [adam][srj5] Have lost interest in my husband, feel totally indifferent. I have hardly spoken to him all weekend, with a desire to avoid him. [choc][srj3] I still don't feel sexually open at all. [falco-pe][nl2] I feel paralysed on the sexual level and it is almost a relief when we don't have sex because of my obstacles. I'm not happy about this. I feel ugly and my body looks ugly. My partner has dubbed me the Ice Queen. [falco-pe][nl2] According to boyfriend I actively avoided any physical contact. Going around the kitchen to avoid touching him in passing. No sexual desire at all, very averse. [falco-pe][nl2]

There can be sexual interest and excitement without the physical ability. Sexual appetite enormous and enthusiastic, with relaxed penis and impotence. [agar][c1] In old men, who, having spent their youth and early manhood in the practice of excessive venery, are just as excitable in their sexual passion at sixty as at eighteen or twenty, and yet they are physically impotent. [Farrington] [agn][vml3] Sexually, I have been much more aware and have touched myself more than usual, but no erection since taking the remedy. This has not caused anxiety, if anything, the opposite. rather pleasant. [dream-p][sdj1] Impotence with increased sensitivity. Orgasm impossible. [mdma][hmd1] Absence of erections, even while indulging in voluptuous thoughts. [nux-m][c1] Desire with relaxed organs. [nux-m][c1] Inclined to coitus but erections weak and of short duration. [nux-m][c1] Lascivious thoughts with impotency. [sel][a1] During coition, feeble erection, too prompt emission, and long-continued voluptuous thrill. [sel][c1] In the sexual sphere there is easy excitement and strong desire, but the male is not highly potent. In the female we see violent sexual desire with involuntary orgasms. [ang][vh1] Excites sexual desire, but causes sterility. [cann-i][a1] Sexual desire, but no erections. [cur][a1]

Or straight forward physical impotence. Erections, but no emissions. [pip-m][a1] Impotence from too much energy directed elsewhere. [querc-r][evans]

This impotence is often related to a feeling of coldness in the genitals. On each occasion he complained of a 'cold, gone,' relaxed feeling about the external genitals, and a sensation as if the penis were absent. [coca][c1] Coldness in the whole penis with formication in the prepuce and cutting, pressing pain in the right side of the bladder. The coldness was painful. I thought an erection would warm the penis but could not achieve one either by fantasizing or direct manipulation. [germ-met][srj5] In imitation of the Greek satyr, the devil in the Middle Ages was often represented with goat's horns, tail and hooves, or it was said that he flew through the air at night on the back of a buck goat. Since theologians in those days believed that angels or ghosts could actually make human women pregnant, it could not be excluded that demons, as well as Satan himself, enjoyed sexual intercourse with people of flesh and blood. A visit from the devil, with the resulting intimacy, never occurred unnoticed, however, since it was common knowledge that his penis and seed felt ice-cold. [lac-cp][vml3]

Or a shrinking or withering of the penis. Diminution and slowness of the sexual powers, which are usually very easily and powerfully excited; the penis is small and flaccid. [agn][a1] The penis is so relaxed that not even voluptuous fancies excite it. [agn][a1] Early in afternoon noticed a feeling of flabbiness in the genitalia, which felt small (second day). [cere-b][a1] Most men have the opposite to an erection: a shrinking penis. [mdma][saunders] Image of naked man, from chest up he is not visible – he is dried out by the sun; he has a dried out penis. [galla-q-r][nl2] Atrophied appearance of the external genital organs. [opun-v][a1] I didn't realize it until later, that my genitals felt shrunken – drawn into my body. [positr][nl2]

There can also be a lack of feeling in the genitals. During the sexual relationship with my husband, I felt my vagina anesthetized like Xilocaína in the teeth. [lepd-s][rsi1] Dryness of vagina. Lack of clitoral response. [mdma][hmd1] In the night, during coitus, little or no sensation. Scarcely any emission or sensation. [cann-i][a1]

This is particularly so in Cereus bonplanadii. Anaesthesia of the genital organs. [cere-b][a1] No feeling at sexual organ. [cere-b][a1]

IX-1 Vulnerability

The most important consequence of a loss of boundaries is that the subject is exposed and open. In HIV the patient becomes open to infection and in the AIDS proving the sense of having lost a protective shell was strong. Felt very exposed – I had no shell to protect me. [aids][nl2] I felt that I had lost my wall, my protection and my shell, and there was a free flow of emotions both in and out. I was exposed, almost naked, with no control. [aids][nl2]

In the birds of prey the loss of strength in their egg shells due to environmental poisoning came very close to making many species extinct, especially the Falcon and the Eagle. DDE, a product of DDT breakdown, accumulated in the falcons and interfered with an enzyme that is important in the production of egg shells. The shells became so thin that they often broke under the weight of the brooding mother. [falco-pe][nl2] The metaphor of the shell comes up in several remedies, particularly the birds. Vulnerability like an egg without a shell. [cath-a][rwt] Physically vulnerable, childlike. Soft thing in a fragile shell. [cygn-b][sle-swan] The remedy has drawn me into my core. I am preparing to shed a shell. It seems to be crumbling all around me and is exposing the next layer – a frightening thing and a glorious one. Today is a good day to die... To be reborn! I am driven deep into my core and find the deeper I go, the more exposed I am. [vacuum][es-vac

However, in AIDS and in a number of other remedies there is a recognition that the lack of boundaries that makes the subject vulnerable also allows connection and communication and so has a positive dimension. Exquisite and precious mental pain – I had no shell for protection. [aids][nl2] I felt like a child, but it was a good feeling. [aids][nl2] Feel tenderhearted, soft-hearted, perhaps vulnerable. Wouldn't take much for me to cry – as if my defences are not there, walls are down. Yet wouldn't say I feel emotional. [heroin][sdj-h] I need to be unprotected. Wanting to be raw, not hidden behind anything. I do not want to be sheltered kept from anything harmful, want to be open to all experience with no boundaries i.e. drive without my seat belt. I sought out an unprotected place to come from. [lac-lup][hrn2] Felt no fear but more aware of danger. Very strong desire not to be at home. Felt I had no protection – felt strong, not like a victim – nothing protecting me. [tung-met][bdx1]] Longing to reach a place of accord, where all defences get let down, and for once hearts reach a place of hopeful joy. [vacuum][es-vac] (*See Connection I-1*)

Most of the modern remedies have a sense of vulnerability. I found, though, that most people, especially those seeking our help, don't feel poisonous and aggressive but rather small. They feel as small as a worm, or worm like, vulnerable. [helodr-cal][knl2] Felt picked on. Very easily offended. Everyone is watching me, flush very easily. Feel vulnerable. [aids][nl2] I felt not completely divorced from what was happening but I felt small compared to the enormity of what was happening. [aids][nl2] I am obsessed about the future and what's going to happen to me. A feeling, nothing specific, of vulnerability. [adam][srj5] Tearful and vulnerable. A situation I would normally cope with seemed threatening. [adam][srj5] The essential process underlying the Arsenicum pathology is a deep-seated insecurity. From this insecurity spring most of the key manifestations known in Arsenicum. The insecurity is not a lack of confidence on a social or professional level, but rather a more fundamental sense of vulnerability and defenselessness in matters relating to disease and death. [ars][vh1] Felt vulnerable, wanted to curl up. [cygn-b][sle-swan] Felt emotionally vulnerable, weepy, scared as there was nothing to relate my condition to. [rhus-g][tmo3] Even the Shark has this vulnerability. Feeling vulnerable, defensive, criticized, I want to hide this weakness. [galeoc-c-h][gms1]

This vulnerability is often equated with a childlike state. The feeling of one who is abandoned, who is bullied and beaten up, a child without protector. [cann-i][sk7] Physically vulnerable, childlike. Soft thing in a fragile shell. [cygn-b][sle-swan] Emotions feel very vulnerable and exposed, almost childlike. [falco-pe][nl2]

And the subject can feel that he or she has to be looked after. I felt vulnerable, that I needed someone to look after me. [aids][nl2] Desired comfort and sympathy. [androc][srj5] Feel helpless, as if I may need to be looked after because I don't feel I can do anything. [hydrog][srj2] "Isolated" feeling as if no one cares for me, or as if there is no one to look after me. [lac-h][sk4] Feeling weak, fragile, lonely. Timid, as if I have to depend on others for everything. Wanted a friend to solve a problem of mine. [lac-leo][sk4] Wanted to be taken care of. [vacuum][es-vac]

The subject's vulnerability makes them cautious. They can feel that they are contributing to their exposure and need to be more closed and secretive. He suspected everything around him, The future appears dangerous to him, as if nothing but misfortune and danger were reserved for him; want of confidence in his strength and despondency. [anac][a1] Feeling powerless and confused. I must prevent this from happening in the future. I must protect myself. [corv-cor][bdg1] Sometimes I say too much about myself to others. Cannot protect myself. Too much is coming out. [germ-met][srj5] I am fearful of exposing my vulnerability. I feel that I should keep my deepest thoughts secret. I need to protect myself. [lsd][nl-lsd] (*See Privacy & Secrecy IX-6*)

This is a little different from the Syphilitic Miasm's paranoia which tends to be projected outwards: others are out to attack me. In the AIDS Miasm the feeling is expressed more in terms of: I am open to attack.

In the Worm and the Dove the vulnerability comes out of their innate gentleness. Gentleness that is hidden through fear of vulnerability. [lumbr-t][evans] Too gentle for the world so appeared retarded or delayed. [colum-p][sej-birds]

In LSD and the Butterfly the vulnerable state tends to be identified with adolescence, when it tends to be matched by a desire for independence and so is often covered up. I have the impression that the essence of this remedy is the state of an unprotected adolescent. The adolescents have the feeling that their parents, though they love their children, do not think carefully enough about protecting them. In this situation, the children are without guidance and feel anxious. [limen-b-c][hrn2] Dreams of being an adolescent; realized adults didn't have all the answers. I felt anxious, unsettled. [limen-b-c][hrn2] Dream: Of being with high school friends. We were going shopping for a couch. We kept trying out different couches and asking for advice, guidance from our parents and sales folk; we were looking to older people to make the decision. [limen-b-c][hrn2] Felt like a teenager, asked out by 2 friends. I really wanted to go out, meet new people, just be out, but I was filled with the realisation that I couldn't. Full of fear, why can't I just do that, why not be adventurous. [lsd][nl-lsd]

Clumsiness also makes the subject vulnerable to accidents. This was particularly noticeable in Dinosaur and Eagle. We had an accident. The car went off the road and looked mangled. [maias-l][hrn2] I had an auto accident during the time of the proving. Driving to San Francisco, a young person plowed into the side of my car. [maias-l][hrn2] Although the bald eagle is seen to be a lord of the sky, it is also often the big, slow and clumsy target of harrying attacks by other smaller, faster birds, including hawks, crows and even smaller birds working in flocks. [haliae-lc][srj5] I was reaching on a high shelf for pots for plants. All the pots and soil came tumbling down. Was knocked on the head, on the vertex. Dirt all over me, and I thought, "This is perfect. This is exactly how I feel." I felt like I had to just give up – give up the bravado. I'm exhausted, I'm just going to rest. I just wanted to go into a little ball and lick my wounds. Felt very much like childhood symptoms. I felt very young. [haliae-lc][srj5] (*See Confusion about Position VII-8*)

In the Goat there is a powerful fear that the subject will be attacked suddenly and the fear of fright is extreme. Fear of being taken by surprise; of being jumped at and not having a single chance to escape: you have had it. [lac-cp][lsy+dmk] This fear strikes inwards (shrinking back), does not come out (contrary to stramonium) and it loads and burdens the organism, especially the heart. The heart cannot bear the sudden frights any longer, it will give way: fear of heart attack from fright. [lac-cp][lsy+dmk] The first reaction (compulsion) is: shrinking back from fright and protecting the sides of the external throat with the hands. [lac-cp][lsy+dmk] This fear and fright is unbearable, you can literally frighten yourself to death. [lac-cp][lsy+dmk]

In the Cat there is a particular vulnerability in the eyes and there is a fear that sharp objects will penetrate the eyes. Mental illusion that the corners of furniture, or any pointed object near her, were about to run into eyes; the symptom is purely mental; the objects do not appear to her sight to be too close (asthenopia). [lac-f][c1] I heard from some patients that they instinctively pulled back, when a finger or another pointed object was pointed at them. Or when a hand, unexpectedly, came close to there face, out of fear there eyes where going to be hurt. [lac-f][wza1]

The vulnerability can give the feeling of being very small, which is the counter to the sensations of being tall. My legs feel shorter. [haliae-lc][srj5] I feel smaller than usual. Usually I feel really big. I'm just thinking about how small I have become. [falco-pe][nl2] When I first put the remedy in my mouth I felt as if I had shrunk, particularly the legs. [neon][srj5] Could imagine myself either very large or very small. My arms could have reached anywhere, or I could be tiny. [plut-n][srj7] I was standing there waiting, and I felt like I was getting really small. All of a sudden I felt small. [sanguis-s][hrn2] It is interesting that the theme of smallness and tiny people came up for a number of the provers. [carneg-g][rwt1] Feeling physically smaller than others. [vacuum][es-vac] (*See Tall VI-2*)

There are also particular feelings of powerlessness. Fear of authority, adults, schooling. Feelings of powerlessness, sensitivity, vulnerability, failure. [aids][nl2] Dream: A small mouse was chasing a big cat. [lac-leo][sk4] I am no person. Feel I have no power when I meet people. [germ-met][srj5] Feeling really powerless and insignificant. [vacuum][es-vac]

Sometimes this is expressed through the image of having no arms or legs. Dream: I had no legs. I was looking at myself from above in a body suit. I didn't have any legs or arms. I was just this trunk in a body suit, and I was hovering above myself. [haliae-lc][srj5] Sensation of not having hands – as if amputated. [galla-q-r][nl2]

Others with more power seem to abuse them. Felt resentful and abused. [androc][srj5] Resentful, feeling aware of being used by husband and family; having to fit into their demands rather than have a life of my own. [adam][srj5] Dream: Sexual experimentation and I was the guinea pig and they were running the tests on me; felt numb and apathetic. [carneg-g][rwt1] Felt invaded psychically and psychologically. [vacuum][es-vac]

Or control them. Each night seemed to be under the influence of something powerful. [cere-b][a1] I feel that I may have been possessed or influenced by a negative entity. [helodr-cal][knl2] Something alien is going on – it's not me – but is it? I feel as if I'm going mad, divided. I want "it" to come out. I feel as if I could be sick and throw "it" up and out, but "it" would have to come from right deep down, "it" is putting out tentacles. I feel disgusted by its presence. It's trying to control me. "It" is a parasite, draining me, a leech, a slug. "It" is slimy and wet and "it" is growing bigger. "It" is real to me and resembles an octopus type creature, something that lives in the depths of the oceans. "It" has got a hold of me and "it" won't let go. It is trying to take me over. [falco-pe][nl2] Felt closed in. My every movement and thought controlled. [germ-met][srj5]

As the subject is vulnerable and dependent there is always a fear of being betrayed or a sense that the subject has been betrayed. Dreams of friends betraying him and felt disappointed. [adam][vml3] For the first two days I have a lot of memories of unfaithful friends. [agath-a][nl2] Felt betrayed by my friends – talking behind my back about my actions – felt paranoid. [urol-h][rwt3] Betrayals, not being treated fairly (very common symptom). [corv-cor][bdg1]

IX-2 Babies, Children & Animals

There is in many of the new remedies a connection between the vulnerable and the young.

This can be through identifying with the subject's own childhood. The food thing is where it focuses for me. When we have our meals together I feel that I am getting this childhood thing; I am being nourished. And this morning I left my lodgings without having breakfast deliberately for the pleasure of coming here and having breakfast with everyone and lighting the fire. [aids][nl2] What I have been noticing is that I want someone else to feed me. It is very difficult for me to feed myself at the moment, as if I am a helpless infant in a cradle. [aids][nl2] (*See The Past II-7*)

Or through feeling childlike. I have had a feeling of being little, feel like a young child. I feel vulnerable. [agath-a][nl2] This afternoon I felt a bit like a lost, fragile, little girl, unconfident, unsure. [falco-pe][nl2] A childlike helplessness, jumping at an attendant and clinging to her can also be a way of coping. [lac-cp][lsy+dmk] Sit there like a small girl who wants to be hugged. [ozone][sde2] Cries, feels babyish apprehension;

fears something terrible going to happen. [pyrus][c1] Feel like a small child – not rational – everything is OK and then panicky feeling – feeling lost – a helpless child. [tung-met][bdx1] *(See Childishness V-3)*

Or through imagery of children and animals, particularly in dangerous situations. Felt really strong love for children. [adam][srj5] Dream: Of a baby chopping up large bone in butcher shop. [limen-b-c][hrn2] Dreamt of babies bathing. [choc][srj3] Dream that two homeless women were giving birth to two babies outside. The babies were like helpless little animals, almost dead. The mothers did not pick them up and I worried that no bonding was encouraged and felt that these modern women should know to do this. [choc][srj3] Dreams of Children and of Animals. [coca-c][sk4] Dreamed of a baby. It was sleeping restlessly, didn't want any covers. Later baby was looking for her potty chair. [helodr-cal][knl2] Horus is often iconographically depicted as a vulnerable child, either sucking at Isis's breast or sitting on her lap sucking his fingers. He is sometimes referred to as "Horus, the child with his finger in his mouth". [falco-pe][nl2] Dream: Cats and kittens clustered around a fire. Frightened of something 'out there.' So the fire was a protection to keep out the beasts. [irid-met][srj5] Dreams of little children. [lars-arg][fkw1] Dreamt about my Alsatian dog (which I would like but haven't got) who wouldn't come when called so this man I knew (one of my son's school teachers) beat him around the ears and I was sobbing for him to stop as it would deafen the animal, the dog was bleeding around his right ear and I was very upset and weepy. [latex][nl-latex]

The Maiasaura dinosaur seems to have been an animal in which the young exploited the natural feelings that adults seem to have for those that look innocent and vulnerable. The juveniles had large heads, short snouts, and huge, helpless eyes. Scientists conjecture that the helpless appearance of the young produced a maternal response in the mothers. [maias-l][hrn2] Dream: I came upon a premature baby sitting in dark city street. The amniotic sac was still intact. On the front part of the baby was a much smaller, nonviable dead twin, attached. It was a dark, damp night. People passing by paid no attention, except for me. I knew it needed help. I hovered around. Soon the sac fell away on its own. It was a little, black baby. I held it. It was alive and slowly responsive. It had straight blond hair and no eyes. There were two nonfunctional, blue eyes when I parted the blond hair. I turned the baby around and on the back of the head was a different face. It was blond and Caucasian and had two supernumerary blue eyes, maybe a third one higher up. They had flat lenses and couldn't see. The feeling: It needed help and nobody was helping. It was a shock. [maias-l][hrn2]

The Placenta is an organ devoted entirely to the care of the foetus and this caring role was evident in the proving. More attentive and protective towards children. [plac][Biggs+] Want to be a proper mother to my children. [plac][Biggs+]

Many of the recently proved animals are ones in which adults have a particular concern for their young. Teams of dolphins can be formed instantly to come to the rescue of a dolphin in distress and lift it near the surface of the water so it can breathe. They will then keep it there for weeks, carefully rotating places until the animal either dies or is healed. [lac-del][hrn2] The mothers are ever alert to potential danger to the young. If the calf should stray near anything harmful or unusual, the mother will push him to safety immediately. [lac-del][hrn2] Dolphins have a special affinity for the ill, especially children who are mentally or physically challenged. It has been reported that dolphins, when confronted with a group of children, will specifically identify and linger with the unhealthy ones. This is said to be particularly true when the children have emotional problems. [lac-del][hrn2] The pride consists of three to twelve females, two to four males, and the cubs. The females share the nursing of all the cubs, guiding them and protecting them daily from a series of dangers. [lac-leo][hrn2] One of the most outstanding characteristics of the elephant is its devotion to its young. The mother stays in constant contact with her calf for the first six months and never lets it out of her sight. The entire herd is ever watchful of the calf's every move. With the slightest hint of danger, all calves are quickly herded into the center and the adults form a protective barrier around them. Under all conditions, even when there is extreme danger to herself, the female will fiercely protect her young. All this maternal devotion to the young is very similar to dolphin behavior. [lac-loxod-a][hrn2] Unlike most mammals, all the members of the pack are deeply involved with the care, protection and feeding of the young. The adults play extensively with the pups – tossing and tumbling with them and enduring endless, sharp-toothed baby nips. The father wolf is an especially attentive playmate for his pups. [lac-lup][hrn2] Very strong sense of responsibility to family, more than duty, they are obliged to care and support. [butteo-j][sej-birds] Baby hawks are very hungry and hawks spend more time than any other bird on finding food for their young. [butteo-j][sej-birds] Protective and caring. [sej-birds]

Even one of the plants has this feature. The young plants usually require a "nurseplant", often a Palo Verde tree, to provide the needed shade for the seedlings to take root and prevent sunburn. [carneg-g][rwt1]

The theme of children that need looking after or the obligation to look after children was extremely powerful. During proving have felt very protective about the children. Haven't wanted to leave them sometimes. [dream-p][sdj1] The maternal animal side came through strongly in images of guardianship and care taking. In addition to animals serving as guardians, images of taking care of animals were reported. Anxiety about who would play the role of caretaker was also an issue. [cath-a][rwt] Dream. I found a robin that had become trapped in a shed it was covered in mud and I set it free. [latex][nl-latex] Was concerned of safety of children. I was just surviving, watching, not doing any action. The world feels very scary in the big global sense. Freaked out about youth, society, where we are going, how we are evolving as a human race. There are so many plant remedies, but our society is not a plant remedy, there is more animal or toxic energy. Lots of adolescents at fair, violence. People are so disconnected, it is frightening. I feel scared for my family for everybody. Feel badly for my children, they can't walk down the street to get a soda. Too many whacked out people. [helodr-cal][knl2] Watch a pair of birds feed their young baby – it can hardly fly. Interested to see that they fly off and leave it to fend for itself if anything frightens them – totally unprotected. They don't sacrifice themselves to try and protect their young. [heroin][sdj-h] Very strong protective feeling towards daughters. Hen and chicks image. Feel more tender towards them then usual. It feels like they are on the brink of adolescence and very vulnerable. Very strong protective feeling, not felt their vulnerability since they were born and very little. [irid-met][srj5] I was worried about my son all night. So I had some fear. I would wake up frequently and look over to make sure he was still in his bed and not still in the water. Several of my dreams, whenever I went back to sleep, we were in the slides or at the beach. I was looking for him in the water, as if I was distracted and I was being negligent and he was in danger. [lac-del][hrn2] Anxious and worried about children that something will happen to them. [polys][sk4]

Especially in dreams where children are in danger. Dream of having to look after a group of children. [aids][nl2] Many dreams dimly remembered – had to look after lots of children, large group of people holding hands. [aids][nl2] Dream: Two limbless babies being cared for. I wanted to look after them, but the caregivers told me it wasn't necessary. [adam][srj5] I had a dream that someone brought me two baby chicks with their beaks broken. [adam][srj5] Stayed at my Father's house and dreamt that partner and I rescued a child being kidnapped in a large American car. There was a lot of compassion and protective feeling towards child. [dream-p][sdj1] The first night I had five dreams. The theme of all of them was caring for another person, very lovingly. It was like a family. In the most marked sequence in the first dream, it was a handicapped person. [buteo-j][sej6] Dreamt of babies, very protective of them. [plac][Biggs+] Dream: Had a baby a year old. Responsibility in taking care of it. Felt very guilty as I ate tomatoes and child is allergic to tomatoes. [lac-del][hrn2] Dream: Pregnant, but not sure if I was, and feeling of responsibility, and not wanting to take on that responsibility. [lac-del][hrn2] Dream of a freak snowfall over fields of yellow corn and oilseed rape. I was trying to save naked babies from the cold and being pursued by hungry fish type reptile. [lac-h][htj1] Dream: Boy is playing on edge of large round precipice. He is not my responsibility, but I am watching him thinking he may fall. He does fall very far down into the center, which is a body of water. I jump in right away, without a thought, to help him. I and another person struggle to pull him out of the water or he would have drowned. He was under for a little long – I wonder, will he be O.K.? Will his mother be satisfied we did our best? [lac-lup][hrn2] Dream: A swimming pool with snakes in it, young children were being thrown in for sport. We caught the snakes, twisted them to break their backs and saved the children. [lsd][nl-lsd] Dream I run after my child which gets into very dangerous situations. I want to save it, nobody helps me, hears me. [ozone][sde2] Dream of taking care of my little brother – a child in the dream. We're in a metropolitan place with tremendous tall signs covered with advertisements. Suddenly he takes off, after something he wants and I can't see him, I'm afraid he'll be kidnapped. [sanguis-s][hrn2] Dream Son is about to blow out his birthday candles and I am upset because people are not singing happy birthday; feeling of anger. [carneg-g][rwt1] Dream: Found an abandoned baby on a doorstep – very emotional – what should I do next – felt responsible. [urol-h][rwt3]

Chocolate has the need to look after children particularly strongly, but it has the distinctive property of ending suddenly and after a certain time the maternal instinct seems to go completely. I love looking after any little animal. I put them in a box, feed them if they are out in a field or look after them if they have a broken wing. But once they are o.k., then that's it. [choc][srj3] I feel my kids are ready to go, but I have to get back to the younger ones to feed. [choc][srj3]

IX-3 Danger & Violence

Throughout these remedies there is a feeling, particularly in the dreams, of violence and danger. It is not easy to categorize but one of the Earthworm provers perhaps summed it up best. The whole world looked grim and violent. Bizarre energy. [helodr-cal][knl2]

There are dreams of quarrelling and fighting. Dream: This is strongest dream I ever had. In the dream I am a man wrestling with another man. I have dark hair, the other guy is blonde. Duality. At some point the other guy plays unfair, he does something that totally offends me (maybe this was done before we fight), so I attack this person. So graphic, I dig the nails of my left hand under the skin of his neck as hard as I can. I can feel the skin break and his blood. I lay into him hard. I am fighting for my life. It is totally graphic. I am enraged, impassioned and wild. [limen-b-c][hrn2] Vivid dreams of fighting. [coca][a1] Dreams about quarrelling. [conv-d][a1] Dream: Short one of gang warfare and knife fights. [lsd][nl-lsd]

Of thieves and robbers. Dream about robbers. Two dark men had come into my bedroom. They sat in my bed and picked out things they wanted to steal. [germ-met][srj5] Dreams of robbers and fights. [gink-b][vml3]

Of general danger and horror. Dreams of danger, and of perils encountered. [cann-i][a1] Dream: War in the jungle like Vietnam. I am an American soldier. I move on from one situation to the next, seeing people being ambushed and killed. I don't see blood. I am trying to survive. I negotiate to keep alive! I move alone in the jungle. I came across a native and another American soldier. The native offered to smoke dope with me and the American soldier. A Vietnamese soldier then took then both away. I felt always in danger. [carbn-dox][knl3] Dreams of the Third Reich. [germ-met][srj5] Dreams of being in an elevator with another woman. Elevator has the bottom open. Have to stand against side and hold on. [germ-met][srj5] Dreams of bomb explosions, of escaping and death in the family; of grave yards, of misfortune. [gink-b][vml3] Horrible dreams, blood and mayhem, awful, shocking. [irid-met][srj5] Fearful dreams of horror movies. [lac-h][sk4] My Nan had come around to stay. In my dream I had woke during the night from noises downstairs. My Nan was screaming and there was a constant knocking on the downstairs door. I ran downstairs to find my Nan in the kitchen the room was trashed and my Nan was standing there hysterical and petrified. There had been poltergeists in the house and as I looked around towards the stairs I saw a large phantom black beast run up the stairs. A powerful spine- chilling dream which left me quite freaked out. [latex][nl-latex] Danger from fire erupting out of a deep pit. [latex][nl-latex] Dream: A dark, wet night. A massive invasion of evil looking bats with cats' faces, coming out of the sky and onto the ground. [ignis-alc][es2] A murderer (a serial murderer of women) had written a book about how he had committed the murders. He had become a celebrity and began running workshops! My feeling was one of fear and horror that murder has become acceptable and even marketable. I awoke feeling anxious. [sal-fr][sle1]

Of people who have been hurt or killed. Dreamed of torture victims. I just remember a snippet of seeing a male torso with a huge cut in his right groin and his penis cut off. He was dead. [corv-cor][bdg1] Dream:

Next night, more sex and death. Murder and disgust. There was a mutilated body in a mangled car at the roadside. Some woman roughly examined the dead body. There was a hacksaw blade. Someone's son was killed. I had to find the body. [maias-l][hrn2] Dreamed of broken windows; of people who fell and broke their bones; of car collision, the cars scraping against each other and tearing the metal. [germ-met][srj5] Dream of murder. [galla-q-r][nl2] Dreamt about a woman and her children being gassed and poisoned by a man in a car. A bad dream. [lac-lup][hrn2]

Of being pursued by dangerous animals and monsters. Dream that a giant black dog, six feet long, four feet tall, a man-eater, was on the loose and after us, especially me. Had to climb a fence out of his reach and cling on for dear life as he jumped up to get me, snapping and snarling, catching my hand. Woke with fear of death clutching at my stomach. [aids][nl2] Dream: Beasts are approaching people from the rear and biting off their heads. I could be both the bitee and the biter. With the bite, you could feel this occipital tension, and then it was gone and so was your head! It was like the twilight zone. [maias-l][hrn2] Then I dreamed about a monster and escaping from it. [irid-met][srj5] When I closed my eyes I had an image of blood red. Then I had an image of black werewolf-like dogs/beasts with white pointed teeth. [positr][nl2] Dreams of being chased and of vicious animals that attack and kill. [tax-br][oss1]

And of being pursued or attacked or murdered. Nasty dream: Someone was trying to kill me and I fought the person by sinking my teeth into the index and second finger, penetrating right into the bone. Dreams of murder committed in the house. [androc][srj5] Dreams of quarrels between near relations, dream of robbers and murderers, who attacked her and her mother. [castm][a1] Dream Someone had entered my room in pitch darkness. I was terrified, wanted to move and get my knife, but was totally paralysed. [coca-c][sk4] Quick, sudden, shocking, and startling dream of being struck in the groin with a blade-like knife, and ripped up through the head. [coca-c][sk4] Frightful dreams; he imagines he is pursued and threatened; he is agitated, screams, tries to defend himself, or to hide. [cur][a1] Dream of ex-boyfriend being violent. [germ-met][srj5] Dreams of being pursued [hir][vml3] Horrible dream of killings, murders and suicides, all vaguely connected with me. It seemed to last for hours and recurred after waking at 3:00 a.m. [hydrog][srj2] Dream: I was caught up in a war and was being tortured, soldiers stuck spikes in my feet. There were lots of faces covered in blood, skeleton-like faces, their skin shrunk against their skulls. [irid-met][srj5] In a vast hotel with damp walls. I'm with a group of youngsters. They want to abuse me. They become nasty. I have to pay them – drugs, nasty, dangerous – how will I get out of it? I feel abused. [galla-q-r][nl2] Dream: Like Pulp Fiction. I and another guy are two henchmen harassing a man. I'm telling the man what a week I've had: two close calls of almost being hurt. My partner pulls a gun on the victim. I am shocked, and then he points the gun at me, and it is apparent that it is me he wants to shoot. I don't know why. [lac-e][hrn2] Dream: Intense nightmare: multiple beings or people against me. Violent interaction with multiple other animals and beings, fighting for my life. People and extra-terrestrials of some sort. Fighting with my hands. They're trying to kill me. [lac-e][hrn2] Dream: My wife was being held forcibly by some men in the kitchen in our house. They were gagging her and she was terrified. I was walking toward her to save her. She was motioning to me to get away, and I was stabbed with swords, killed? He chopped me up with a sword. Do I want to die or do I want to go? [lac-lup][hrn2] Dream: Calling 911, "Man entering home. Mother has been knocked down." Two sons tell me a weird man outside is trying to get inside the house, and we run around locking doors. As I am locking the last door, the man bursts in and knocks me down, beats me. Terrified, protective of kids. Dream was powerful enough to wake me, fast, energetic, active, fearful. [lac-lup][hrn2] Night restless, although very sleepy, constantly twisted and turned, and when I did sleep dreamed of being chased and when overtaken and about to be killed I could not make a sound to called for help. [xan][a2]

All these might also be expressed as fears in waking life. He sees thieves in his room, and therefore hides himself under the bed. [ars][a1] The fear I have is becoming extremely intense: when I hear the door make a noise in the dark I think that my final hour has struck. [ozone][sde2] I have animal instincts, feel all my senses are alert to stay alive. [plut-n][srj7] Hallucination at night of threat of being attacked. [carneg-g][rwt1] Annoyed with partner for watching gratuitous scenes of domestic violence on trash TV after we had just watched a good film. Violence disturbed me. [latex][nl-latex] The world seems difficult and potentially dangerous, threatening maybe. In the world I feel potential danger. [rhus-g][tmo3] Feeling I'll get stabbed. When I see a knife I feel the world is dangerous and someone could grab the knife and stab me. [rhus-g][tmo3]

There can also be a sense that the subject is about to undergo a terrible ordeal. On going upstairs, all colours seemed incredibly bright and the walls were pulsating in towards him and out again. This felt similar to an LSD experience years ago. Overwhelmed by terror, panic and fear, like a psychic attack. Then specifically became fear of being psychically tested as if confronted by something absolutely horrible, as in a "cult initiation ordeal". [androc][srj5] Fear, anticipation in pit of stomach.

Foreboding. [positr][nl2] Feel like my hands are being tied up and bound, as if I have been kidnapped and am about to go through an ordeal. [positr][nl2]

In Positronium fears, particularly those of being tortured and murdered by a serial killer were very strong. Have become paranoid that one of my students is going to stalk and murder me. There has always been something a bit creepy about him, but I have managed to push the feeling to one side. He has become obsessed with serial killers and devours books on them. He talks about walking down street, realizing that no-one is aware of his existence and how he has the desire to smash someone across the head with a hammer or drop a heavy shopping basket on a babies head, then they'd notice him. This really freaks me out because I know he has been attracted to me since the beginning of the course. He was staring me all the time in a really unnerving way and not taking notes as he usually does. Now I'm paranoid that he's going to turn into a serial killer like the characters he is so fascinated by, and I'm going to be his first victim. My big fear and delusion is that I'm attracting this in some way because it's part of my energy field and unless I do something about this, my energy is going to attract this more and it is going to happen, but I didn't know what to do so it's a bit scary. [positr][nl2] I was reading a Sunday supplement which contained an article about a woman who married a man who had been imprisoned for murdering his family. He was the perfect husband for about 15 years. Until she became depressed and he murdered her then killed himself. I became paranoid and scared that my partner had a lot of suppressed violence and that he would murder me at some point. [positr][nl2] Facing my worst fear; being trapped, as in a basement or cell, with a man who is going to torture and kill me slowly with great malicious delight. Cannot escape it, no way out. This is it. [positr][nl2]

Polystyrene has a fear of being attacked or taken away, Had the fear that the ferocious dog that was "behind me" might bite me. So thought that I should keep a doberman or a Alsatian dog. [polys][sk4] Had the constant fear that some person or group or the police would take me away. [polys][sk4] I felt one can't trust anybody, and was treating everyone with suspicion, doubt, fear. [polys][sk4] and it is a remedy in which will act violently but only when the enemy seems weaker than the subject. Had the feeling in the morning that someone would harm me and I should threaten him. But wanted to threaten him only if he was weaker than me. [polys][sk4] Violence – desire to strike, to clench teeth together. Feeling of being threatened and that I should protect myself by being violent. [polys][sk4]

IX-4 Rape, Child Abuse & Incest

The varied issues of sexuality, vulnerability, violence and childishness come together in the themes of child abuse and rape. Although it is extremely unlikely that these crimes are more prevalent today than they have been in the past (in fact the reverse is probably true); they are issues of which people are much more aware than ever before and around which there is much fear.

The Cat and the Stingray are both animals in which all sexual intercourse has an element of violence and rape but which are still part of the way of things. The actual mating in the cat appears to be a mix of pleasure and pain; the tom grasps the queen by the back of the neck and holds her securely while mounting her. The penis of the tom has spines which stimulate the vagina, leading to ovulation. While the queen does allow the mating to occur, she usually screams during the process; it doesn't sound particularly like a pleasurable scream. [lac-f][vml3] Thus one can see the mix of sexual desire, even need [intercourse is required to stop heat cycles] with the feeling of rape and of prostitution. I would suspect Lac-f. to be a possibility for addition to the rubric sexual desire increased while nursing a child. Also such rubrics as coition, painful." [Don Hamilton, DVM] [lac-f][vml3] Dreams of sexual intercourse; many dreams of being pursued for rape, even by relatives. "I have since then found it to be one of the remedies indicated in patients with a history of incest." [Chhabra] [lac-f][vml3] Courtship and mating in elasmobranchs is behaviorally complex and anything but tender. The male assesses the females reproductive condition by sampling chemical signals. The male bites the female prior to, and often during copulation. This helps to hold the female to ensure successful copulation. Males can spend considerable energy trying to mate with reluctant females. Unreceptive females will stab males who grasp their fin margin with their tail sting. Persistence is a necessary attribute for courtship. When a female is receptive, the pair swims parallel to one another. As the male holds the female's fin margin in his mouth, he will lift her disc, pivot underneath her, and insert a single clasper. Sometimes several males on the scene will attempt to dislodge the successful male. [urol-h][rwt3] During the mating phase, females spend the morning buried in the shallows often in groups or lie side by side and on top of one another and form large aggregations called piles. Buried females are apparently trying to avoid amorous males. The whole reproductive phase lasts several weeks. [urol-h][rwt3] Females are noted to mate with many males. [urol-h][rwt3] Females can die from the wounds and fatigue of courtship. [urol-h][rwt3] Dream I am in my hotel room; I hear the door open and close and all of a sudden there is a man laying on top of me; he starts pushing and thrusting; I can't get him off; I try to get up and can't; his weight is so heavy; I try to scratch him but he won't budge – the dream was so real that I thought I was awake. [urol-h][rwt3]

In a number of remedies there are dreams about being raped. Dream: he took me down a ramp to a car park underground, with the truck's lights off and no lighting in the car park. I knew he was going to rape me and that the car lights were off to show that he knew where he was going, he was in charge, he had all the power. I was a helpless victim, pleading with him not to do it (and at the same time wishing that I did have the opportunity to have sex with someone I love). I felt I couldn't escape, but meanwhile there was another one of me upstairs, who knew where I was and what was wrong. Upstairs I was organizing a wolf to track me and the man down and SORT HIM OUT! Then I woke up feeling very tired and worn out. [aids][nl2] Dreams of men going to attack her. [buteo-j][sej6] I woke up after a bad dream. In the dream, a man had come into my bedroom I was lying on my stomach in bed. He lay on top of me. I pretended to be asleep. He got off me, but stayed in the room. When I got a chance, I ran out of the room, but in the next room were other people who wouldn't let me escape. I felt I was a prisoner. [latex][nl-latex] Dream: Sexual experimentation and I was the guinea pig and they were running the tests on me; felt numb and apathetic. [carneg-g][rwt1] A gang took my Harley Davidson away. They were threatening. I was in a room lying on the bed, knowing they will come in to rape me because I was not impressed or afraid by their threats. I knew where and how to escape. [corv-cor][bdg1] Woke from a dream of rape. [haliae-lc][srj5] Dreamt last night – which was of a sexual nature, the major themes were of helplessness, powerlessness even though I was the more powerful entity, of shame, of self disgust, of others being disgusted with me, of feeling forsaken, of no one else caring. Also a sort of moral tension was present – I felt I had to partake in the sexual act and part of me felt I really didn't want to. This part of me felt bullied and disempowered. However another part of me was aware of partly enjoying what I was doing but felt bad. [falco-pe][nl2] Dream of a man who tried to have sex with me. He didn't succeed, but he had made a hollow in the area between the vagina and anus (perineum). [germ-met][srj5] Dream: about to be raped. [germ-met][srj5] I dreamt first that I was raped by a revolting looking man. I was in a house that I didn't know or recognize and he forced me to have sex. [positr][nl2] Dream of being threatened and menaced outside car and house by loads of men. Feel very alone and very threatened. [positr][nl2] Dream of rape. [musca-d][stew+]

Or about others being raped. On going to bed and closing my eyes – a vision of a bleeding, beaten woman standing by the road in tatters. I'm still feeling bruised. [carbn-dox][knl3] Dream: Hearing about a woman who was raped and two women who were murdered. Feeling of threat. [tung-met][bdx1]

There can be a fear that she will be raped. Fear that someone was trying to find out if I was home so that they could come and rape and murder me. [hydrog][srj2] Fear in the dark of being mugged or raped. [ozone][sde2]

There can also be dreams of being the rapist. Dream: Raping a junior colleague because she had teased me. [lac-h][sk4]

In Polystyrene the fear of being raped is strong but there is also an indifference. As in so many things the subject is insulated from the true horror of the world around them. Feeling of a constant threat of being assaulted, especially by the opposite sex. I felt that it could be anyone, may be even someone from your own family, it may be someone honourable, and it is sudden and from someone you didn't expect. [polys][sk4] Dream: Indifference to being approached by four men who had the intention to rape me. [polys][sk4]

In Diamond the major themes of the remedy revolve around the female energy being suppressed and abused by male energy. Vagina still feeling very overused, all day. Idiosyncratic, it felt like I'd slept with every bloke in the universe. [adam][srj5]

Issues of powerlessness and shame are clearly relevant. (*See Vulnerability IX-1 and Shame & Humiliation XI-3*)

There are many dreams about or connections to child abuse.

The Wolf is the archetype for the abuser of children. In Europe, the wolf had a reputation as a child killer, and thus all wolves were seen as a sinister menace to society. There aren't any documented incidents of wolves attacking people. [lac-lup][hrn2] The fairy tale, Little Red Riding Hood, comes from Europe and tells of the horrible, trickster, monster wolf who eats an innocent, little girl and her kind grandmother. [lac-lup][hrn2] And this came through in the proving. Dream: Intruders got daughter. Black magic, voodoo needles in her eyes; calling 911. My children are being hurt! [lac-lup][hrn2] A neighbor is riding on the front hood of his baby sitter's car while she is driving. An old man who looks demonic is speaking to him. I suspect the child is being abused. I talk to the mother. I'm concerned but not emotionally upset. "Who is your pediatrician? Can I be of help?" [lac-lup][hrn2]

The domesticated animals, the Cat, the Dog and the Horse have all, as species, been abused by man. We find with children who have been abused, a humiliating situation as if they were kept on a lead. [lac-c][lrp1] The use of the term, "breaking," reveals a great deal about the relationship that man has had with the horse over the centuries. [lac-e][hrn2]

In Rhus glabra there is a feeling of having been abused and an anger at this. The picture is compelling with extensive reference to betrayal, being used, stabbed in the back, feeling cheated and hurt. It is essentially a picture of abuse. [rhus-g][tmo3] I felt abused and I feel hatred for the people who hurt me. [rhus-g][tmo3]

The dove, by its very gentleness, is the archetype of the victim. Sex and sexual abuse (cooing, my little dove). [colum-p][sej-birds]

There are dreams of being abused. I was a schoolgirl and dreamt (in the dream) that I was being sexually abused by a teacher at school (although in this dream nothing physical happened, he only said things – what he said was indistinct, but somehow I had my legs in the air with knickers showing and he made a comment about knickers and periods). This dream upset me so much that I was crying at school and the headmaster took me aside to comfort me and find out what was wrong. I asked for a female teacher to be present before I told him (not because I was worried about the head, but felt I needed female presence because of the nature of the problem – also because it was the thing to do). So he went off to get someone. Another, young male, teacher came to comfort me meanwhile and put his arm around me and I thought how nice it was that he was prepared to do that when teachers were scared to because of accusations of sexual abuse. He took me to my next class (which was having a class photo taken with toddlers and a dentist) and other girls discussed the fact that they'd been scared of the teacher I dreamt about after they'd dreamt he'd sexually abused them, but actually in class he was ok. I found this reassuring. The young male teacher stayed with me and we left school at the end of the day together. He started coming on a bit strong (cuddles and verbally) which made me feel very uncomfortable – he wanted me to stay the night at his house. I said I had to get home – it was 10.30pm and my parents would be worried as I hadn't gone home after school, and he said he'd fallen in love with me. [heroin][sdj-h] Dream: My mother lines me and my siblings up at a bar about waist height. She does this to spank us. [galeoc-c-h][gms1]

And of abused children. Had a dream last night that I walk into a room to find two young children who are silent and I see that one is mostly naked and her clothes are torn and her body is bloody and the horror of the realization that she has been raped chills me. [corian-s][knl6] Three skinny, impoverished ragged children in the inner city. Eerie feeling, had to open my eyes to get the vision out of my mind. [coca-c][sk4] Dream involving the children and also a sexual element, but not sure if they were connected. There was a pole, like a maypole without ribbons, and a feeling that I had to put a stop to something. [hydrog][srj2] Dream of children, women, child abuse. [ozone][sde2] Dream of children, women, child abuse. [ozone][sde2]I dreamt of a ship voyage with sexual abuse survivors. [plut-n][srj7]

And a sense of being, or nearly being, the abuser. Felt very sexually aroused by image of young male child. [aids][nl2]

In several remedies there are strong Oedipal issues, particularly between girls and their fathers. Dream that she would kill her father; she tried to cry out, but could not, on account of which she was very oppressed; a kind of nightmare. [castm][a1] Horrible dream of my dad trying to seduce me. [plut-n][srj7] I dreamt of my father's death and felt that my emerging sexuality was to blame. [plut-n][srj7] Woke from a dream. Weird dream: I am making love to my father whilst my mother is busy with housework in the same room, (very Freudian). It feels very mundane and normal – everyone does it! [sal-fr][sle1]

There are several remedies with dreams of incestuous sex between brother and sister, they are usually attended by strong feelings of shame. I was in a multi-storeyed house that was so huge that it occupied a block. I had three sisters and a brother, and there were also some other people in the house. Two of the rooms in the upper right corner of the house were filled with very sensuous, sexual energy. I found myself in one of these rooms kissing my brother. I was getting ready to take off my clothes, when I opened my eyes and saw one of my sisters in the room. I tried to explain to her that I didn't know what was happening; the sexual impulse had been just too strong to resist. She left the room in a hurry, and it was apparent that she had told everyone else, when later they all looked at me with disgust. I was at a loss as to what to do. [coca-c][sk4] Dream: I met my wife. We took the elevator upstairs. I ended up seducing my wife's sister. I'd just told my wife how much I loved her. Both women didn't have much clothing on. [maias-l][hrn2] Dream: My sister and I are in bed, we are intending to make love. We are self conscious and awkward and don't know what to do. I realize that I don't want to touch her genitals. [lsd][nl-lsd] Recurrent dream of younger brother embracing me warmly, during some celebration in my honour, and later not leaving me and putting me on a bed. While earlier I had been touched by his gesture, I later felt it was not correct, rather was shameful and embarrassing. Woke up feeling why am I suffering this sort of dream when my relationship with him is soft, delicate and tender, and he is very dear to me. If it were to happen in reality, would feel hateful and angry towards him, would not want him around, would lose faith in the relationship, in people – very traumatic.

I would always have to be on guard with someone I am always at peace with, safe with, on whom I can rely. [polys][sk4]

There are also a number of remedies that have dreams in which the subjects incestuously abuse their children. Not surprisingly these were extremely disturbing for the dreamers who felt terrible shame after them. Dream: I am in a building I do not recognize, and I am with a baby. It is a baby girl. I am changing her and I put my hand over her crotch and feel sexually aroused. Immediately I catch myself and say to myself What are you doing?! This is sexual abuse! This is incest! The feeling is I am horrified and worried for the baby. It dawns on me that just this single incidence can be traumatic for the baby. With a great deal of worry I check her face to see if she is showing any indication that confirms that what just happened was traumatic to her. I feel shame while I tell this to Walter and I feel disturbed, horrified that my subconscious mind can produce something like that in a dream. Does that mean that at some level that is in me? Have I done something like that in any lifetime? This dream was upsetting and continued to be upsetting for several weeks. [carbn-dox][knl3] Dream: This morning woke up – weird sexual dream about my stepdaughter disturbing. [carbn-dox][knl3] Very ashamed, can't even write it down. In dream had intercourse with my son, was bizarre. Just wanted to make him feel good. Wanted to turn him on. He was into it, but he didn't know what he was supposed to do. We were in middle of action when started to dream it, no foreplay and stuff. End of dream. Husband and I had conversation with son about sex, he asked about mating animals. Woke up very ashamed. It stuck with me all day. Very ashamed of myself. Son is very sensual being. I never had a dream like that before. [helodr-cal][knl2] Embarrassing dream: Me [male] and my family are living on an island kingdom with a castle. I am the mother. My beloved son goes off to the crusades and he comes back half nuts, crazy on this wild stallion that is vital and beautiful and untamed. It comes running at me in this field and I have this stake and I plant it in the ground and the horse impales itself and dies. My son is very upset. He embraces me, his mother, and he kisses me and then it becomes sexual and I am willing and aroused. He says this is not moral and rejects me and I go to the beach to hide and find a place to sleep but all the huts are full. I sit on the shore and wait for whatever will come. [lac-loxod-a][hrn2]

IX-5 Anxiety, Fear & Paranoia

The state of vulnerability and the sense of being in a violent and threatening world inevitably lead to feelings of anxiety.

The anxiety that is so well known in Arsenicum. The least trifle fills her with care and solicitude. [ars][a1] He is anxious and trembling and is afraid he shall not be able to prevent himself from killing a person with a knife. [ars][a1]

Is also found in other remedies. When walking he felt anxious, as if some one were pursuing him. [anac][a1] Trembling anxiety in legs, stomach and chest. Fear as if something terrible would happen. [androc][srj5] Extreme apprehensiveness and sadness, and constantly inclined to cry. [castm][a1] Feels very badly, has an ill-defined bad feeling in the evening and at night. [cere-b][a1] Overpowered by indescribable anxiety. Feeling of anguish increased with failure of every effort to strive against the weariness; torment only diminishes with perfect rest. [coca][vml4] Weeping, fear to be alone, fear of meeting an accident while driving. [coca-c][sk4] Intense anxiety, with palpitations. [conv-s][jl1] I took the first dose with considerable apprehension. [maias-l][hrn2] A third had difficulty coping with people and had anxiety attacks which caused him to miss work for a week. [mdma][saunders] Low-grade anxiety without obvious cause. [mdma][hmd1] Nervous and afraid we were going to crash. I didn't like it at all. Sure that the driver was going to miss signs and traffic lights. [falco-pe][nl2] While we were walking along the dark road with no pavement, I was anxious about the cars. My two friends were making me very anxious because they were walking in the middle of the road. [latex][nl-latex] Very anxious; she always started up in fright if any one opened the door, and her body trembled visibly. [mosch][a1] Disposition to worry about something, he hardly knows what. [ptel][a1] Melancholy, ill-humour, and anxiety, as if a misfortune would happen. [rhus-t][a1] Fretful about trifles or only fancied occurrences. [meph][a1] Anxious, and full of care. [tell][a1] On the next morning woke with great anxiety. [phos][a1]

There is a sense of foreboding. Accompanied by an apprehension of misfortune and anxiety. [anac][a1] "Existential" anguish. [anh][jl1] I had a feeling that something bad was going to happen. It was beautiful all around me. The sun was bright and the hills, the ocean. Then I saw the black storm clouds approaching us. [cann-i][sk7] Apprehensive about the shift in consciousness and nervous someone would notice. It is reminiscent of L.S.D., the 'shifting edges', before the full blown trip arrives – an uneasiness and unsureness about which way things will go. [choc][srj3] Great apprehension. [coca][a1] Was trying to go over my dreams, and I suddenly thought about the remedy. I got a huge sense of fear, just a tremendous feeling of fear. It first came like a free-floating panicky fear. [maias-l][hrn2] The same sense of danger; being just around the corner is present again. [haliae-lc][srj5] Sense of fear. Vision: The shadow of death creeping in, like it did in the movie, Ten Commandments".

[haliae-lc][srj5] Went to neighbours for a drink this evening – felt on the edge of a panic attack all evening, not sure quite why, just this feeling of apprehension. [falco-pe][nl2] Anxiety, as if something were about to happen. [mosch][a1] My mind was greatly oppressed with melancholy; tears would start without cause; a feeling of dread, as if awaiting something terrible, yet unable to resist or move, overcame me. [phos][a1] Fear that something is going to happen, with breathlessness, sense of foreboding. [plut-n][srj7] Very restless mood, with anxiety and apprehension, that constantly clawed at her heart. [rhus-t][a1]

That is particularly well described by one of the LSD provers. Put the phone down and was immediately hit by a 600ft wall of anxiety. Felt an all consuming despair, hopelessness and desolation hit me from out of nowhere – not especially linked to anything (vaguely to a money situation we have at the moment but way, way out of all proportion). Total anxiety, despair and desolation leading to panic. I couldn't feel my link to spirit at all for the first time in my life. The image was of previously having lived in a bubble of life beliefs, consciousness, etc., floating in nurturing blackness (space?), but that the bottom of the bubble had burst, destroying all my beliefs, awareness, trust and everything that is life. I'm free-falling downwards through oblivion. There is no bottom to the fall and no-one/nothing can help me. [lsd][nl-lsd]

This anxiety can deepen and become fear, terror or panic. Panic, terror. [berlin-w][hmd2] Very scared of driving in a car, obsessed with crashing and accidents and death. [adam][srj5] A very deep fear and panic felt in abdomen. [androc][srj5] Indescribable fear that something terrible is going to happen to him. [cact][hr1] I felt very scared and alone, like I can't connect with people, everyone having a great time and I felt very alone. It was extreme fear, I was terrified of everything, wanted to get away from everyone. [falco-pe][nl2] Fear I may lose my mind, or even die. Fear about the proving. Feel I could bash the car so I have to make a real effort. [hydrog][srj2] Put safety chain on door when enter house. I'm panicky and afraid that someone will break in. I don't want to be on my own. [sal-fr][sle1] Horrible visions, fears they will take objective form; when sitting still and thinking. [lac-c][c1] The fear I have is becoming extremely intense: when I hear the door make a noise in the dark I think that my final hour has struck. [ozone][sde2] Sudden attacks of fear – in despair – heaven has turned against me, everything is opposing me. [ozone][sde2] Locked and bolted the house because I felt scared. [plut-n][srj7] I fear people. Fear of being attacked and hurt. [rhus-g][tmo3]

Throughout a wide range of remedies there is a feeling that the subject is being conspired against, that someone is plotting against them in some way. Feelings of Paranoia. [aids][nl2] Felt like I was being lied to. [aids][nl2] Felt every one was talking about me in an unkind way. [aids][nl2] Suspicious. Mistrustful. Felt that people were plotting against me. [aids][nl2] Bad paranoia, that people hate me, anyone just walking down the street hates me. I think they will hit me. [adam][srj5] Anacardium individuals can become real misanthropes, with a fear of associating with others. Eventually they will reach a stage of paranoia where they suspect everybody and feel that they are being followed, pursued by others who want to do them harm. [anac][vh1] When his friends were talking, he became very suspicious and fearful, but had no fear of strangers or the police. [androc][srj5] Deceitful. Suspicious. [berlin-w][hmd2] Quite suddenly, or so it seemed, about 10.30, this spooked, very scared, paranoid feeling came on, like there was somebody threatening about. [falco-pe][nl2] I felt mistrust, suspicion and paranoia. I think I'm dangerous to people and they can't cope with me. [hydrog][srj2] Others are hiding things from me. [galla-q-r][nl2] Suspicious – felt that people were saying bad things about me. [lac-cp][sk4] Feelings of persecution, suspicion and paranoia all day. I suspected people (fellow homeopaths) had taken my ads down in the shopping centre or had the feeling that a parent had been listening outside the classroom all the time while I was teaching their children. Feeling as if somebody is watching me, persecuting me! Someone behind my back all the time? [latex][nl-latex] Woke about 7 a.m. Felt a huge fear in the pit of my stomach. Was terrified that someone would find me out. I know I've done something really dreadful and that I would be discovered. I need to do all my paperwork to cover my trail, I've got to hurry to do everything. [latex][nl-latex] Night full of vivid, slanderous dreams, wherein everything seemed to conspire against him, and from which he woke very much excited. [mosch][a1] The other significant thing in terms of interactions was this sense that people were somehow after me for something. That I was almost being hunted. Slight paranoia to it. [sanguis-s][hrn2] Delusion of being watched by a thousand eyes. [musca-d][stew+] I have been a lot more verbal about my paranoid thoughts. [vacuum][es-vac]

This feeling is particularly strong in the drug remedies. Distrust and resentment; thinks companions are laughing at him; wants to do them violence. [anh][c1] He grows suddenly suspicious of all persons and things. [cann-i][a1] Husband wants to go out for a walk. I don't want to go. I feel paranoid that someone will see me and think 'on drugs' and arrest me or cart me off to an institution. [choc][srj3] The most unpleasant after-effect is paranoia which is frequently reported by heavy users. [mdma][saunders]

IX-6 Privacy & Secrecy

Privacy and secrecy are important issues in modern society. We actually have very little privacy and the Big Brother of Orwell's dystopia is sufficiently present to be acceptable and is even presented as light entertainment. Although the primary Big Brother is, as it was in 1984, the government or the authorities; there is another expression of this theme in which everyone is the observer and Big Brother is the collective society. (*See The Observer II-5*) This voyeurism seems to be driven by curiosity rather than by malice and is therefore not so threatening. In the unbounded Global Village everyone is subject to gossip and observation as they would have been within the closed community of the local village.

At the same time privacy is an important issue and has come to be regarded as an inalienable human right.

This contradictory approach is common in the world of HIV where privacy and openness are both often taken to extremes. They are both also major themes in the AIDS Nosode and in the AIDS Miasm. A prover has requested that her identity be revealed in association with this proving thus providing a gift for the homœopathic community as well as transforming her suffering into a personal as well as public understanding of the remedy. This act strikes me as being typical of the dynamic which the disease and the remedy set up. On the one hand there are dirty secrets, the Syphilitic aspects of the nosode, while on the other, there is the desire for openness, candour and above all for intimate contact and a flow from within to without, without to within. [aids][nl2]

The large houses that were an important them in AIDS dreams often contain an element of privacy or secrecy. Dreams about a big, old neglected house, which he recognized as a house belonging to an old school friend. In his dream this house had a secret staircase, from where he could spy on everyone. He was spying on his sister who had an important meeting. The meeting was about a mortgage, which she deserved to get. There were other, unknown children watching with him, and it felt as if they had a common secret bond. There was great excitement and anticipation about whether his sister would get this deal. [aids][nl2] Dream: He said, 'I live underneath'. We went down to his place. It looked derelict outside, rundown, and I thought, 'nobody could live inside'. But inside it was like a palace. There was a huge hall and lots of lovely antique furniture. It was beautiful. I asked him, 'How much do you pay rent for this?' It seems he was allowed to live there by the owner. In the house was a very nice piano – just the right size for our house. I asked him if he thought the owner would sell it. He said he doubted it. He lifted the top of the piano and inside it was a bit like an old radiogram, but it was a CD player. As I looked at it, it shrank and became a wooden cased CD player – modern machinery. [aids][nl2] Dream: went to a house with the possibility of buying it. It was on the corner in an industrial estate with lots of scrap metal around, but it was only an ordinary house behind a very high wooden fence around it and there were no views because it was contained inside the fence. The house was like a Tardis because it was much larger inside. There was space in the hall and the staircase and the landings were wide and the view from the lounge was of pretty gardens and the view from the upstairs rooms was a view of the rolling fields. It was in need of renovation, it was empty but it was tatty and it needed to be redecorated. My family were with me and there was a very contented feeling as if I was home. It was the difference between the little outside and the big inside that was strange. [aids][nl2] (*See Houses XII-3*)

Dreams about toilets (*See Shit & Toilets X-4*) often also contain issues of privacy and embarrassment. I dream that I am looking for a toilet as I need to poo. But everywhere I go there is either a very dirty toilet, or one with no lock, or one with people in the cubicles. When I woke up I thought that I must actually need to go to the toilet, so strong was the urge in the dream, but I didn't. [aids][nl2] Dream I am at work and I have to go to the bathroom and get up to wipe myself and see that my client can see through and is looking at my hairy genital area. I am more surprised than ashamed. A little embarrassed I go behind the wall. [corian-s][knl6] Dreamt of sitting on the loo with a policeman staring at me. I realized I hadn't closed the door. [lsd][nl-lsd]

In several provings there are issues about being observed or spied upon. I did not like the feeling of scrutiny and being accountable and observed. [lac-h][htj1] Dreamt I was being watched. [lsd][nl-lsd] Dream: My conversations were being heard by someone in another room through a microphone. I tear off the microphone with a feeling that I am being spied upon, being watched. [polys][sk4] A feeling of lack of privacy. The second prover had a dream with a feeling of being exposed as with a one way mirror (like in a dolphinarium?). [lac-del][hrn] There are also symptoms relating to privacy being invaded. In a dream, a woman had taken a section from my own personal journal and read it. How she got it I don't know and she would not tell me. I asked her where she found my journal. She would not tell. I became very angry and threatening toward her. She was quite indifferent to my feelings. The angrier I became the more she ignored me. The next scene was a crowd of people. She was there. I went and confronted her. She tried to ignore me. I pushed her, yelling, threatening. A woman came to me and said something mean. I pushed her away. The woman who took my journal said she didn't know where the journal was because she had given it to other people to read. I began to scream at her that I was going to kill myself and she'll be sorry. She'll see, I'll show her. I felt humiliated, trespassed upon, ignored, disregarded, my privacy totally invaded which created anger and violence in me. [corv-cor][bdg1] For the first time I felt my privacy was invaded. [lac-h][htj1] Do not like this scrutiny, my own of myself or my supervisor of me. It almost feels like an intrusion. I must be more private than I thought. [lac-h][htj1] Dream: Intruder breaking into the house. [carneg-g][rwt1] Feeling of invasion/violation/people intruding into my life. [carneg-g][rwt1]

Or confidences being broken. Dream: A woman confides in me about money problems, and I discuss it in front of another. She feels that I have violated confidence. [lac-e][hrn2]

In Polystyrene there is a powerful sense of insulation from what is going on in the world. However, there is a corresponding openness to the world. This is expressed particularly in the dreams where the home lacks privacy and is open to view. Dream: I was with a group of people and a person was showing us his house which was big, majestic, had stained glasses and resembled a European church. Everyone was impressed. Then I took them to my house which was princely, with huge rooms and a lot of furniture. There were new things in it but these seemed out of place. As we came out, there was a big lounge with many chairs in it. I realized that there was a restaurant adjacent to my flat. The two were merged into each other so that there was no clear demarcation between them. I wondered, without any feeling of anxiety, where I would put the door so that people coming to the restaurant wouldn't enter my house. [polys][sk4] Dream: My house consists of a single room surrounded by two open balconies on either side, so that there is no privacy. Also I realize that there is no ceiling and anyone from the surrounding sky-scrapers can look inside. [polys][sk4] Embarrassing dream of changing in a friends house while the window was open so that other people could look inside. [polys][sk4] A similar feeling was strong in the proving of Rubber which is a closely related remedy. Dream of being in some holiday chalets where everyone could see into each others place – no privacy. [latex][nl-latex] Feel need to shut curtain, which I would normally have open, did not want to be seen. [latex][nl-latex] On the way back to the campsite I turned my torch off in the lanes when cars passed so they wouldn't see me – (my usual reaction would be to turn it on so they didn't hit me). [latex][nl-latex] Dream: An old lady sitting in a large old house in a high backed chair, wearing pyjamas and watching TV. She was alone in the house and a group of us took a shortcut through her house. [latex][nl-latex] When

I wasn't talking, I found it interesting to look around at all the people in the pub. Noticed some security cameras I hadn't seen before – thought it was odd in a pub where people are supposed to relax. [latex][nl-latex]

Secrecy is also an issue in several remedies including AIDS. The identity of this man and his case history is not known. It was shrouded to 'protect' his family. Likewise the homœopathic pharmacy who ran up the potencies wishes to remain anonymous. Hiding, concealing, even lying because of self loathing and mistrust have shown themselves to be characteristics of the genius of this remedy, as also is the opposite trait: of openness and candour [aids][nl2] The Aztec legend tells the story of a princess who was left to guard a great treasure, while her husband was away to defend the borders of the empire. During his absence she was attacked by his enemies but although tortured did not reveal the treasure's hiding place. The soldiers killed her in revenge for her silence. The cacao plant sprouted from her blood and since then the fruit was regarded as hiding a great treasure in its seeds, as bitter as the sufferings of love, as strong as virtue and as red as blood. [choc][srj3] Although the patient has all these strange feelings, yet she goes around all day about her business, and no one knows them unless she confesses them. [lac-c][k2] Feeling as if something needs to be hidden. [lac-h][sk4] Bought on impulse four Groucho Marx disguises. [lac-loxod-a][hrn2]

Getting a picture of some remedies can be difficult and repeat provings are needed, they want to keep their secrets. This was the case in AIDS, Results, of the initial provings, though portraying some symptom pattern, did not convey the 'shape' of the remedy. Therefore, I sent some pillules to Mariette Honig in Holland who carried out a similarly exhaustive, yet, ultimately unilluminating, proving. The verified symptoms of these provings have been included in the extraction presented. However, the picture of the nosode emerged with flying colours when in 1994 we carried out two group provings amongst students at The School of Homœopathy. [aids][nl2] and in Heroin.

In Oak one of the few solid symptoms we have is: Not quite capable of stating his own case. [querc-r][c1] In spite of several provings the real picture is yet to emerge.

The most secretive of all remedies appears to be the Rat. The main theme in Sanguis soricis is secrets. Listen to the words of the provers: "Didn't want to be seen. People who sit all day looking out of their secret worlds. We were having a secret affair. Something about this stuff wants to remain hidden." These are deep, dark, profound secrets. [sanguis-s][hrn2] Didn't want to be seen, would stay in the shadows. [sanguis-s][hrn2] Preferred darkness to a lighted house. Reading in the dark. [sanguis-s][hrn2] Secrecy is a part of the way of life for the Rat. Many have extensive, subterranean tunnels where they live their lives without ever coming to the surface – mating, feeding and foraging underground in total darkness. [sanguis-s][hrn2] The remedy was another that was reluctant to give up its secrets to the proving. Repeating the proving remedy. Something about this stuff wants to remain hidden, and I want to find out what that is. [sanguis-s][hrn2]

IX-7 Trapped

One of the important feelings if the AIDS Miasm that seems to contradict the lack of boundaries is the feeling of being trapped and hemmed in.

This comes partly from the fact that you need to be able to find boundaries in order to escape them. If they are not there you can never cross them to reach the freedom of the other side.

However, more important is the fact that without boundaries there is nothing to stop others from coming in and holding and controlling the subject.

In Diamond there is a powerful feeling of female energy being trapped by the power of masculine force. Aware of having been trapped in a role, always left holding the baby. [adam][srj5] Desire to run away – in a balloon – up and out of it all. [adam][srj5] Exceptionally strong desire to leave my marriage and children, to live a clear unmuddled life alone. [adam][srj5]

The trained Falcon is a lover of freedom but is the animal that is most thoroughly trapped and restricted and this came through in the proving. I feel cramped. Like there is absolutely no space for me. [falco-pe][nl2] I feel like that reined in wild stallion who is terrified and has to fight free. I became totally detached and very angry and vengeful even though I knew these were wasted feelings. [falco-pe][nl2]

It is also a feature of the Eagle. Eyes feel nearsighted. Don't want to look far away. Don't want to go far out of my house either, not even to the market. Don't want to go far outside my territory. [haliae-lc][srj5] Wanted to escape and fly away. Phoned the airlines, trying to fly away. [haliae-lc][srj5]

And of birds in general. Birds live in air, supported and carried by it, can soar and dive there is a tremendous sense of Freedom. Freedom of movement, expression, from attachment. For freedom to be a concept there must be the opposite e.g. an absence of freedom. Freedom will be an issue for people needing this remedy. Freedom/Lack of Freedom. Imprisoned in body, Imprisoned in society rules, Imprisoned in obligation e.g. should, – responsibility, duty, right and wrong. [sej-birds] Macaw had much entrapment. [ara-mac][sej7] This yearning for freedom was very strong. [buteo-j][sej6] Feel trapped. [cygn-b.][sle-swan] Crammed in and didn't belong. Want to be myself, liked being the outsider. [cygn-b][sle-swan]

The image used in the Falcon proving is of the wild stallion, and freedom is also an issue for the Horse. Man has subjugated the horse and used it for a variety of horrendous tasks. The horse, first and foremost, has been used in battle. Everywhere, wars were fought on the backs of these unfortunate creatures, who died in untold numbers, without the slightest idea of what the screaming and shooting was all about. Next, the horse was used and abused on the farm. Day in and day out, horses pushed and pulled and carried heavy loads until they dropped from exhaustion. The final insult was that once their usefulness ended, they were sent to be killed and made into glue. The rodeo and racetrack provided other settings for horse suffering. Certainly they love to run, but spurring and whipping diminish the pleasure. [lac-e][hrn2]

And for other domestic animals such as the Dog and especially the Cat. Cats that have run wild tend to grow larger than normal, probably because there is an abundance of natural food and because they lead a more healthy life. Moreover, it has been found that feral cats are not only larger and fiercer than domestic cats, but that their descendants return to the form of the tabby, the colour of their ancestors. The domestic cat is less removed from its wild ancestors than, for example, the domestic dog, and has remained more independent than the latter from human beings. [lac-f][vml3] Within a relationship, a clinging or grasping partner evokes a sensation of claustrophobia or constriction. 'Women stick to you like a limpet' was how one male patient expressed it. There is a great fear of attachment and an aversion to persons who 'hang on to your apron strings'. [lac-f][vml3] On the physical level a Lac felinum person is intolerant of constriction, especially around the neck. [lac-f][vml3]

Yet even the dog's wild cousin experiences it. Dream: Pursued through old building. Despair of being trapped with no way out. [lac-lup][hrn2]

The Berlin Wall's purpose was to trap and imprison people and this is a part of the remedy picture. Feel trapped, unable to break free. [berlin-w][hmd2]

In the Cactus this feeling of being trapped or caged is a very physical one. Whole body feels as if caged, each wire being twisted tighter and tighter. [cact][hr1]

Germanium is perhaps the most specific AIDS Miasm remedy and the feeling of being trapped or a prisoner is a keynote. Felt not enough space in bed. It's a big bed. [germ-met][srj5] Felt closed in. My every movement and thought controlled. [germ-met][srj5] Felt uncomfortable if any one stood close to me. Felt uneasy and paranoid in class.

Feel as if done something wrong. [germ-met][srj5] Feel like a prisoner. [germ-met][srj5]

Again the wild animal metaphor is used. I'm desperate. I want to die. Feel the power to kill. Feel like a wild animal locked in. It's strong, so intense. I hate so strong, feel a terrible disgust and I'm afraid of what I'm able to do. It's completely impossible to be in it and impossible to get out of it. [germ-met][srj5]

Iridium and Positronium both have a strong feeling of being oppressed and trapped. A sudden, very deep desire for wilderness, space and air and height. [irid-met][srj5] Today I noticed how narrow my life feels, and what I feel like doing is making my life even narrower. [irid-met][srj5] I felt all closed in like I couldn't move, I couldn't breathe. I felt oppressed by being in this room, there's no space. It's funny but I felt like that tonight when I was sitting outside. There were lots of clouds in the sky and it felt like they were coming down on me. Like the sky had been really close and the clouds in the sky were nearer to me. [irid-met][srj5] Had this longing to find real wilderness. Britain is too full, nothing is really alive anymore except people. The world really feels too oppressed with people and roofs. I kept saying to partner, "Why do we live in this dreary, ugly place, where people know nothing about freedom, and certainly nothing about discovery or mystery, just tarmac and roofs." It struck me that the world was too small for me, and thought "That's got to be something about the remedy, something around pressure." [irid-met][srj5] I have been told that I seem irritable. I don't feel it. I just feel that I want to be quiet and left alone. I don't want anybody to make a fuss. I just want to be peaceful. [positr][nl2] There seemed to be nowhere for me to sit and just be. I felt angry that my space was being invaded. [positr][nl2] Anxious, scared and restless, hard to sit still. Felt as if he would explode in a building society waiting in a queue. Felt trapped but decided to stay, the queue seemed to take ages. [positr][nl2]

Drugs are often an attempt to escape the feeling of being trapped. Desired alcohol and drugs, a feeling of wanting to escape. [androc][srj5]

And Drug remedies encompass that feeling. Had an image of a hedgehog's face. Overwhelming desire to curl up under the duvet and to keep warm, so I did. Tightening around right side of jawl felt like being outside, roaming around without any possessions, to have the freedom to go where I want to go when the feeling took me. I felt very restricted. [choc][srj3] Dream: I was in a muddy swamp. It was quite yucky and I didn't know how to get out of it. [heroin][sdj-h]

The reaction to this trapped feeling is a desire to be out in the open. There is a powerful desire to be outside and particularly to be in and with Nature. Feel need to be outdoors, in air surrounded by trees even when raining, need air and space and beauty all around. [adam][srj5] Resentful of having to be inside in this weather. Wanting open air. Wanting to be very physically active. [limen-b-c][hrn2] When I look, I want to see far distances and sky, not houses. Went to estate agents to look at country houses. [choc][srj3] Overwhelming desire to be in the country. [hydrog][srj2]

Being outside also tends to ameliorate symptoms. I feel trapped. Getting out of the house ameliorates. [adam][srj5] Took a walk in the woods and found it very refreshing. [lac-lup][hrn2] Everything provokes laughter, quite contrary to habit; this was especially noticeable on going into the open air. [nux-m][a1] I sit down and can't fully concentrate. I need my space. I feel hemmed in. Went to park, drove, didn't want to be round streets and houses. Happy at the park, singing. [positr][nl2] Worse in the house, relieved by walking in the open air. [rhus-t][a1] The symptoms decrease by walking in the open air, but they return when sitting. [ambr][a1] if you force them to take a brisk walk, especially in fresh air, they feel better. [cann-i][vh1] Symptoms seemed to lift when I was able to be outside and garden or walk. [carbn-dox][knl3] When outside and looking at people, thought to myself I know them. People were friendlier to me. Thought I could start a conversation with strangers. [germ-met][srj5]

X-1 Infection

Infection is a doubly important issue in HIV. In the first instance because it is an infectious disease and in the second because its pathology is to allow other infections to take hold in the body.

When the mechanism of AIDS was first beginning to clarify it was feared that it was extremely infectious. The appearance of AIDS in haemophiliacs and intravenous drug users indicated that it was an infectious disease and that the infectious agent was carried in the blood. The appearance of AIDS in female partners of high risk men, indicated that the infectious agent was probably present also in semen. The cases of babies suggested that breast milk might also be a carrier. The obvious conclusion was that all bodily fluids, including saliva, were possible carriers of the infectious agent. What had at first seemed to be restricted to a particular, and somewhat isolated, community; now came to be seen as a plague that would affect everyone. A simple kiss could be a death sentence. [aids][nl2] It has since become apparent that it is an infection that is very difficult to pass on. In almost all instances penetration, either sexual or with infected equipment, is required to cause infection. The only other mechanisms are from mother to child through the mixing of blood during birth, or from contaminated blood products. However, the myth of infection has become part of the genus of the disease and it is found in the Nosode and throughout the Miasm.

Several remedies including the Nosode have dreams about AIDS. Dreamt that a friend told me a mutual ex-boyfriend had all along been having sex and therefore (sic) we were both at risk from HIV and AIDS. [aids][nl2] urol-h][rwt3] Dreamt of friend having AIDS, also that I had cancer and that my sister had her eyes and mouth stapled shut. [lac-h][htj1] Dream: Woman was complaining about classmate because he had HIV and that he had diarrhea and would never clean the toilet. [urol-h][rwt3]

The most powerful perhaps being Iridium's. Dream: My child had AIDS. Met man in front of a marquee who was losing his hair and teeth although he was quite young. He was trying to talk about AIDS to me. I was thinking I knew I would outlive my child. [irid-met][srj5]

There are dreams about infection in general. Dream: I was supposed to be going somewhere to meet some people to run some kind of training, and I had to be there by 6 o'clock, but on the way I found all these boxes of tampons and I was thinking 'wow, that's really nice, they are unbleached ones'. But then I thought they might be infected because they were out on the street. [aids][nl2] Dreams of epidemic, contagious diseases, and especially of hydrophobia. [anan][a1] Dreamed I was taking a boat trip to a party at a country club in San Jose. The boat started taking on water and there was urine in the water. I was mad that my party clothes were getting ruined. It was hot and stuffy because the captain turned off the ventilation due to a crew member getting sick with strep throat. The captain didn't want the disease to spread. While on the boat we were passing what looked like a war zone, buildings burning and buildings that are now rubble (like they were bombed out). It seemed like a foreign country. [helodr-cal][knl2] Dream: I lift up my sleeve to discover that I have some horrible skin disease on my left arm. The doctor informs me that my disease is somewhat incurable. [lac-h][sk4] Dream: I was in a group under threat – my van had a 'bug' which was a harmful illness somewhere in the back of the van so I had to wash all my clothes, sheets, etc. but I had packed up my house so had to stand my washing machine in the street and run it off the car! [latex][nl-latex]

In the Swan the feeling of being diseased is part of the more general feeling of being excluded, an outsider. Felt pushed aside by family. They were well and I was ill. [cygn-b][sle-swan](*See Isolation II-8*)

There are also dreams about horrible diseases in others. Dreamt I was in a car accident which ran over my dog, but when I got home he was alive, but a different colour and had a horrible septic state all over his paws and legs, which had taken the fur off, leaving raw flesh. [aids][nl2] She is dreaming about the loathsome diseases of others. [anac][a1]

And in the self. Woke up with the sense of having a deep, deadly disease. [coca-c][sk4] This is particularly a feature of Lac caninum. Woke at daylight, feeling that she was a loathsome, horrible, mass of disease. [lac-c][c1]

There is a fear of infection. Afraid I would catch germs from a patient. [limen-b-c][hrn2] Had a cup of weak caffeinated coffee, I felt infected by the woman who offered it. I didn't really want it but had a fantasy she couldn't have coffee alone, and I didn't want to reject. Because of the proving I thought "shit" then "sod it". [positr][nl2] Dream: One woman is disgusted with my bathroom because I have cloth towels rather than more sanitary paper towels for drying hands. I think she is overly critical but also wonder if maybe she has a valid point. [galeoc-c-h][gms1]

The fear of contamination by a dirty and contaminated world and the need to maintain, or to obtain purity is particularly strong in Fire. To maintain my own purity, I feel the need to avoid contamination from others. It's as if it can rub off. [ignis-alc][es2] I felt I had come into a den of iniquity in the bowels of the earth. I was watching the backs of people sitting at the bar with their pints of Guinness and thinking

'Those poor, unfortunate, lost souls – they are beyond redemption'. I felt I had to get out of the place quickly before I got contaminated. [ignis-alc][es2] Avoiding people who I feel will contaminate me, i.e. people who are too emotional, slow, dirty, over needy, untogether in any way. [ignis-alc][es2] I feel like I'm standing way above the earth looking down on a cesspool of ignorance and vulgarity, a stab city market place of vice, corruption and perversion. I cannot be part of it – I do not know how to exist in it. [ignis-alc][es2]

And the expected corollary of washing. Washing her hands always. [coca][sk7] Extreme fearfulness with hiding is common in cats. Arsenicum album often helps. One can easily imagine the ever washing cat as an arsenicum! I wonder even about Lac-f. belonging in the rubrics mind: washing, always washing her hands, mania for bathing, etc. [Don Hamilton] [lac-f][vml3]

These are symptoms of the Syphilitic Miasm as well. There is a distinction though. In the Syphilitic Miasm the feeling is that others, even other diseases, are out to get the subject and they are deliberately targeting him or her. In the AIDS Miasm the world is a dirty, infectious place and the subject is open to that infection. Everything he sees appears foul and nasty. [cur][a1] This is the same distinction that is found between the forms of paranoia in the two miasms. In the Syphilitic, people are out to attack the subject, whereas in AIDS the subject is vulnerable and lives in a violent world. (*See Anxierty, Fear & Paranoia IX-5*)

The AIDS Miasm also has the feeling that they are likely to contaminate others, this is an underlying feeling in Syphilitic remedies as well, but it is not one that the subject can admit, even to him or herself. Whereas it is more openly expressed in the AIDS remedies.

The feeling that disease is an entity, one that has taken over the subject is also apparent. Something alien is going on – it's not me – but is it? I feel as if I'm going mad, divided. I want "it" to come out. I feel as if I could be sick and throw "it" up and out, but "it" would have to come from right deep down, "it" is putting out tentacles. I feel disgusted by its presence. It's trying to control me. "It" is a parasite, draining me, a leech, a slug. "It" is slimy and wet and "it" is growing bigger. "It" is real to me and resembles an octopus type creature, something that lives in the depths of the oceans. "It" has got a hold of me and "it" won't let go. It is trying to take me over. [falco-pe][nl2]

This is also a Sycotic symptom but in Sycosis it is because the subject is weaker than the powerful influence. In the AIDS Miasm it is because the subject has insufficient boundaries to prevent the influence from entering.

There is in many of the AIDS Miasm remedies an anxiety about health. I am generally quiet serene myself except that I seemed to get unusually upset when I get a symptom. It occurred to me that weeping over my itchiness was unusual. Normally I would just shout and curse angry, but this time the reaction is somehow feminine. Not wanting to talk. [positr][nl2] As a natural consequence of such a lifestyle, of such intense identification with earthly pleasures, once they begin to suffer from some kind of disturbance in their health, they become overwhelmed with a fear of dying. The fear that pleasure may end and be replaced by suffering is unbearable. They become restless with a constant fear of death. [anan][vh1] The essential process underlying the Arsenicum pathology is a deep-seated insecurity. From this insecurity spring most of the key manifestations known in Arsenicum. The insecurity is not a lack of confidence on a social or professional level, but rather a more fundamental sense of vulnerability and defenselessness in matters relating to disease and death. [ars][vh1] Anxiety about my condition during flu-like symptoms. [choc][srj3] Discouraged about his health. [phos][a1]

And a fear that the subject has some disease. I am concerned about my health. Think I have TB or pneumonia. I am sure I will die. [adam][srj5] Particularly cancer. Fear of breast cancer because of aching in the breast and arm. Feel a certainty of breast cancer. [adam][srj5] I have a constant fear of cancer. When I think of being with cancer it explains the state that I feel – the sense of dis-ease. I don't feel myself, I feel unattractive and ill, run-down. [latex][nl-latex] Fits of fear of cancer. [ozone][sde2] Fear of cancer is getting obsessive. [plut-n][srj7]

X-2 Flu & Non Specific Infections

The infections that are damaging in AIDS are not directly caused by the Virus but are ones that are allowed in by the weakened immune system. Although the original syndrome was defined by a few specific infections, PCC and Karposi's sarcoma in particular, these were just the ones that stood out because of their general rarity.

The overwhelming feature of AIDS and of the Miasm in general is non-specifity. The most common veneral disease in the modern world is non specific urethritis (NSU), and the quality of being ill-defined, non specific and hard to pin down is very important in the pathological manifestations of the AIDS Miasm.

Sometimes symptoms are just confused. Complains without knowing what ails him; complains much, but of nothing in particular. [mosch][fr1]

But in other cases they are described as being like a cold. The mind is much confused, as if a cold were coming on. [anac][a1] Feel that

I am sick (fifth day). Feel like one recovering from a cold (third day). Went to bed feeling miserable. [cere-b][a1] Still feel like I am fighting a low-grade cold. I have not had this little energy in a long time. I feel really wiped out – always ready for nap. [lac-loxod-a][hrn2] Cold like symptoms – sneezing twice with a runny nose, worse for a draught. [latex][nl-latex] In myself it set up all the symptoms of a common cold. [oxyg][c1] Felt as if I had another cold coming on – before the effects of the last are over! Draggy feeling, sniffly, upper respiratory fuzziness and heaviness. Mentally fuzzy too. [positr][nl2] It's often said that taking Ecstasy affects your immune system, making you more likely to catch a cold afterwards. [mdma][saunders] I feel slightly hazy and distant, like the beginning of a cold. [irid-met][srj5] Ache. Felt like a full-on head cold aggrevated by. movement. Nasal obstruction. Spaciness. Kept saying to myself this cannot be the proving. [lac-del][hrn2] I had all the symptoms of a common cold without a cold. [vacuum][es-vac]

The symptoms seem most to match those of flu. General feeling of malaise, with aching in the lower extremities, and premonitory symptoms of fever. [ptel][a1] The next day she felt, in the afternoon, chills and feverishness by turns, and general malaise. [rhus-t][a1] Feel tired, my head feels thick, heavy and boggy as if a headache is coming on. [adam][srj5] Feeling of physical misery. [anh][jl1]

And they are repeatedly described as flu-like. Flu like sensation. [aids][nl2] Thought I was getting the flu. [adam][srj5] There have been reported cases of allergies to scorpions developing in people working with them, to an extent that the effect would be felt even if there was a scorpion in the neighbouring room: the effect resembled a "flu" – constant sneezing with profuse nasal secretions and lachrymation, nausea and a headache that felt as if there were hammers beating in the head. Eyes were burning and hands trembling, all better fresh air. These "flues" appeared in the provings. [androc][srj5] Anxiety about my condition during flu-like symptoms. [choc][srj3] I feel like I have the flu. Headache, tired. [corian-s][knl6] Influenza-like symptoms. Malaise. [mdma][hmd1] Influenza. [gink-b][mp4] Felt like flu – hot dizzy and aching all over. [germ-met][srj5] Felt whole head and body aching as if I was getting flu. Cold symptoms coming out. Bunged up with cold in the nose. Spent the morning in bed. [latex][nl-latex] The bark of the willow contains salycilic acid, which has been used in herbal medicine, and as aspirin in conventional medicine, to relieve the pain of headaches, rheumatism and flu. [sal-fr][sle1] Flu feeling in back of head, lots of catarrh and coughing with fuzzy feeling in the head. [tung-met][bdx1]

X-3 Dirt

The feelings of danger from infection are often expressed as issues about dirt. Several of the new remedies are substances that are generally regarded as dirty, particularly the Housefly, the Rat and the Worm. Earthworms are slippery and slimy and evoke all sorts of reactions. Usually, unlike a fear of venomous creatures there is primarily an initial disgust over the earthworm's slimy and soft exterior and then a protective feeling (unless you are a young boy with plans). [helodr-cal][knl2]

Two of the remedies derive their names from the Greek word for smell. The name Osmium is derived from the Greek word 'osmos', meaning 'smell', because of the nasty smell of osmium tetroxide. [osm][stj2] The name derives from the Greek which means to smell, to spread odour. [ozone][sde2]

General issues of dirt are found in some remedies. Thought I was surrounded by dirt. [adam][srj5] Theme: Putrefaction or purification. [Sherr] [androc][vml3] Feel like I'm waging war on dirt. [ignis-alc][es2]

And there are dreams about dirt. Dream: I went to the elevator and someone had put and set off a bomb in the lobby elevator panel but I wasn't worried. I was going to use it anyway. The elevator came. The door opened and inside was empty and filthy – like a homeless person lived there – filthy clothes, a cardboard box, grime on the walls. It was too disgusting and I left. [helodr-cal][knl2] Dream: I was in a muddy swamp. It was quite yucky and I didn't know how to get out of it. [heroin][sdj-h] Powerful dreams of Dirt, Infection and Shit. [positr][nl2] I am having dreams of dirty going to clean. [cath-a][rwt] Dream: I am trying to find a way to purify myself, and so I go down to the water's edge and begin to pour huge buckets of Bay water over myself and down my throat. But I realise the water is polluted and full of mud and shit, and I gag. [vacuum][es-vac]

The Housefly is one of the "dirty creatures" and the theme of dirt is very important in it. Favourite sources of food material are garbage dumps, trash cans, fecal matter and spoiled and rancid foods. They are often thus vectors of disease. [musca-d][stew+] One prover thought he was being followed by garbage. [musca-d][stew+] Many provers expressed disgust with their surroundings. [musca-d][stew+] One prover who had seemed to enjoy every moment of the proving got quite upset after finding out it had been a "grotesque substance". [musca-d][stew+] There was a lot of talk about putrefaction, rotting garbage, maggots, corruption, excrement, toilets, sewers, tunnels and dirty water. [musca-d][stew+]

Dirt and pollution tie in with the feeling of ecological doom. Dreamt of going on holiday to the seaside, our favourite beach polluted by a nearby factory newly-built. [falco-pe][nl2] Dream of dirty water, sea with wild big waves, but it is black almost like liquid tar. [ozone][sde2](*See Nature I-7*)

Issues of dirt and disgust often congregate around the theme of food. Dream: somebody had cooked some food, and I filled up my plate and took a mouthful and it was so disgusting, I thought I can't eat this, but I didn't want to insult the person who had cooked it, so I was like trying to throw it in the bin without them seeing. [agath-a][nl2] I urinate on a tray in a restaurant. Surprised at myself for doing it. I tried to hide the evidence. Waiter came to collect the tray. I looked at the ground rather than at him – hoped he wouldn't notice. [phasco-ci][rbp2] Garlic cooking at college, I normally love the smell, but it smells rancid, foul and impure. [lsd][nl-lsd]

Particularly in Falcon. I still have a disgust around food. I don't want to prepare or eat it. [falco-pe][nl2] Had thoughts that when Misha tells us the remedy I will throw up because it is so disgusting. [falco-pe][nl2] Dream of a picnic with lots of traditional food that was seen as a joke, cleared away and the real food brought on – a corpse and other revolting edibles instead. I was revolted but not totally surprised. [falco-pe][nl2] Went round Tesco's tonight, had to get away from the meat counter because something smelt so strong. It was a disgusting smell – just had a whiff – it could have made me feel sick, was really strong. [falco-pe][nl2]

In Oxygen the metaphorical corruption of society is an important issue that reflects the decay of the subject's person and situation. Corruption is another important theme in this remedy. In the initial stages they abhor the thought of corruption. They can't even accept small favours and little presents, because they feel it to be the beginning of the end. It is a sign of their fear to be polluted by corruption. [oxyg][stj2] In later stages they may also start to neglect themselves, their house or their business. They will lead the life of a tramp, dressed in rags and muttering to themselves about the injustice of it all. They like to shock others with their appearance and the things they say. [oxyg][stj2] I hadn't wiped my anus properly after the toilet and forgot to wash fully in the shower. I am usually more thorough than that. [rhus-g][tmo3]

Several remedies have a dirtiness of the person and particularly smell. Constant smell before the nose, like pigeon or chicken dung, especially when smelling his clothes, or his body. [anac][a1] Feel grubby even after a shower. [hydrog][srj2] The secretions are foul, urine smells like violets, belchings like radishes and axillary sweat like garlic. [osm][mp4] Evolution of such a persistent odor, that for the remainder of the session, the patient had to sit apart from his fellow-students. [tell][a1]

Feeling dirty and at the same time not being bothered to do anything about it are strong in the trio of related remedies Plutonium, Positronium and Rat, particularly the latter. I have been feeling very shitty, very polluted, very dirty. Regarding my skin eruptions, my friend joked that I looked like a bloody leper and I felt she had put her finger on it. It is making me feel suicidal. [plut-n][srj7] Don't feel like washing or bathing. It all feels too much effort and I can't be bothered. Wearing the same dirty clothes for ages. [positr][nl2] Feel dirty all the time; can't bathe or wash my hands enough. [sanguis-s][hrn2] Averse to bathing. Irritated and impatient with the amount of time it takes to groom myself, washing hair, brushing teeth, etcetera – when will it end. [sanguis-s][hrn2] Had the idea that bathing may antidote this proving, while I begrudgingly took a bath because I smelled. [sanguis-s][hrn2]

The Stingray is the garbage collector of the oceans, hoovering up rubbish from the sea floor. In the proving there were dreams of racoons which are notorious for scavenging in garbage cans and collecting rubbish. The remedy's dreams include a theme of trying to keep clean while having to negotiate the filthy rubbish. Dream There is a new way of collecting garbage – trash is enclosed in plastic and then thrown in another car that looks like a plastic covered tube; I keep thinking that it looks like a condom. [urol-h][rwt3] Dream: Filthy barnyard – I am concerned about keeping white towels clean. [urol-h][rwt3]

Dream of treasure, to be found in a dump – waste land in a city, big gates. They say "This is where the treasure is to be found, but if you want to get it you have to walk through the dump and get shit on your feet." [tung-met][bdx1] This tungsten dream is an excellent example of the theme of finding the treasure within the shit is an important lesson of the AIDS Miasm. It was echoed in a less dramatic Vacuum dream. Dream: I looked down on the ground where there was dirt and semi-moist soil and saw coins. [vacuum][es-vac]

X-4 Shit & Toilets

One of the specific themes around which dirt issues are gathered in the AIDS Miasm is that of shit and toilets.

Several animal remedies are taken from anal or preputial gland secretions. Some of these substance, especially Musk and Ambra grisea are important ingredients in very expensive perfumes, again finding treasure amongst the shit.

Crack Willow subjects like those in Ambra tend to use the phrase "I feel like shit". Feel like shit all day. [sal-fr][sle1] An Ambra grisea woman feels that something is wrong with her that needs to be covered up. There is an intensely dirty feeling about herself. The expression "I feel like shit" aptly describes the main feeling of Ambra. The feeling is that something in her is intensely disgusting and that this part should never be exposed or she will be completely forsaken. [ambr][sk7]

Carbon dioxide, again like Ambra, has issues of embarrassment around stool. Embarrassing to talk about my stool (to supervisor). [carbn-dox][knl3]

Several remedies had dreams where shit is an important factor. Dream: Deck/sidewalk made out of stone with walls that go up to the waist; like a rail of stone. Sense of medieval time. Sense that the sea is beyond that deck but I don't see it. I stand close to a big door looking at this man that [who] is sweeping the floor of this deck-sidewalk thing. His broom is made out of sticks with small branches at the end gathered in a bunch and tied around a pole. There are lots of little mounds of dog shit or animal shit all over. He goes around sweeping, pushing the shit from one place to another trying to gather it, it is not sticky shit, but somewhat dried up shit. He is ranting and raving about the stupid idea of building this sidewalk, now he has to clean the shit on it. I start to help him clean the shit but I don't see myself using a broom, I am wondering how he will discard it. No dumpster or bag in sight. [carbn-dox][knl3] Dream: My sister-in-law needed to change the baby's nappy. She rushed into the loo and threw the nappy out spraying small pieces of shit. I had to go into the loo to wash. [heroin][sdj-h] Dream that I was peeing shit! Doctors are confounded. Then everyone got ill. Whole world turned to shit. (This is all quite matter of fact as far as I am concerned.) [latex][nl-latex] Primitive dreams of sewers and man eating sewerage. [plac][Biggs+] Dream of being covered in excrement. [musca-d][stew+] I dreamt that I had a shit and then wiped my anus only once or twice, as I was going to wash it in the bidet. But for some reason I couldn't so I had to pull my trousers up and go around dirty that day which was very unpleasant. [plut-n][srj7] Dream: Crossing a large park which was so dirty in the centre that I thought that the entire city came here to evacuate their bowels. Later, I realized that the periphery was clean and decided to walk along the clean portion henceforth. [polys][sk4] Tuesday night dream of bursting and ending up with a pile of shit. [positr][nl2] Dream: Helping man with a very large catholic family by changing the baby's diaper, but there were no diaper wipes in the diaper bag so I had to use paper towels. [urol-h][rwt3] Dream: Men were cleaning a porta-potty; wondered who would do that as a job? Watched as shit poured over them. [vacuum][es-vac]

In Eagle there were a number of dreams of passing stool by accident. Dream: I have to shit but am too interested in studying. As I lean over, a constipated stool falls out of my rectum. I take a detailed look at the stool. Two are hard and round bits with one flat bit. I want to leave it on the floor but not in my friends' house. I throw it out of the window to the street below. [haliae-lc][srj5] Dream: I had a BM in my pants while riding in a car, getting it all over the seat. The stool was like clay. I was embarrassed but not mortified. I just tried to clean it up before anybody noticed. I don't know why or how it happened. [haliae-lc][srj5] Dream of defecating in pants in a car with six people. Friends finding out. Embarrassing, humiliation and trying, holding to denial of it. [haliae-lc][srj5]

Dreams of toilets are common in these remedies. Snapshot of being in a public toilet, a very highbrow young woman was there. She was wearing a black velvet dress studded with diamonds. She had hung a 2 piece on the door of the toilet. The top had an embroidered dragon on it. [positr][nl2] Food dreams and going to the toilet – interrupts the meal. [tung-met][bdx1]

They fall into two basic categories. Usually the issue is the dirtiness of the toilet. I dream that I am looking for a toilet as I need to poo. But everywhere I go there is either a very dirty toilet, or one with no lock, or one with people in the cubicles. When I woke up I thought that I must actually need to go to the toilet, so strong was the urge in the dream, but I didn't. [aids][nl2] Dream of large derelict house and a toilet with a load of raw vegetables floating on the top. [androc][srj5] Finding a clean pot to urinate in inside a soiled public toilet into which I had walked barefoot. [coca-c][sk4] I am back at my convent school, I want to go to the toilet. A nun shows me where to go. The toilet is strange like a bowl set into the wall and I have to sit in the water in the bowl. A female saint appears, glowing in the room. One minute she is talking to me, the next thing I know she is a tiny, grotesque, rubbery head floating in the toilet which I am sitting on. [falco-pe][nl2] My eldest is asleep wrapped up in quilt on public toilet floor. I thought, oh, how disgusting, I must wake him and move him, then I think, oh well, he chose to sleep there, leave him alone. [heroin][sdj-h] Dream: A patient, who was paralysed, was lying in a dirty toilet with blood shot eyes. I had to pick him up, support him and take him for a CT scan to a diagnostic centre nearby. The man was very bulky, but I managed to reach him even though I had a tough time doing it. [lac-h][sk4] Dream: We went to a large urinal that was dirty, unwashed. I could not urinate because of the dirt. [lac-h][sk4] Dream: Passing stool in a dirty toilet. Dirty embarrassing feeling. [polys][sk4] Dream: Woman was complaining about classmate because he had HIV and that he had diarrhoea and would never clean the toilet. [urol-h][rwt3]

But in quite a few the issue was privacy. Dream I am at work and I have to go to the bathroom and get up to wipe myself and see that my client can see through and is looking at my hairy genital area. I am more surprised than ashamed. A little embarrassed I go behind the wall. [corian-s][knl6] Dreamt of sitting on the loo with a policeman staring at me. I realized I hadn't closed the door. [lsd][nl-lsd] Dream was sitting on the toilet in the bathroom and the door was wide open; my father and brother-in-law were sitting on the couch watching football right in front of me. [urol-h][rwt3] Parents toilet, door didn't close because carpet crumpled. [tung-met][bdx1] Dream I was going to the loo in pub and there was one toilet in the open. The rest of the toilets were in cubicles. I used the open toilet. An old lady walked in and looked at me in disgust. [vacuum][es-vac] (*See Privacy & Secrecy IX-9*)

X-5 Insects, Worms & Vermin

The animated expressions of dirt are insects, worms and vermin. A few of the remedies fall into this class but there are probably many more insects in particular that should be considered. (The cockroach, the flea and the head louse are just a few of them.)

In Chocolate, perhaps because the substance contains cockroaches, there is a desire to eat worms and insects and dreams of them. The American Food and Drug Administration has published a monograph for chocolate manufacturers which specifies that up to 4 per cent by weight of chocolate may legitimately contain 'cockroach parts', since it is apparently impossible to prevent these bugs from contaminating the vats in which chocolate is manufactured. [choc][srj3] I wanted to eat beetles, big black ones, this morning. Desired the crunch as when you eat celery. It surprised me. [choc][srj3] A vivid dream of worms – they were dark and fat, but I wished they were red and thin. I felt very excited by the worms. [choc][srj3]

Other remedies have dreams of eating worms or insects. Dream about flies. Lots of fly's eggs mixed in with white rice in the boot of a car. I knew they would hatch out and he was waiting for it to happen. Sense of fear of the swarm of flies. Nearby there was a honeycomb and I knew the flies were going to go to that when they hatched out. [aids][nl2] Dream: People are eating worms – they are red and chilli flavored – a man says you get more heat if you eat the fatter worms; someone says that they aren't big enough to eat you and then shows us people who are deteriorating because the worms are eating them – you can see them writhing under the skin and there are holes in the skin. [urol-h][rwt3]

Coriander is a foodstuff but the odour of the plant is striking. It is completely pervaded by a distinctive smell of bed bugs. Indeed the name of the plant comes from the Greek word koris (bug). [corian-s][knl6]

The sensation of bugs under the skin is in several remedies. Last week or so constantly feeling as if insects are crawling around the back of my neck and shoulders, whether they're there or not. A feeling of being got at. [agath-a][nl2] But it is a particular keynote of cocaine. Sensation as of small foreign bodies or of worms under the skin ("cocaine bugs"). [coca][tl2] These worms are projected only on the Cocainist's own person or clothing. He sees them on his linen, in his skin, creeping along his penholder, but not on other people or things, and not on clothes brought clean from the laundry. [coca][c1]

Many remedies have general dreams or delusions about insects and vermin. He sees vermin and bugs crawl about his bed, from which he wants to escape, and constantly throws away whole handfuls of them. [ars][a1] Thoughts about red worms crawling together with very little dirt, compost store, and bait shop. Thought also that I had worms in my stomach. [coca-c][sk4] Dreams of millions of ants. [Swoboda] [gink-b][vml3] Dream: Scorpions infesting the house. [helo-s][rwt2] Imagines she sees spiders, snakes, vermin. [lac-c][k2] Dream: I found insects and cockroaches in my pants, and thought to myself that my maidservant doesn't wash my clothes properly. [lac-cp][sk4] Terrible dreams of sleeping on garbage riddled with ants, worms, maggots, bloated rats, smaller insects, smells of rotten things. I am lying down in it with my mother. Could not fall back to sleep after seeing we were in the garbage. I did not mind too much about the ants. Baby, embryonic mice and animals all dying from the cold and being hurt. A disturbing, horrible dream. I often dream of maggots and worms, having the maggots or worms inside of me. This was more about being immersed in them. [lac-lup][hrn2] Dream: Scorpions lying in wait in people's shoes. [lac-lup][hrn2] Dreamt of cockroaches, feared them. They were behind net curtains, their bodies just lying around, maybe dead, red and shiny. I hate their antlers. I was scared and disgusted by them. I had to get someone else to remove them. [lsd][nl-lsd] I dreamt that my husband and my two youngest children were trying to get into a modern house so that we could live in it, but it was infested with rats and mice. [plut-n][srj7] Delusions: Saw hundreds of small, black bugs running across the floor. [sanguis-s][hrn2] Distressing dreams of vermin. [phos][a1] Dream: My daughter told me she had worms – my son had worms as well. I realised I had them too. I felt horrible when I woke up. A few days before the dream I was paranoid I had lice. [vacuum][es-vac]

Polystyrene has the dream of rats but the insulating effect of the remedy means that it lacks the usual fear. Dream: About ten or fifteen small, round rats, without the usual fear. [polys][sk4]

In Falcon the element of shame was very strong and this affected the dream of vermin. Dreamed of having head lice. I was combing through my hair with a lice comb and when the comb came out it was clogged with bugs which looked more like wood lice. When I tried to wash the comb under the tap, the bugs wouldn't come out. Every time I combed through the comb was totally clogged with the bugs. There was a crowd of people around me saying it was because I was dirty and disgusting. [falco-pe][nl2] (*See Shame & Humiliation XI-3*)

The Oak Gall Wasp is a parasite and this feeling come though in the proving. One member of the group was ostracized, being called a parasite. She did not dare even to use a pen for fear of being further ostracized. [galla-q-r][nl2]

Other remedies also have delusions or dreams of being infested by parasites. Start to imagine I've got worms, parasites, in me, think, is it that raw liver I ate. Feel I've infected myself – done myself damage by eating raw liver, why did I do it? It was stupid, I should have cooked it more. [heroin][sdj-h] Dream: I had a cut in the sole of my right foot – inside the cut were two layers of spam – in between the spam was a rectangular 'nest' of flies eggs. Completely revolted by dream all day! [phasco-ci][rbp2]

XI-1 Lack of confidence

Lack of confidence is a key issue in the AIDS Nosode, Feelings of being awkward and shy – averse company and talking. [aids][nl2] Lacking in self confidence. [aids][nl2] and throughout the Miasm.

Lack of confidence is an issue in the Sycotic Miasm where it is important for the subject to be as strong as possible so he can reach as high a place in the hierarchy as possible. In the Syphilitic Miasm if you are not stronger than others you will be destroyed. In the AIDS Miasm the feeling is that the subject is just a small and vulnerable child in a vast unbounded and dangerous world. This afternoon I felt a bit like a lost, fragile, little girl, unconfident, unsure. [falco-pe][nl2]

The subject feels that he or she is not up to the task in hand. He is separated from the whole world, and has so little confidence in himself that he despairs of being able to do that which is required of him. [anac][a1] He has not confidence enough in himself to undertake and perform voluntary motions. [ang][a1] Overwhelmed and inadequate. [helo-s][rwt2] Want of self-confidence. [lac-c][vml4] A feeling that I am lacking somewhere. I feel that my teachers made a hundred from zero, and that I can't even maintain the hundred. Helpless. [polys][sk4] I couldn't think from very low self confidence. [rhus-g][tmo3] Worried if I said things wrong, if I gave the wrong impression. [rhus-g][tmo3] Uneasiness respecting one's children, affairs, and the future, with want of self-confidence. [rhus-t][a1] Feelings of being hopeless at everything and useless. [sal-fr][sle1]

This makes the subject timid. Want of vigor, timid, apprehensive. [pip-m][a1] Dream: Feeling I was doing something and feel a failure. [positr][nl2] Timid, mild, and insecure. [tax-br][oss1]

Awkwardness and insecurity tend to be worse in company. Most of the symptomatology of this remedy revolves around the idea of not being able to loosen up, to relax and "exchange", to let go when in the company of other people. [ambr][vh1] Bashful: timid: ill at ease in society. [coca][tl2] Mind: Awkward. Felt unusually socially awkward and did not know what to say. [lac-leo][hrn2]

The everchanging and unfixed world of the electronic age does not have markers against which worth can be measured. This leads to fluctuating assessment of self worth. Sense of superiority and well-being. Sense of depression and inferiority. [anh][c1] I have to do something; make my mark. [phasco-ci][rbp2]

Generally this is an underestimentation. Lack of confidence. I feel worthless. I haven't got a life. All that I have revolves around boyfriend.

[adam][srj5] Low self esteem. Felt I am not worthy or not pretty or not interesting enough for people. [adam][srj5] Feel worthless. Why even bother trying to get things done? What's the point? [vacuum][es-vac]

This is particularly so in Eagle. Am thinking about taking a job that would put me in a high class, but don't know if I would want to work with those kind of people – downtown people into their careers who make hundreds of thousands. They make me nervous. Afraid they will snub me. So much to do with worth. What am I worth? [haliae-lc][srj5] What is my position in society in relationship to career, how friends view me and relationships with men? [haliae-lc][srj5] I was in a depression, unlike anything I have felt for a long time. Deep sense of low self-worth. Feeling invisible, uncared for and envious. I was lethargic, couldn't do anything. [haliae-lc][srj5] Inner vision: I was a male Indian. I thought, "I'm not a brave. I don't deserve this feather". [haliae-lc][srj5]

There is also a tendency to be critical of the self or to believe that others are critical of the subject. Delusion, hears unpleasant voice about himself. [coca][sk7] Critical as to own appearance. Lac felinum patients not only have a feeling of being stupid, but are quite convinced that this is the case. They perceive themselves as being of insufficient or only average intelligence; they have a desire to know more and be capable of more. They received the message from their parents that they were 'only a silly little kid'. Hence the feeling of being 'incapable, thick and stupid', good for nothing. Secondly, we also find feelings of worthlessness or inferiority, [as in Lac equinum]. [lac-f][vml3] Dream: Of being criticized or accused wrongly of doing something. [polys][sk4] Seeing attacks where there are none, feeling not good enough. [positr][nl2] Whatever I do, I feel that somebody will criticize me, that I do something wrong. [germ-met][srj5] Sensitivity to criticism. [tax-br][oss1]

XI-2 Old, Ugly & Fat

The inability of reality ever matching the pervasive ideals of youth and beauty result in a feeling of being old and ugly. (*See Youth, Beauty, Peace & Love I-8*) The tendency to extremes (*See Extremes VI-1*) and confusion (*See Confusion VII-1*) result in a lack of understanding about body image and especially about weight. This is expressed pathologically in the large number patients with eating disorders. In the provings it tended to be expressed as a feeling that the prover is fat. Feel fat! [adam][srj5] I feel fat. [corian-s][knl6] Dreams: Sitting in dark room huddled up in chair. Dark haired woman passed by, said: "Boy are you getting fat." I said: "Oh don't tell me that." [corian-s][knl6] Feel fat. [haliae-lc][srj5] Feel like I'm gaining weight, but am actually losing weight. [haliae-lc][srj5] I'm ripping all my clothes. I'm so much fatter that I'm not aware of my width, and I'm catching on things. [haliae-lc][srj5] Feel really fat today, almost a paranoia that I've put on weight. [lsd][nl-lsd] Feels fat. [plac][Biggs+] I've put on weight as I've been eating crap. [positr][nl2] Felt I'd put on more weight than I had. [positr][nl2] Dream: Gained a lot of weight and looked grotesque in the mirror. Niethammer in 1974 recounted a story of a priest in the seventeenth century to the effect that after the Indians had been eating the fruit for about three weeks, the priest could not recognize many of his friends because they were temporarily so corpulent. Several provers described bingeing and reduced appetite with weight loss in a similar pattern. This also manifested in the form of hallucinations or bodily distortions, which predominantly reflected 'looking older'. [carneg-g][rwt1]

There are also strong feelings that the subject is ugly. Felt ugly, miserable and generally fed up with myself during menses, more intensely than I usually would at this time. [adam][srj5] Looking in the mirror is weird. Feel ugly. Very pale. I feel I look ugly, pale, big body and butt. [haliae-lc][srj5] I felt and looked absolutely worn out. I look ugly. The skin on my face is very flushed. Some whiteheads have appeared. I've been feeling bad all morning. I woke with a puffy face. I definitely feel less attractive, ugly. [agath-a][nl2] We find feelings of ugliness with a revulsion for oneself [as in Lac caninum]. Inferiority feelings such as these seem to be a common characteristic of Lacs, at least those of all domesticated animals. On looking in the mirror, a feeling that she looks horrible. [Müller][lac-f][vml3] I felt that I looked strange when I looked in the mirror; I looked wretched, as if I hadn't slept much. [latex][nl-latex] Face looks completely ravaged. [latex][nl-latex] Predominant feeling today and yesterday is of feeling ugly. I tried on a couple of dresses and looked at my hair which is so fine, and I feel masculine, ugly I don't feel feminine. I do feel that I look like a man. [lsd][nl-lsd]

In the proving of Swan the story of the Ugly Duckling that was really a Cygnet seem to have a particular resonance. Isolated by feeling ugly, dirty and unworthy. [cygn-b][sle-swan] Felt I was ugly inside and wanted to be beautiful. [cygn-b][sle-swan]

There is an unhappiness or distaste at the subject's own body. Very unhappy with my body, I want to escape from it, to run away from myself. I want to go from me. [adam][srj5] Really loathed my body. [positr][nl2] Felt really fat and repulsive, didn't want partner to look at me or touch me. [positr][nl2]

There is also a tendency to neglect appearance. The moral sense is lowered and he neglects his personal appearance. [cocain][a1] Yesterday didn't take a shower all day. Normally I never do that. Just didn't care. Kept thinking: OK tomorrow morning, but I didn't. Finally took one at 1 pm. The last weeks I took normally two showers a day. I just didn't care about hygiene. [helodr-cal][knl2] Haven't washed my hair for weeks, I'm too tired, indifference about looking after myself. [falco-pe][nl2] I feel dishevelled in appearance. [plut-n][srj7]

However, the most important feeling is the delusion that the subject is old. The delusion tends to be about the state of the body. Dream: I am in a seminar with a group of strangers. Somebody tells me that my hair has turned white on the back of my head, which I hadn't noticed before. [aids][nl2] Premature old age, with apathy and melancholy. [agn][c1] On looking over this remedy as a whole it will appear to you that you have studying the characteristics of one prematurely old. [ambr][k2] I look old and wrinkled. [helodr-cal][knl2] Feeling old, really old. [haliae-lc][srj5] This is a conflict I have anyway, on the one hand feel childish and immature and on the other feel my age, my years. This is something I feel is me anyway, but it was much worse. I felt so old. [falco-pe][nl2] I look older. [germ-met][srj5] Delusion of being old. (Compare Sequoia, another 'fossil' tree as old as Ginkgo.) [gink-b][vml3] One prover described herself as 'feeling old like an old mother,' while the mother of another prover said: 'you look like an old woman'. [gink-b][vml3] Sitting there in the morning, bent over, with no contact with the surroundings and concentration problems, tired and dull, forgets to cook (which she always liked to do), and dreaming that her hair gets grey. A full picture of a lonely, withdrawn, demented old person. [Swoboda] [gink-b][vml3] Feel like a crippled old man. [hydrog][srj2] I feel empty, old and tired. [galla-q-r][nl2] Dream: All my hair has suddenly gone grey. I look in the mirror with surprise and realize that I need to dye it. [lac-h][sk4] I am feeling very old and not very well. [lsd][nl-lsd] I feel as if I am old and waiting to die, as if there is nothing to live for. [plut-n][srj7] looked down at my body and it looked old – the flesh sagging over the bones – I didn't realize this was a clear delusion until I arrived at school and thought about it. [positr][nl2] Overwhelming feeling of being old. [seq-s][vml3]

XI-3 Shame & Humiliation

Some of you will remember a prover coming forward to join me upon the occasion of the ECCH & ICCH Case Conference in Holland in May 1995 and again in UK at the Society of Homœopaths Conference later that year. Her story was and is deeply shocking and provoked strong responses amongst participants many of whom were critical of what had occurred when she laid her soul bare. This response is typical of the feeling tone associated with AIDS: shock and condemnation – anything not to be contaminated by association! [aids][nl2]

There is throughout the AIDS Miasm not just strong feelings of being criticized but a powerful sense of shame. This feeling is central to the genus of the state, but it is not easy to quantify or pin down.

It can be expressed as a feeling of having done something wrong. Eating too much chocolate is considered bad for your health and statements like 'I have been naughty' are always associated with the consumption of a bar of chocolate. [choc][srj3] Felt uncomfortable if any one stood close to me. Felt uneasy and paranoid in class. Feel as if done something wrong. [germ-met][srj5] Afraid of the police – of being caught and unveiled. [germ-met][srj5] I have a guilty feeling if I get too much attention. I am afraid of bothering others. [germ-met][srj5] Dream: That I have committed a terrible crime. [latex][nl-latex] In a DIY shop, their computer wasn't working. I had to stop myself saying "Is it something I've done?" I realised it had been on the tip of my tongue to say this more than a few times since taking the remedy. Strange – 'Guilty as if he has committed a crime'. [latex][nl-latex] Felt guilty. Felt I had been remiss in reporting. I felt that I blew it. I did it wrong. I was selfish. Disappointed. I really want to be part of the proving. I felt like it was all put on me. [galeoc-c-h][gms1] According to an old legend the Cross was made from its wood, on account of which it was degraded to be a parasite. [visc][vml3]

However, even with this feeling there is some recognition of the fact that it is not the subject's fault. Had lost sight of the fact that I had not done anything. All I saw was the criminality of it. [heroin][sdj-h] Dream: Feeling of unfairness and humiliation; I was working part time as a cashier and accused by female boss of stealing; she called in the police who strip searched me in front of the police and other employees; woke up weeping; overwhelming feeling of humiliation, anger, injustice, helplessness; felt like other people were controlling me. [urol-h][rwt3]

In Lac humanum there is a feeling that the subject does not have the power to control themselves and are ashamed of it. Feel very, very remorseful and guilty after having done something wrong, although while doing it am unable to control myself. Later, also seek the power to control myself, along with repentance. [lac-h][sk4] Embarrassed and hiding, thinking what others would say about him when he could not control his urge to eat much and frequently. [lac-h][sk4] They may try to cover it up. Feeling as if something needs to be hidden. [lac-h][sk4] As does the Koala Bear. Covering up what one has done wrong. [phasco-ci][rbp2]

In Lac humanum there is also the feeling that what they do is not appreciated. Felt ignored, like I had no value. Felt that people don't understand or consider me although I try to help them in many ways. Felt the need of someone who understands me. I felt it is preferable to stay alone and concentrate on your aim, because then you have a position and people appreciate you. [lac-h][sk4]

In the Miasm there is shame about sexuality. Dreamed I was pregnant. Mixed feelings – felt ashamed to tell my family. [hydrog][srj2] A horridly unnatural and amorous dream resulted in a seminal emission, about 3 a.m., which was so large that the passage of it through the urethra caused pain enough to awaken me; penis erect; sensation of sickness, shame. [pip-m][a1] Being prude and shameful is a way to suppress it (the sexuality of the remedy). [lac-cp][lsy+dmk] Dream I am at this place and going to be married but I don't know to whom; the man comes and says he will take care of it; I think what if he substitutes himself for the groom and the marriage is not legal but I've already slept with him on the wedding night; the guests and the wedding party start to arrive; some one goes out to get me panty hose; I am feeling very troubled; I feel ashamed. [urol-h][rwt3] (*See Sexuality VIII-5*)

This was particularly strong in Falcon. Dreamt last night- which was of a sexual nature, the major themes were of helplessness, powerlessness even though I was the more powerful entity, of shame, of self disgust, of others being disgusted with me, of feeling forsaken, of no one else caring. Also a sort of moral tension was present – I felt I had to partake in the sexual act and part of me felt I really didn't want to. This part of me felt bullied and disempowered. However another part of me was aware of partly enjoying what I was doing but felt bad. [falco-pe][nl2] I couldn't make love. I realised I saw this as humiliating, like it was the act of a prostitute. [falco-pe][nl2]

And the theme of prostitution appears in other remedies. Kept thinking about ex-girlfriend prostituting herself (news just heard). Why was she doing it? Did she have to? Did she enjoy it? I'm shocked and feel it like a punishment that I know what she's doing – as though I can't leave my past behind. I wonder if it's a reaction to her not being able to find the kind of love she wants. She had high expectations of what love should be. I suspect she has found a way of justifying it to herself. [heroin][sdj-h] This was an animal remedy with a dirty feeling about oneself, a feeling of not being respected, of being treated contemptuously. The conflict of submitting oneself, of degrading oneself to save relationship or for money. The theme of the prostitute who submits her body, her respect for money. To get his food, the wild cat became the domestic cat of today. "The trick had been to control their fear of humans, to learn to tolerate handling and even enjoy it, as the necessary price that had to be paid for an easy life. In a way they had to prostitute themselves, but once they had mastered the art, the rewards were impressive. They allowed the domestic cat to live longer and more healthily than its wild ancestors They made a choice, gave up their independence, their wildness, their freedom, their respect – for food, for survival." [Chhabra] [lac-f][vml3] Dream of deciding to leave home and become a prostitute in the city. [plac][Biggs+]

The feeling of shame can be fairly general. Shame and Disgrace. [androc][vml3] Reached right down into a mirror of my real feelings and I saw a dark secret full of a sense of deep humiliation and shame and despair. [falco-pe][nl2] I am still feeling irritable and in a desultory mood that doesn't want to shift. All sorts of images are triggered in my mind of unattained ambitions, ways I've let my parents down, and of shameful episodes in the past. [heroin][sdj-h] Humiliation, feel like I'm whipping myself. [lsd][nl-lsd] Rats are among the most despised creatures on the face of the earth. [sanguis-s][hrn2] Totally worthless. I was not dirty but I had reason to be ashamed. Ashamed almost to be seen, as if there was something unclean about me. [vacuum][es-vac]

The feeling often comes out of a sense of inadequacy, that the subject is making a fool of him or herself. I imagined everything I said was wrong – that I had offended someone – that I had committed some sort of faux pas – that I was gabbling. [aids][nl2] Suspicious/confusion that people are making a fool of me, laughing at me. [adam][srj5] The patient has an embarrassed air; the bashful state is very characteristic in certain connections. [ambr][a1] There is such difficulty in communicating with others at any level that the sight of people laughing creates an aversion to laughter, almost a disgust! It is also in the nature of this remedy to have a tremendous concern about others: "what will they say", "what will they think about me" are typical exclamations, especially if something 'bad' comes out. [ambr][vh1] I feel very ashamed of all the bad things I have ever done or said. I feel like people can see through what's on the surface to this horrible person underneath. [positr][nl2] Easily feels ashamed. Won't try new things for fear of making a mistake. Question their own abilities. She feels self-conscious, and inferior to others. [tax-br][oss1] I had a feeling like I was afraid that I was going to be 'found out'. I felt inadequate. [sal-fr][sle1] I do have a strange feeling of being very aware of my own delusion – that there is something wrong with me and I am not good enough. [sal-fr][sle1]

This can be a childlike state. An old memory sprang up in me (an image of the way that my dad used to look at me) and a feeling of shame. It was the shame I'd felt as a child that made me hide things I'd broken. It is the shame I feel now. I am seven years old and forty two years old at the same time. [plut-n][srj7]

However, the essence of the feeling comes in a state where the subject feels shame or humiliation but it is the bad behaviour of others that has led to this situation. This leads to the double distress of being badly treated and feeling responsible for it. Felt lied to, angry, frustrated. With people but had feeling they did not like me. Sitting there and not wanting to be sociable. Feeling they don't like me. Not like me at all. Feeling like people are looking at me and saying "she's no good" [aids][nl2] I felt like I had been treated badly, a mixture of insult and humiliation. [adam][srj5] Sensation of being wronged, of being betrayed, which affects my social relationships. [adam][srj5] Feels like we're the American Indians. "Here's 24 dollars worth of beads for your island, idiot." In the pit of despair. [haliae-lc][srj5] Lac caninum also shows autodepreciation; the dog will never be equal to man: it is the key note "contemptuous with himself". [lac-c][lrp1] We find with children who have been abused, a humiliating situation as if they were kept on a lead. [lac-c][lrp1] Felt that people were trying to put me down, blame me, find fault with me, criticize me. Became tearful from this. [lac-leo][sk4] Felt that they were making me feel inferior or low. Began "firing" back, and putting others down. [lac-leo][sk4] The gray wolf is a proud, intelligent, family-oriented, and highly socialized carnivore, but he has been despised and feared by most societies. [lac-lup][hrn2] Feeling criticized. Feeling judged. Feeling angry. Feeling stupid. Feeling isolated. Feeling incompetent. All these are old symptoms but with an intensity that is overwhelming. [lsd][nl-lsd] Guilt and the sense of self being judged, criticized. Shame. [colum-p][sej-birds]

XI-4 Self Hatred & Self Harm

The feeling of shame combined with the feeling of powerlessness can result in a powerful hatred of the self. Disgust with herself. [gink-b][vml3] Felt that I hated all people and also myself. [galla-q-r][nl2] Felt disgusted, hopeless, good for nothing, as if there was nothing in life to live for; to continue to live is the most painful thing. [lac-h][sk4] Received a long letter from a patient today; haven't even read it, can't be bothered. Very unusual. In terms of indifference, I have felt disgusted with myself; one of these violent and malicious feelings. God, I feel so wretched. [neon][srj5]

This sense is perhaps strongest in Germanium where the subject feels worthless and hateful and believes that he or she is despised by everyone including him or herself. Other people do pleasant things. All my energy I use to keep an intense rage distant so that I won't hurt myself or the kids. Everything was heavy and felt impossible without meaning. Terrible anger. Bad conscience and crying afterwards. Could not do what I had planned to do, because I felt so terrible and everything was chaos. [germ-met][srj5] I am probably incurable and that's my own fault. [germ-met][srj5] Feeling a total failure, I would prefer to die. Very unmotivated. [germ-met][srj5] Whatever I do, I feel that somebody will criticize me, that I do something wrong. [germ-met][srj5] Everything is my fault. I asked for 'drubbing' (beating) and I have got it. [germ-met][srj5] I don't like to be me. Want to be different. Have a distant feeling to myself yet long for physical contact, a boyfriend. Not able to do something about it. [germ-met][srj5] Don't understand anything, the meaning of life. Feel also strength somewhere inside. I wish a change could happen. I ought to bring myself together and change. It is silly of me to go on like this. I despise myself. I am hard on myself, but I don't deserve anything else. I think other people are silly, too. [germ-met][srj5] Feel envious of a colleague who I feel manages so well. When I compare with myself I feel worthless and nothing. I feel like talking badly about her to my friends and I do this, even though she is not present. [germ-met][srj5] Concern that people may not like me. So afraid of what others think of me. [germ-met][srj5] If I were me, nobody would like me, so I try to be what I think others expect me to be. I don't think I can be loved with all the parts of me which are ugly and bad. Lonely feelings. [germ-met][srj5] I'm desperate. I want to die. Feel the power to kill. Feel like a wild animal locked in. It's strong, so intense. I hate so strong, feel a terrible disgust and I'm afraid of what I'm able to do. It's completely impossible to be in it and impossible to get out of it. [germ-met][srj5]

The self is seen as something horrible. Felt that I did not have the right to be with others. I feel that I'm sucking them out. Throwing my dirt at them. [galla-q-r][nl2] Had an explosion for not being the perfect person. I was really pissed off at the situation. I felt out of control, helpless, and lashed out with vehemence and anger at the situation and myself. I'm in the "Valley of Discontent" and want to get out of Sacramento. [neon][srj5] Self-contempt from sexual abuse. [agn][c1]

In Lac caninum the feeling is that the self is so loathsome the subject cannot even bear to touch his or her own body. Woke at daylight, feeling that she was a loathsome, horrible, mass of disease. [lac-c][c1] Could not bear to have any one part of her body touch another; felt if she could not get out of her body in some way, she would soon become crazy. [lac-c][c1]

There can be a desire to rid the self of that which is horrible within. I feel like vomiting out all my insides. I want to get rid of everything inside me I physically feel like vomiting all my stomach and even all my breath. I want everything to get out of me. [adam][srj5] Something alien is going on – it's not me – but is it? I feel as if I'm going mad, divided. I want "it" to come out. I feel as if I could be sick and throw "it" up and out, but "it" would have to come from right deep down, "it" is putting out tentacles. I feel disgusted by its presence. It's trying to control me. "It" is a parasite, draining me, a leech, a slug. "It" is slimy and wet and "it" is growing bigger. "It" is real to me and resembles an octopus type creature, something that lives in the depths of the oceans. "It" has got a hold of me and "it" won't let go. It is trying to take me over. [falco-pe][nl2]

The feeling of self hatred can come to be expressed in self destructive behaviour. I am deeply in touch with a self-destructive sense inside. The part of me that wants to disintegrate and die. Dis-integrate; the opposite of integral oneness, the opposite direction. [haliae-lc][srj5] Feel self-destructive, like eating greasy fatty junk food, not exercising, slowly kill myself that way. Why care? [haliae-lc][srj5]

Aggression that often comes to be turned on the self. Extreme aggression: towards self and others. [berlin-w][hmd2] Had strong feeling, like a visualization. I picture myself lying on floor in fetal position and being shot in the head like a horse or a dog. Almost welcomed it. Then thought my children still need me. [germ-met][srj5]

And ultimately self harm. Paroxysm of insanity impelling him to attack himself; he strikes, scratches, and tears himself with a sort of relish, and without feeling any pain. [cur][a1] Don't see why I am here. I can't bear it. I go mad. I hate myself. I want to beat myself and I do it. Tear my hair. Stop when it hurts too much. It is like hell! [germ-met][srj5] Rage because I left gas ring on for 3 hours, want to beat my head. Have image of stabbing head into a pulp with big sharp knife and of slicing body. Very violent. Hate knives. [heroin][sdj-h] Tendency to inflict self-harm; burnt palm, and made a cut with a pen knife. [lac-h][sk4] Self mutilation; slow fascination with watching a knife cut through my skin, or an artery, watching the blood; watching myself bleed to death. [positr][nl2]

XII-1 Boundaries & Obstruction

The AIDS Miasm is about the removal and dissolution of boundaries, however, boundaries are very important because there is a compensatory need to build barriers, even if this effort ultimately proves to be ineffectual.

Beavers are known for their building of magnificent barriers. The Berlin Wall was the symbolically most powerful barrier of the early electronic age and also a symbol of those barriers collapsing. The Ozone layer is a very important barrier and again is one that is being breached. Feeling in a cloud as if beneath a glass dome, separated from others. [ozone][sde2] Feeling as if I were surrounded by a layer, not like a wall, but softer, almost like a mist. [ozone][sde2]

The feeling that there is a barrier between the subject and the world is common. Spacey, not spaced-out feeling, as much as if a fog is between you and the other person – like looking through a wet window or a pane of glass with rain on it. It was disfigured, disoriented, disassociated feeling. Heard people talking, sounded like the hum of bees. [lac-del][hrn2] Sat in a dream and all is unreal and through a kind of invisible veil. [tung-met][bdx1]

There are several remedies in which the sensation of a barrier could be seen as a keynote. In Polystyrene the theme of an insulating barrier runs right through the remedy. Feeling like there was barrier. [polys][sk4] Rubber is used to form a barrier in many ways, particularly in the condom that was used to make the remedy and the theme of a barrier was very important in the proving. It was often expressed as a blockage or obstruction that needed clearing. Dream: Aware that toilet was blocked, could feel myself pushing white tampon down toilet with index and middle finger of left hand. Could feel the pressure of my fingers. Felt I had to unblock this as it was a responsibility to others to make it work properly. [latex][nl-latex] Dream: Two patients, I was sister in charge of ward. Patients were wearing white gowns, stained with haematuria, beds were also wet where their catheters had blocked and overflowed around the catheter and leaked into the bed. I studied the catheters to see the cause. The end of the catheter end was faulty and I remember pushing the end with my left index finger. The valve was not working properly. There was some sort of blockage, and by pushing it I could release the valve. [latex][nl-latex] Feeling of being obstructed in my attempts to do anything. There are things in the way. Progress is difficult, feeling undermined by other people, friends and family. [latex][nl-latex] Constipated – bowels feel blocked. [latex][nl-latex]

Being separated from the world is very important in Oak Gall, Afternoon feeling – a heavy curtain hangs between me and others. [galla-q-r][nl2] Black painted fence. [galla-q-r][nl2] I felt as if we were all under a thick blanket. [galla-q-r][nl2] but there is a suggestion that this does not work. A man is brick-laying a wall, he says, "now, no-one will get in". But the wall is not effective. [galla-q-r][nl2] I felt as if a wet mist hung over everything, surrounding nothing. [galla-q-r][nl2]

In Eagle there is a barrier but it often seems to be one of distance, the subject feels far away. I was trying to connect with husband. He starts sharing with me about his seminar. Daughter was calling me, "Mom, Mom.... Dinner on the table." There was this glass wall between us that neither one of us could traverse. [haliae-lc][srj5] There is some kind of barrier or buffer. There's a distance between me and everything outside. [haliae-lc][srj5] Things weren't up close. Something between me and everything else. [haliae-lc][srj5] Again the breaches of the barrier are important. Like being in the edge of an abyss, a crevice that's cracking deeper all the time. A crack that gets deeper and longer. [haliae-lc][srj5]

For the Koala Bear the barrier is a way off hiding guilty secrets. Have to hide a secret; make smoke screens. [phasco-ci][rbp2]

In Plutonium the barriers are again isolating. Felt as though I was wearing a mask, looking through two holes. [plut-n][srj7] I feel as if there is a veil between me and the rest of the world. Like a very fine net curtain. I felt isolated and alone. [plut-n][srj7] But they are also heavy and oppressive. On waking, emotional heaviness, a dark cloud all around me. [plut-n][srj7]

This oppressive aspect of the barrier is also important in Iridium. Felt very low again, like being covered by a heavy blanket. I felt weighed down by it. [irid-met][srj5] Feeling of being pushed down. [irid-met][srj5]

However, it is in Germanium that this heavy and oppressive cloud is most firmly settled. The proving of Germanium is firmly engraved in my mind. A heavy turgid atmosphere prevailed, as if a thick grey cloud had settled over our minds. Communication during the proving was difficult. Provers were irritable and suffered extreme and long lasting fatigue. Germanium proved to be a powerful substance, capable of affecting people for long periods of time in a lingering manner. [germ-met][srj5]

In several remedies there is an oppression of breathing or of the chest. Sensation as of weight on chest. Oppressed asthmatic breathing. [berlin-w][hmd2] General numbness with weight on chest. [cocain][a1] A number of provers experienced coughing with wheezing and difficulty breathing or asthma. One prover in particular experienced a severe acute cough and breathing problems. She described it as hard to breathe, rattling, and then exhausted from coughing, cough until she threw up. She had severe bronchitis with a tickling in her throat and feeling as if couldn't get enough oxygen. [helodr-cal][knl2] Dreams of choking/difficulty breathing. [helo-s][rwt2] In bed, afraid I could not breathe through my nose. [lsd][nl-lsd] Chest heaviness. Like something pushing down, like heavy blankets, like a lead apron feeling. [galeoc-c-h][gms1]

In some remedies it is difficult for things to reach the subject. I was just reading and it wasn't actually reaching anywhere in my head. I felt a bit sort of scrambled. [agath-a][nl2] Feel kind of dull in general – felt relaxed and fuzzy and dull as though in a pool of water where all the stimuli come to you through water. A pleasant sensation. [lac-loxod-a][hrn2] Sudden loss of his senses. In this condition he thought that his fingers and toes were cut off. [mosch][a1]

This is often described as the subject being wrapped in cotton wool. Everything's kind of distant, like being wrapped in cotton wool. [haliae-lc][srj5] "Lac felinum patients have a sensation as if various parts of the body are packed in cotton wool. One patient with chronic sinusitis had a sensation as if his head were packed in cotton wool. Another had a sensation as if anaesthetized. One patient had a dream that her hands were packed in cotton wool, reminiscent of velvety paws." [Müller][lac-f][vml3] One hypersensitive patient to whom I gave a single dose of Nux m., 30, said it seemed to put a coat of cotton wool over her. [nux-m][c1]

XII-2 Obstruction of the Senses

The sense of obstruction or of a barrier is found particularly in the senses.

In the sense of sight this is usually in the form of a veil in front of the eyes. Sensation as of a mist or cobweb before the eyes. [agar][k2] Turbid sight, as through a mist. [ambr][a1] Sees as through a white gauze. [ars][a1] Weakness of sight recurring periodically; objects appear to be obscured. [cact][a1] Stars, clouds, and on viewing fixedly a distant object, mist before the sight. [castm][c1] Sensation of impaired vision, with a veil in front of the eyes. [gink-b][jl1] It looks as if there is a fine mist, or smoke over everything. [latex][nl-latex] Vision was a little cloudy, like looking through a thin veil or light fog. Things were not completely in focus. With headache. [neon][srj5] Confused sight, as if directed through a veil. [plat][c1] She was obliged to hold objects near in order to see distinctly; at a distance everything seemed enveloped in a smoke or mist, but she could long retain distinct vision by holding objects near her. [phos][a1] Everything seems in a mist, with some loss of consciousness. [phos][a1] There are also cataract like symptoms. Sudden dimness before the eyes, so that she thought she would become blind. [mosch][a1] Sensation as if the cornea is covered with a milky layer. [ozone][sde2]

Focus can be difficult. Very bad eyesight. They often go out of focus, usually when I am tired or nervous. [adam][srj5] Impaired accommodation. [anh][jl1]

In Rubber the difficulties in seeing and hearing are an expression of a more general feeling of being unable to penetrate a barrier between the subject and the rest of the world. I had a dream that something was wrong with the windscreen wipers on my car – they were too furry. [latex][nl-latex] The feeling of disconnection becoming more intense. Very low. Like trying to see through thick murky liquid – hard to hear properly (especially on the right). Hard to see properly, focussing takes effort. It is not so much that my eyes can't see but that my brain can't function to perceive what is seen. [latex][nl-latex]

Hearing can be hard. Dream of talking to another long distance over the phone with a poor connection. [helo-s][rwt2] People talking in restaurants and couldn't understand what was going on; couldn't hear it. [helo-s][rwt2] Communication and messages were another theme found in the proving. Much of the communication was associated with frustration or feeling blocked in efforts at communication. It is interesting to note that the bird is voiceless. [cath-a][rwt] Unable to hear properly; everything seemed distant. [irid-met][srj5] Can hear myself talk as if in an echo chamber, as if listening to someone's talk. [galeoc-c-h][gms1]

Or muffled. Hearing very muffled. [lsd][nl-lsd] Hearing as if through cotton wool. [ozone][sde2] Tickling in the ears, as if a veil were drawn over them. [phos][a1] Buzzing in ears. [ignis-alc][es2] Ears feeling very blocked. Adding to the sense of being separate from the world. Sensation of pressure in the ears as though plugged. Sound slightly muffled. [latex][nl-latex]

The most common symptom is some form of tinnitus, which is found an almost all AIDS Miasm remedies. Ringing in the ears, or rather roaring. [agn][a1] Roaring and whistling in the ear. [ambr][a1] Roaring before the ear. [anac][a1] Noise in the ear, like the running of a river, continuing all night. [cact][a1] All sorts of noises in the ears, even whistling and cries of animals. [cur][a1] Heard people talking, sounded like the hum of bees. [lac-del][hrn2] Right ear ringing so loud I can't hear the T.V. [latex][nl-latex] Hearing feels bad again today. Whooshing noise in my ears constantly. Adds to the continuing feeling of being immersed in something thick and hard to move through. Worse in right ear. [latex][nl-latex] Sudden, very transient rushing into the ear, as from the fluttering of a large bird, now in the right, now in the left side. [mosch][a1] Singing tinnitus. [mosch][c1] Buzzing in ears; as if stopped.

[nux-m][c1] Deafness with noises in the head. [querc-r][c1] Noises in the ears. [phos][a1] My body hums. My ears, the world hums. High pitched, not disturbing. I just notice it. [galeoc-c-h][gms1] Mild to strong tinnitis, both high and low register. [vacuum][es-vac] My ears were ringing very noticeably when I just woke up today. [vacuum][es-vac]

The sense of smell can also be lost but that is much less common. Smell seems to have disappeared almost completely, although the nose is not obstructed. [anac][a1] Smell blunted; could not tell whether or not tincture of asafoetida was a perfume. [anh][c1] Anosmia. [cur][a1] Due to the strongly aromatic odour, taste and sense of smell are blocked for some time. [propl][vml3]

XII-3 Houses

The house was a very important image in describing AIDS Nosode symptoms, You have all spoken about houses and rooms; it was as if I had moved. I had fully moved into my house and I can go right up to the window of my house. This isn't a dream or anything, this is an image. Whereas some people are saying they felt persecuted so they would go back into themselves, I actually felt quite safe to go right up to my very extremities and what the hell, it doesn't matter what people say and I can go right up to the window and right into the bay and move right round. So it is the opposite of what everyone is saying. [aids][nl2] I felt that there were people who just went terribly serious and I had to move right back from anybody who was serious because the message was that life is too short and the house is too big. Let's explore every room. A very expansive feeling. [aids][nl2] and in the AIDS dreams. Dream: A Georgian terrace on a high pavement and I had a smaller apartment within this large house, but I remember there were lots of weird things going on with drug dealers, threats and violence and I had big, strong male friends and I took them up there to protect me but the drug dealers had gone. The house had a top layer which I left derelict so that nobody would suspect that on the basement level I had a beautiful house, so half of it was derelict and half of it was really beautiful downstairs. [aids][nl2]

The house is an obvious metaphor for the self, particularly in defining inside and outside.

One of the contradictions in Anglo-Saxon societies is that we have reversed the expected relationship between inside-outside and private-public space. In European societies outside is public space, while inside is very private. In Anglo-Saxon societies outside space is private, we do not like being approached in the street, but inside space is very often public. Hence the street cafés of France and Italy and the pubs and bars of Britain and America. The shopping mall is an attempt to reverse things again. By putting the street indoors it is hoped to again make it public space again. This reversal can become applied to the self and lies at the heart of some of the pathology of the AIDS Miasm. The self becomes public: everyone can criticize and observe you. While the outer world becomes private and you are unable to communicate and interact with those around you.

For several of the remedies the building of the house is extremely important. This applies to the Beaver's lodge. Of all mammals, the beaver is the most efficient and technically proficient when constructing its dwelling. The animal converts his living environment into different levels of water. This protects him against enemies on river banks and guarantees a quick escape through the underwater entrance to his lodge. [castm][mp4] The beaver's greatest achievement is its construction of a dam, which can sometimes reach a length of several kilometres. To build the dam, the animal gnaws trees in such a way that they fall into the water, and then transports them through the water. The lodges and dams are waterproof. [castm][vml3] And to the Butterfly's cocoon. At the pupa-cocoon stage, Limenitis bredowii builds a silk house around itself and hangs there quietly, until its body disintegrates and magically transforms into that of the complete, adult butterfly. [limen-b-c][hrn2] Dream: I was walking through a beautifully decorated house. It was decorated in pastels and white and had flowing curtains. [limen-b-c][hrn2] Dream: Of strange, dark cities. Of life around the gardens now in pain. Of lots of big structures. Of industry and dark, big, old, buildings. [limen-b-c][hrn2] Also to the Wasp's oak gall.

Houses appear in many dreams and are often a vehicle for expressing feelings about the self.

The house can be a crowded place, lacking privacy and a separate space. Dream: I was living in a loft space with my husband. A large, loft-like space with partitions/walls built in it to make separate rooms. I came home one day to find several college-age kids had moved in with us – they had torn down the partitions to make it open space again. They did not seem concerned that we had already been living there and did not want any room mates. [lac-e][hrn2] Dream: I was with a group of people and a person was showing us his house which was big, majestic, had stained glasses and resembled a European church. Everyone was impressed. Then I took them to my house which was princely, with huge rooms and a lot of furniture. There were new things in it but these seemed out of place. As we came out, there was a big lounge with many chairs in it. I realized that there was a restaurant adjacent to my flat. The two were merged into each other so that there was no clear demarcation between them. I wondered, without any feeling of anxiety, where I would put the door so that people coming to the restaurant wouldn't enter my house. [polys][sk4] Dream: My house consists of a single room surrounded by two open balconies on either side, so that there is no privacy. Also I realize that there is no ceiling and anyone from the surrounding sky-scrapers can look inside. [polys][sk4] Dream: Went to friend's home in New Mexico; she had a house with no front or back; walls in house are wide open to the forest and wilderness; animals coming right in house; she would think nothing if mountain lions killed a rabbit in the living room; didn't phase her but freaked me out. The whole animal kingdom was in the house – no walls – the whole universe felt in the house. [carneg-g][rwt1] Dream: Living in a house with a ton of people – old storey house with many bedrooms and beds in them; people were sleeping in the hallway. [urol-h][rwt3]

There are many dreams of large houses. Dream about a large Victorian house which I have never seen. [androc][srj5] Magnificent Castles; far off places and fantasy. [helodr-cal][knl2] Dreamt about being on a college campus and visiting sororities. Each one in a different setting and huge like castles or giant apartments. [helodr-cal][knl2] Dream: I was in a communal house, a big house, with lots of rooms and bathrooms. [lac-del][hrn2] Dream: Going from place to place in a deserted, big building like a palace. I saw the rooms, mostly from a height with fascination on the one hand and sorrow on the other. [lac-h][sk4]

Or a desire to move or to improve the house. Dreamt of longing to move to a bigger house with a walled garden. [adam][srj5] I am the head in a house which is made of dirt, and get my grown son moving to work hard with me and accomplish a job that will help us to grow. [coca-c][sk4] Dreams of wanting to live in a new house. Looking for the Realtor to look for a new house. [haliae-lc][srj5] Dreams of buying house. Dreams of selling house. [ignis-alc][es2] During the proving I frequently dreamed of being in houses – people showing me around their houses. [galeoc-c-h][gms1]

In some dreams the house has unexplored or secret areas. Dream: Whilst showing someone round my half finished house, I discover some new rooms and stairs that I had not noticed before. [heroin][sdj-h] Dream: In the house, but the house is much larger with more rooms and hallways; some seem to be hidden unless approached from the right direction. [urol-h][rwt3] Dream of a building with lots of rooms and floors, strange architecture. [plac][Biggs+]

The house can be under threat of being broken into. Dream: I was in a lonely house and wanted to shut all the windows to be safe from robbers, but wanted also the sunlight to come in and so I couldn't keep everything shut. I was wondering how to be safe. [lac-leo][sk4] Dream: Intruder breaking into the house. [carneg-g][rwt1] Feeling of invasion/violation/people intruding into my life. [carneg-g][rwt1] Theme I am being attacked and intruded on, but If I defend myself in the right way, I will not be hurt. The area of intrusion is generally in the home, the area that one generally feels safe and secure. When one is not protected, there are feelings of anxiety, edginess and fear. [carneg-g][rwt1]

Or of being destroyed. Dream: My place got screwed up, no shelter, a big piece of open property with junk lying around. [lac-lup][hrn2] Dream of an earthquake. House appears to be falling down. [ozone][sde2]

The car is the house in miniature and a space that is extremely isolated. This space can be important in further detaching the subject from the world. Driving seems to be a big time for the euphoria. The sensation of speed and the visual. [haliae-lc][srj5] I was flowing in the car. Driving to a destination and not being driven. More a sense like floating without the tension of driving. [haliae-lc][srj5] Drove partner to town, actually he drove, and as soon as we got into the car I had the waves of alteredness and detachment come over me, there is a definite link to being in the car. [falco-pe][nl2] Difficulty focusing my attention while driving, with a sensation of gentle floating. [germ-met][srj5] I felt better when driving the car fast with company and loud music. [hydrog][srj2] Feel as if I am the only person. Feel like I'm in my own little capsule sitting very still and yet being moved. Thinking of nothing, just driving and staring at the road. [irid-met][srj5]

XII-4 The Skin

The most important barrier for people is their skin. It is also the primary site for miasmatic expression. In Psora, the Itch, there are eruptions that are chronic, long lasting and relatively stable. In Sycosis the theme of growth is manifested in growths, warts and excresences. In Syphilis the skin symptoms tend to be destructive and necrotic. In AIDS the skin symptoms are non-specific, they are likely to change and they tend to make the subject aware of their skin.

Dryness is a common theme. Skin itching and lips very dry. [choc][srj3] Very dry skin, this is completely new. [lac-h][htj1] Dry facial skin, especially forehead and cheeks. [lars-arg][fkw1] My skin got very dry and itchy. [sanguis-s][hrn2] (*See Thirst & Dryness IV-5*)

There is an awareness of the skin. Woolly feeling and hyperaesthesia of the skin. [anh][jl1] The fine skin and glossy hair of the young women among the arsenic-eating populations is remarkable, and is comparable to the fine coats of arsenic-fed horses. On the other hand, "staring coat" in animals, and "dry, rough, scaly, unhealthy-looking skin" in human beings are keynote indications for the remedy. [ars][c1] I am more aware of the surface of my body. [agath-a][nl2] More awareness of skin surface. [lac-lup][hrn2] In the shower I am aware of my short hair and skull, and of the soles of my feet, which have velvety feeling. [plut-n][srj7] I felt movement on the skin over my ribs, as if fur or hair on my skin was touched – a rippling movement. [plut-n][srj7] Sharks have toothlike structures on the surface of the skin called denticles. If you rub a shark from head to tail, the skin feels almost smooth. If you rub the skin the opposite way, it can cut. [galeoc-c-h][gms1] As if I can feel my skin. [galeoc-c-h][gms1] I am noticing an overall feeling of increased awareness of the skin all over my body, in the form of a gentle, pleasant buzz. [vacuum][es-vac]

This is most pronounced in Iridium where there is a concomitant sensual delight in touching the skin. Dreams of babies and frogs legs, smoothness of skin. [irid-met][srj5] A sensation like something is sticking on the skin. A sensation like my clothes are sticking to my skin. A tight sensation. [irid-met][srj5] (*See Touch XII-5*)

In some remedies the skin feels softer or different. Skin is paler. Feels more feminine, round and soft. [adam][srj5] My skin on my face feels softer, not so dry. [falco-pe][nl2] Skin feels softer, a hardness is gone from it. Feels squishier, more pliable. It reminds me of my mother's skin, which gives me the creeps. Not wanting to be like my mother. [haliae-lc][srj5]

Many of the remedies like Rhus tox are powerful skin irritants in their natural state. If the skin brushes against the seed mantle [especially if it is rotting], intense skin irritation occurs, sometimes only after 1 or 2 days, which is called ginnan-kabure in Japan. It usually disappears spontaneously after a week. [gink-b][vml3] A peculiar kind of skin disease, called Tahiti, arevareva, results from the daily use. The skin is covered as in leprosy, with large scales, which fall off and leave lasting white spots which often become ulcers. [pip-m][a1] In the skunk these glands are extremely developed for defence purposes: the discharged fluid causes a terrible stink as well as extreme irritation of the skin. [meph][vml3]

There can be rashes and eruptions. Skin red. Sore, itching eruptions. Red, sore, painful itching on soles of feet and palms, around the veins, alternating sides or on both sides. [androc][srj5] Woke in the morning completely covered with poison oak all over body. [limen-b-c][hrn2] A scarlatina-like rash over the body. [coca][c1] Every prover who had ever had herpetic eruptions had an outbreak during the proving. [musca-d][stew+] I have vesicles everywhere, on abdomen, back of legs and chest. Feel OK. [positr][nl2] Have blisters, red and sore, all over. Ears, left elbow and both heels very sore. The skin symptoms are very intense. I scratch until they are sore, it feels better for scratching, but the scratching makes it worse. Arms, legs, chest, abdomen, back, elbows all feel burned, red, sore and swollen. [positr][nl2] Covered with a rash resembling measles; his face, neck, and throat swollen. [rhus-t][a1] When she awoke, next morning, her body was covered with a copious miliary eruption, on the third day the rash disappeared, and there was an abscess formed at the right knee, which broke on the eleventh day, and was followed by death on the fourteenth. [tax][a1] After two or three days an eruption makes its appearance, such as he had never had; small red pimples, very bright red and very sharply defined, with minute vesicles upon them, first on the lower extremities, then also upon the upper, most on the left side. [tell][a1]

Itching is also common. Itching of the skin all over which changes place from scratching. No place is exempt from this. [agar][k2] Itching-stinging in different parts of the body, obliging him to scratch. [agn][a1] Corrosively stinging itching upon the body here and there, especially upon the back and thighs, with desire to scratch; scratching relieves for a short time. [anac][a1] One woman said she had been tormented for the last two days and nights with irritation of skin, which she compared to being in a bagful of fleas. [ars][a1] Itching in face, shoulder, abdomen, and feet, relieved by scratching. [cann-i][a1] Felt for two days, more on second day, intolerable itching over the whole surface of the body. On the third day it was perfectly unbearable. After annoying me very much, it gradually left me. [cere-b][a1] Itching scapulae, shins, forearms, top of pelvic arches and forehead. In some areas, I kept on scratching until I bled. [choc][srj3] Skin in general is more sensitive, and generally more itchy and tingling. [haliae-lc][srj5] I had prickling sensations on the Friday night as physical sensations, and isolated, sort of specially more on the face, but anywhere in the body, but definite prickling, which I don't normally get. [agath-a][nl2]

It is often has a sensual or voluptuous dimension. General voluptuous itching over the whole body, which spreads still more by scratching. [anac][a1] Itching is intense, "voluptuous", it keeps moving around, have to scratch until it is sore. [positr][nl2] Scratching myself feels so pleasurable. [sanguis-s][hrn2]

In Cocaine there is a very characteristic sensation. Sensation as of small foreign bodies or of worms under the skin ("cocaine bugs"). [coca][tl2] A characteristic symptom of Cocaine poisoning is a sensation as if small foreign bodies were under the skin, generally like grains of sand; or else as of a worm under the skin. "You imagine," he says, "that in your skin are worms, or similar things, moving along". [coca][c1] If you touch them with wool, and especially with absorbent wool, they run away and disappear, only to peep cautiously out of some corner to see if there is any danger. [coca][c1]

In Diamond the skin is sensitive and painful. Skin very painful. Whole body is sensitive, bones aching, skin hurts. [adam][srj5] Skin painful – feels prickling and cold. [adam][srj5]

In Anantherum the skin is tender, liable to break and becomes bruised. The skin is very tender, it breaks, ulcerates, and suppurates readily. [anan][a1] Blotches and swellings on various parts of the body, as if he had been beaten. [anan][a1]

In several remedies the skin is not able to repair itself as it should. Wounds slow to heal. [plac][Biggs+] In Kauri there is the signature of the unhealing wound: the resinous gum which oozes (in the case of old wounds, for hundreds, even thousands of years) from damaged branches. [agath-a][nl2] Blood would not clot and wounds would not heal. [visc][ptk2]

Hair is an extension of the skin and it figures in several remedies. There is a desire to cut the hair. Desire to cut hair so that it is short and bristly. [choc][srj3] Husband cutting his hair. [coca-c][sk4] Desire to have my hair cut right now. I do. [germ-met][srj5] Shaved off my beard after more than 25 years. Don't really know why just felt that I should give it a go, don't like it and will grow it back. Face feels very cold, exposed to the elements. [latex][nl-latex] There is a tendency for the hair to fall out. The hair falls off. [cur][a1] All the hairy parts became denuded. [tax][a1] My hair is falling out – mainly on the left side. [sal-fr][sle1] Or to become white. The hair loses its gloss, and finally turns white. [cur][a1] The hair becomes matted and frizzled like wool. [cur][a1] (*See Old, Ugly & Fat XI-2*)

An important feature of recent years is the popularity of body piercing. This seems to me to be a characteristic symptom of the AIDS Miasm. It both draws attention to the skin and increases awareness of it and it does so by breaching the integrity of the skin. It is another form of the unhealing wound. One person had the first of many piercings immediately after coming into contact with the AIDS Nosode proving. There is a fear of things that things might pierce, especially in Lac felinum. Dream: I was trying to remove a block in the needle of a syringe by blowing in air and sucking it out. In the process, I accidently swallowed the needle and I was frightened that it would perforate through my stomach. I imagined the needle piercing through my stomach wall and the fear kept increasing in my mind. I did not know what to do and was afraid that I would die. [lac-h][sk4] I heard from some patients that they instinctively pulled back, when a finger or another pointed object was pointed at them. Or when a hand, unexpectedly, came close to there face, out of fear their eyes where going to be hurt. [lac-f][wza1]

The other way in which the skin is an important theme in the Miasm is in nakedness. It is as if the skin is enough of a barrier and the subject does not want to make it even worse by adding clothes. There is also an element of connecting to the primitive and natural. Another recent vogue, tattooing is probably linked to this. The young assistant of the session has a tatoo on his arm and I feel slightly attracted by that, I find it sexually animating. [heroin][sdj-h] There are general nakedness symptoms. Delusions, fancies and dreams about nakedness. [Sherr] [androc][vml3] Delirium, strips himself. [conv-s][jl1] I lay naked outside in the wind. [haliae-lc][srj5] I was at a meeting with many other people – all people had clothes on except me; it didn't bother anyone except me. [helo-s][rwt2] In Silesia, it is said that angels put gold at the foot of the rainbow, and only a naked man can obtain it. [irid-met][srj5] Dreams: Running naked with breasts exposed. [lac-e][hrn2] Dream: Lost clothes, looking for something to wear, so I wrapped self in rug. [lac-leo][hrn2] Shamelessness, uncovers. [plat][c1] Tendency to uncover completely in sleep is a leading note of it. [plat][c1]

There is a sensuality in nakedness. I wanted to do something wanton and sensual and extravagant, last night I felt frustrated – I wanted to swim naked in the sea or ride a horse naked or something naked. [aids][nl2] Tremendous pleasure at smoothness of skin of inside of arm, against side of body (was walking around naked from waist up most of day). [haliae-lc][srj5] Getting dressed, didn't want to put clothes on, wanted the freedom of nakedness, chose clothes for their lack of restriction. [irid-met][srj5]

But it is not usually sexual. I imagined being naked, not having sex, with female houseguest. (Male prover) [irid-met][srj5]

There is no embarrassment at nakedness. I felt like doing something mischievous. I had no embarrassment with nakedness. [aids][nl2] In dream, was on a train to California. It stops in the desert. I stepped out naked onto the desert. There are a lot of stones mixed with seashells and cacti growing like seaweed. I am delighted and call to a young girl to come and see. It was like looking at the bottom of the sea, seashells. We are snorkelling on dry land. A delightful dream. People were showing up. I was naked but had no shame or embarrassment. I did put on a long T-shirt. [maias-l][hrn2] Dream of being naked (used to dream of this as a child with great embarrassment) now I'm not embarrassed at all. [galla-q-r][nl2] Dream: On the way another car passed by with another group of people all of whom were also naked. We all waved and shouted greetings to each other. I was neither surprised nor embarrassed about being naked or being in the company of naked people. It all seemed okay. [lac-h][sk4]

And the subject can be better for being naked. Feel better on disrobing for the night. [cere-b][a1]

XII-5 Touch

Touch is the physical expression of recognition of the skin and of barriers in general.

There can be an aversion to touch, as it emphasizes the subject's openness and vulnerability. I don't want to be touched or talked to. [adam][srj5] Sensitive to touch, uncomfortable from pressure. [coca-c][sk4] Aversion to touch. A fuzzy angora sweater felt irritating to me. [haliae-lc][srj5] Shrinking feeling on being approached. Aversion to being touched. [lumbr-t][evans] According to boyfriend I actively avoided any physical contact. Going around the kitchen to avoid touching him in passing. No sexual desire at all, very averse. [falco-pe][nl2] My skin feels very sensitive and I don't want anyone to touch me. [heroin][sdj-h] Aversion to being touched. [hydrog][srj2] If anyone actually pokes me with their finger like that, I get violently angry it's an invasion of my space. [agath-a][nl2] During the second month of the proving, the spine, from the last cervical to about the fifth dorsal vertebra, became very sensitive, and the seat of a peculiar sense of irritation, which made the prover dread having the part touched or even approached; this dread was disproportionate to the actual sensibility of the part when pressed or rudely touched, for this sensibility was not really very great. [tell][a1] The symptoms are agg. by touch. [tell][jl1] *(See Vulnerability IX-1)*

In some remedies it is a form of restriction. Can't bear to be hugged; it makes me feel restricted. [ozone][sde2] *(See Trapped IX-7)*

The remedy which has the greatest aversion to touch is Lac caninum. Sensitiveness of the abdomen so that the sheet cannot be permitted to touch the skin. [lac-c][k2] Could not bear to have any one part of her body touch another; felt if she could not get out of her body in some way, she would soon become crazy. [lac-c][c1]

In Selenium it is touching of the hair to which there is an aversion. The symptoms are agg. by touch and pressure. [sel][c1] Pain in the hair when touched. Don't want the hair touched [Boger]. [sel][vml3]

There can also be a numbness and lack of feeling in the skin. The skin feels numb, and is insensible as far as the knees, without being cold; the hands have but an indistinct sensation; the skin seems to have gone to sleep, but there is no tingling. [ambr][a1] External numbness of whole body in the morning and weakness. [ambr][vml4] My skin feels numb, less sensitive to touch. [choc][srj3] Lips and face so numb that she tried some time before she could speak. [cocain][a1] (*See Anaesthesia III-3*)

Many of the animals that have been proved recently are ones that take delight in tactile contact, and this came through in provings. Just like elephants and whales, dolphins love constant physical contact with one another. They rub their bodies together affectionately along their entire length while swimming and touch and pat each other throughout the day. They also engage in a curious maneuver where one dolphin will slowly push another dolphin around with its beak in the other's genital slit. [lac-del][hrn2] Elephants are highly affectionate creatures. The whole family moves as one, and the merest whimper from a calf causes them to stop and patiently wait until the problem has been solved before moving on. From playtime to the moments of greatest danger, elephants will be in constant physical contact with one another – touching, nudging, caressing, and even kissing by putting their trunk tips in each other's mouths. [lac-loxod-a][hrn2] Play is a big part of the life of the wolf. Making body contact, chasing, bumping, teasing, rolling, kissing, biting are everyday activities in a healthy wolf pack. [lac-lup][hrn2]

There can be a desire to make contact through touch. Became aware of a man's hair and had an intense desire to touch it, to make contact with it. [choc][srj3] Desire to touch and be touched. [mdma][hmd1] Wanted to touch and stroke people. [falco-pe][nl2] I sort of had to keep touching everyone. [agath-a][nl2] Desire to touch people, be near them, feel their presence, feel connection, to have fun with them, to laugh with them. Normally I want time to myself. [lac-del][hrn2] Desire to being caressed in an 'appropriate', way making love on her own conditions, cuddling dreams of dogs and fishes, of coats and furs. [lac-f][wza1] Dream: Unknown man afraid of being touched. He is asked to pick me up so I am stretched lengthwise over his back, our bodies touching from shoulders down. He can do this and it is big deal since he is afraid of being touched. [lac-lup][hrn2] Wanted to plait a girl's hair (another student who was sitting in front of me in class – I don't know her well enough to do this!). [lsd][nl-lsd]

There is often a sensuality to the touch. Wearing light things instead of dark. Want light next to my skin. Desire for yellow silk underwear. [adam][srj5] Feelings concerning the texture, smoothness, warmth and 'melting in the mouth' qualities were most venerated. [choc][srj3] Tremendous pleasure at smoothness of skin of inside of arm, against side of body. [haliae-lc][srj5] Increased sense of sensuality to the skin, pulling on jeans is a luxury, I feel like a kitten, soft, cuddly and warm. [haliae-lc][srj5] Impression that I have a luxuriant, soft growth of beard on my face and chin, like a woman's pubic hair, although I am clean shaven. I enjoy the imaginary sensation of stroking it. [plut-n][srj7] More tactile and affectionate than usual. [positr][nl2]

This is usually not sexual but it can be. Sexual desire increased, easily excited by clothes and pressure. [lac-h][htj1]

There is an enhanced awareness of texture in many remedies. Textures and shapes seem different – like a new way of seeing. I seem to have a fascination with certain objects and textures, like wood on doors or colours of hair. [choc][srj3] Feel I am noticing the surface texture of things more than usual. [lac-h][htj1]

Mescaline has the distinctive symptom of the hallucinations being increased or enhanced when the subject is touched. Impressions of sound and visions heightened by any marked stimulation of skin. [anh][c1] Their delusions and illusions are greatly affected by skin contact; if somebody caresses them, the visions or sounds are heightened. [anh][vh1]

The most tactile of all the remedies is undoubtedly Iridium. It is one of the hardest of all substances (Diamond, the very hardest, has similar symptoms but they are not as pronounced) and it is one that does not give in to outer pressure. Yet its proving produced an impressive array of touch symptoms, particularly a sensuality through contact with the skin. Skin felt very alive, tactile, fingertips felt awake. Feathers felt amazing. Skin to skin; very aware of contact of surfaces. [irid-met][srj5] When a friend visited, she touched me a lot, and I noticed it. I've not touched people as much as I normally do. [irid-met][srj5] Desire to touch backs of hands on face. Enjoy touch on skin. Old memories of gentleness, delightfully feminine. Wearing bright pink (unusual!) and stroking my legs. Enjoying my skin, touching bottom, stroking it. Dancing erotically at 8.00 a.m. [irid-met][srj5] Had sensation of someone touching my knee while eating supper. [irid-met][srj5] Woke in white softness, like rabbit's fur. [irid-met][srj5] The cat got hold of my hair and started to groom it. She has never done this before. [irid-met][srj5] Delight at seeing my own female form in mirror, desire to shave legs so they would be smooth. Highly sexual, more refined, dressed in best clothes today. [irid-met][srj5] Curled up stroking body, especially legs, feet together, Feeling as if they were magnetic. [irid-met][srj5] No desire to touch, make love to husband all week in spite of easy, relaxed week. I feel detached from him, as if this is a problem within me. [irid-met][srj5] Still want to touch husband. Not wild desire but more like a pet dog. Affection rather than desire. Getting him cups of tea, stroking him. [irid-met][srj5]

XII-6 Portals

The opening through a wall or boundary not only breaches it and

opens it up to the other side, but it also defines it as a boundary and not just an ending.
The bridge and the rainbow are symbolically seen as paths that cross the boundary between the earthly world and the spiritual one. The bridge symbolizes the passage from one shore to another, the transition between two states or desires in coflict. [ang][ggd1] In Judaism, Islam and Christianity, it is interesting to note that the angel, being slightly more than human and slightly less than god, is considered both a winged messenger, and a bridge between heaven and earth. [irid-met][srj5]

The Raven, the Falcon, the Eagles and birds in general fulfill the same role. In Native American belief, the eagle is a spirit of great vision, wisdom and power, one who sees clearly and travels high, one who opens the magic door and can carry you to the place of vision and communication with Great Spirit. [haliae-lc][srj5] The Peregrine Falcon has been regarded as a mystic bird and often as a messenger from another world, a stranger in ours. [falco-pe][nl2] Biblical writers described God-sent ravens sustaining the prophet Elijah during his retreat to the desert. [corv-cor][bdg1] Less sense of individual duty, more need to connect with the other world. [haliae-lc][sej-birds]

LSD and Mescaline are seen as doors to a deeper and more spiritual world. Hence Huxley's choice of title for the "Doors of Perception" in which he describes his hallucinogenic experiences. It was a doorway into places I am certain I dreamt about in my childhood, crystal dimensions, where I could taste colours and touch sounds and smells with my hands from the very first trip on. [lsd][nl-lsd]

Doors lead to a feeling of being closed in and shut off from the world. It's a very closed sensation as if I've been closed out. A feeling of being shut out as if the door was closed. [aids][nl2] Dreamt about big red door, I saw it but did not go through. [latex][nl-latex] *(See Isolation II-8)*

But they are also the opening through which a hostile world can come in. He felt so scared he had to shut the door, with a feeling that something would appear from behind it if he left it open. Intense but very rapid fear, immensely powerful and very upsetting. [androc][srj5] D. made a hole in the wall of the workshop yesterday for a cat-flap. I was worried about stray cats, rats, squirrels coming in. [agath-a][nl2] Delusion that people are about to burst through the door. [plut-n][srj7] Dream: A door being pushed in and me trying to press with all my body weight against it to not let it in as I felt whatever it was, was going to harm me or my girls. [vacuum][es-vac] The paranoid feeling I was writing about is also a vivid fear of war. Images of having the door kicked in by armed forces, the suddenness and fear, the terror. [vacuum][es-vac] *(See Vulnerability IX-1)*

Doors, windows and openings are particularly important symbols in Neon. Looking out of the window at the night sky, it suddenly cracked open and a great darkness revealed itself. Infinity was blackness. It was deeply disturbing. [neon][srj5] I notice a foolish and irresistible desire to spy on my partner through the keyhole in the door to his study. I now remember doing this a couple of times yesterday (on the first day of the proving) as well. I am finding it ridiculous, laughing to myself. I feel like a mischievous child, doing something it shouldn't do, giggling away to myself. It makes me feel excited in a childish sense. I have never felt compelled to spy on anyone ever – be it through a keyhole or otherwise. Very strange. [neon][srj5]

The delusion that someone is knocking or calling was also strong in Neon. Twice thought I heard someone at the door but when I checked there was no one there. [neon][srj5] Twice at 5.45 am I was awakened by hearing a doorbell – leapt out of bed to open the door but no one was there. [neon][srj5] Dreamt that I was knocking on many different doors. Nobody opened them. [neon][srj5] Though it was found in other remedies as well. He imagines he hears his name called by the voice of his far-distant mother and sister. [anac][a1] Imagines someone calls him. [cann-i][a1] Hearing things like someone knocking at the door, someone calling my name, the phone ringing but nobody knocked, no one called. [corv-cor][bdg1] Woke at 6.35 a.m. convinced I'd been woken by my daughter shouting "Mum, come quickly!" Rush of adrenalin. [positr][nl2] Dream: There is someone pounding on the door of my apartment; woke up with a lot of fear. [carneg-g][rwt1]

XII-7 Mouth, Anus & Vagina

The physical portals that are opening between the self and the outside world are important sites of pathology in the AIDS Miasm.

Many of the drug remedies but especially Speed and Ecstasy have a tightening or clenching of the jaw which contrasts with Ecstasy's main symptom of openness. Gritting and grinding of the teeth while sleeping. [cann-i][a1] The teeth of right side of mouth seem to him to be clenched. [cann-i][a1] Grinds teeth whilst asleep. [cann-i][c1] Various muscular side effects are common, as though some muscles react against the drug's demand to let go. These include holding the jaw tightly clenched, eyes flickering from side to side, muscle twitches, nausea and cramp, especially as the drug first takes effect. Generally these side-effects soon pass. [mdma][saunders] Three quarters of the subjects experienced jaw tension or teeth clenching during the session, sometimes accompanied by shaking. [mdma][saunders]

This, and grinding of the teeth, are found in other remedies.

Grinding teeth. [adam][srj5] Hunger, with sensation of fullness in the stomach; even the little he eats causes clenching of the teeth and contraction of the throat. [anan][a1] Convulsive grinding of the teeth. [ars][c1] Jaw tightened up. Tried to release it but could not. [carbn-dox][knl3] Contracture of the masticatory muscles. [conv-s][jl1] Speediness, clenching teeth, irritable with the kids. [germ-met][srj5] Grinding teeth. [irid-met][srj5] Felt like I was grinding my teeth in my sleep. [galeoc-c-h][gms1] I'm clenching my teeth – my jaw feels stiff. [vacuum][es-vac]

There are symptoms of crumbling, loose and missing teeth or decay of the jaw. Teeth feel loose and squidgy in sockets (bottom front). [aids][nl2] The jaw affection, called "Phossy-jaw" by the work people themselves, is accompanied by profound adynamia, and not unfrequently ends in death. [phos][c1]

Decaying teeth are often found in the dreams where their symbolic role as guardians of the inner self is clearer. Dreamt my bottom teeth came out, and I put them back the wrong way. [aids][nl2] I dreamt of a party, it's my party and lose my (false) teeth. Then the party starts to turn really sour, with people being nasty and thoughtless. It gets worse and worse until the dream is a nightmare. [aids][nl2] Dreams about the falling out of his front teeth. [conv-d][a1] Dream: My mouth was full of broken, crumbling teeth. [irid-met][srj5] Dream: Teeth falling out, pulled them out. It was so real. I had braces on my teeth as well and I pulled them off. I just wobbled all my teeth and they were loose and rotten. I had a handful of molars, which someone had later stolen to sell. [lac-lup][hrn2] Dream: Two teeth are wobbly and fall out. I feel horror. [positr][nl2] Dream: Looking at my teeth in the mirror and seeing the top two in the front had an inscribed circle of decay on each of them. [vacuum][es-vac]

Cocaine is an anaesthetic that is particularly felt in the mouth and face, the quick test for it is to rub it against the gums and see if the powder causes immediate numbness. Cocaine causes a numb feeling on the tongue. [coca][a1] Lips and face so numb that she tried some time before she could speak. [cocain][a1]

The Butterfly has a very similar symptom and the effect is also explicitly felt in the vagina as well as the mouth. Stranger, of it forms sudden is anesthetized. Of one moment for other, every area of the lips, upper and below, in the same intensity whole region, I feel as if it had won a place anesthesia of all the lips. I didn't place anything that can have anesthetic action. This picture a lot is impressing me, therefore it is completely anesthetized. [lepd-s][rsi1] During the sexual relationship with my husband, I felt my vagina anesthetized like Xilocaína. [lepd-s][rsi1]

XII-8 Death

The ultimate boundary is that which lies between the world of the living and the world of the dead.

There is in the AIDS Miasm there is a strong fear of death. Excessive fear of death. [cur][a1] Fear of death came up more than usual during the proving. It wasn't the fear of ageing. It was fear of the finality, that one day you won't see the light, or breathe the air, or live to contemplate overcoming your problems. [haliae-lc][srj5] Apprehension of death, and excessive timidity about dying. [mosch][c1] Great fear of death. [nux-m][a1] Anguish with fear of death and sighs. [rhus-t][a1] Constant fear of death. [phos][a1]

The fearful delusion that the subject is dying. He seemed to have the one idea that he should die and soon be dissected. [cann-i][a1] He became possessed with the idea that be was about to die, from which he cried out, "I am dying; I shall be carried to my death-chamber". [cann-i][a1] (The feeling of) what it would be like if I were dying. [corv-cor][bdg1] She thought that she had no place in the world, life was wearisome, but she had great dread of death, which she believed near at hand. [plat][a1]

Or even that he or she is dead. Feels as if dead. [anh][sp1] I woke up and could not feel the usual sensation of my heart bulging or beating through my ribs while lying on my left side. I felt shock and thought 'perhaps I'm dead'. Groped for pulse and was reassured to be able to feel it. [choc][srj3]

In some remedies the thought of death is welcome. Had strong feeling, like a visualization. I picture myself lying on floor in fetal position and being shot in the head like a horse or a dog. Almost welcomed it. Then thought my children still need me. Woke up writing a poem about death being my lover. Comparing her sweet kiss to a lover's kiss that turns sour. The earthy taste of her other lips that are a portal to the sweet comfort of the grave, rather than a source of the pain of life and the sweet waters of Lethe suckled at her smooth cold breast. [positr][nl2] Feels an acceptance of death, and welcomes it with a sentimental longing. [tax-br][oss1] Been longing just to be done with life. I no longer actively engage in fantasies of suicide, but I have this bone weary exhaustion with life. [vacuum][es-vac]

Many of the remedy substances have an association with death. "In Asia," states Alain Eid in Butterflies and Moths of the World, "moths are held in special esteem; they are believed to be the manifestation of dead souls who have returned to protect the living." [limen-b-c][hrn2] The Mayas had believed that the drink made from the cocoa seeds would nourish them after death. [choc][srj3] The name Falcon comes from the Latin falx, a sickle and alludes to the sharp beak that, like the grim reaper, brings sudden death. [falco-pe][nl2] Egyptian priests used it to embalm mummies. [propl][vml3] In pre-Christian times willow was traditionally placed in coffins or planted on the grave, to enable the spirit of the corpse to rise and free it from the body. [sal-fr][sle1] Orpheus wore a willow branch that allowed him to enter and leave the underworld. [sal-fr][sle1] In parts of Asia, it was assumed that people changed into cats after they died. The Chinese believed that as soon as cats reached a certain age, they could change into other creatures. [lac-f][vml3] Locals in the Solomon Islands believe the ghosts of the departed inhabit the bodies of sharks. [galeoc-c-h][gms1]

In some remedies there is an awareness of death and the process of death. He imagines a bier is in the side-room. [anac][a1] Dark curtains in my room as in a crematorium. Sadness. Death. The curtains are a separation. [galla-q-r][nl2] In the house that I live in, there was someone who was in their dying process and died during the course of this. After working all day, I would be up most of the night with this person often, was very exhausted because of that. [sanguis-s][hrn2] During the proving, one couple saw a ghost, and two of the provers made a connection to a sibling who had died in infancy. [sal-fr][sle1] Thoughts of death before going to sleep – for no reason! [latex][nl-latex] I'm obsessed with ageing and death. [vacuum][es-vac] Have a feeling of understanding of the Last Judgement, when the dead rise up from the graves. [vacuum][es-vac]

Hydrogen is a remedy in which the link to the living world is tenuous. Subjects may feel that they have not properly been born or that they are well on the way to the state that follows death. I feel my connection with the physical world is very loose, as though my soul was separated from my body. I have thoughts that this is a bit like dying – not unpleasant. [hydrog][srj2] Wrote a letter to my son, "to be opened after my death", not morbid, nor do I feel a premonition of death. It's something I've always meant to do – a sort of resolving. Wept with emotion as I wrote it. [hydrog][srj2] Thoughts of death – thoughts went back to doing dissection as a medical student. [hydrog][srj2]

In Fire the most important theme is one of purification, of burning away that which is evil and dirty to reveal that which is clean and pure. It is therefore this part of the process of death, the cleansing of Purgatory, that is most important. Dream: I took a group of my friends to Purgatory. It was a large, stone building in space, very dark, shiny damp. [ignis-alc][es2]

Snakes and dogs have long been regarded as the psychopomp, the being that leads the dead into the underworld. There are dreams of snakes. Had a dreadful dream about a snake. I was being pressured to do heavy psychotherapy with a man I didn't like – a trainer. I thought the whole thing was dangerous, but went in because lots of people were doing it. A small boy of eight to ten was there. He stuck his tongue out at me, it turned into the most disgusting, slithery snake, pink and revolting, which went for my throat, It wrapped itself around my neck. I can't describe the repulsion I felt, nor the fear at being controlled. I said I repudiated it. The therapist in the dream said it's not about sex, this snake, its about the evil within which must be cleansed. I woke up shouting "I refuse to accept this snake!" but the feeling stayed. Fear; I had to put the light on – revulsion, horror. [aids][nl2] Dream: A snake wound itself around me while I was travelling in a train. I wasn't scared, picked it up and threw it out, although it was slippery. [lac-h][sk4] One prover had delusions about snakes; imagined she was surrounded by them; was afraid to close her eyes at night for fear of being bitten by a large snake which she imagined was beside the bed. [lac-c][c1] Dream of being at a party where she had a snake in her bag. The snake is somehow let loose; it is enjoyable for her. But fearing that other people will be bitten, she puts it back into her bag. [lac-h][sk4] I own a lot of snake paraphernalia and I noticed it more. Picked up a romance novel while at grocery store (never before had done this), and the first line on the book jacket is that a guy gets a poisonous snake in his mouth and it killed him. [lac-loxod-a][hrn2] Dream. Green snake was trying to attack me and I kept having to throw it away to protect myself but it just kept coming back. [latex][nl-latex] A nightmare: seven black snakes come from a box and I am quite scared of them. [rhus-g][tmo3] I saw a king snake on the road and pulled over to watch its serpentine moves, to see it coil in reaction to a passing car then carry on across the road – watching it move into the grass. I suddenly thought, "Darn, I should have grabbed it," brought it home to live in our yard, to protect us from rattlesnakes – and then I remember the proving, the feeling of having to grasp, to possess, to own something of nature, to use it for my own purpose without regard for its purpose. [sanguis-s][hrn2] In some of these this role is explicit. Dream: On a picnic with friends. We were playing mono-acting when a pregnant friend collapsed. We were going to give her a cardiac massage, when a python encircled her abdomen. [lac-h][sk4]

There are dreams of dogs. Dreamed a lot of things but general theme was confusion and chaos. Lots of dogs in dream, then I turned into a dog. [irid-met][srj5] Some of which make the connection to death. I dreamed that my father was dying of tuberculosis. When I told him about my dream (in my dream) he felt that this sealed his fate. We got involved in a group which is involved in the rituals of the process of death. Everybody was very accepting, including myself. It was idyllic. There was a lovable, frisky puppy-dog, black. [agath-a][nl2]

In Fire the animal that is most important is the cat which seems to represent a connection to the Evil that exists on the otherworld. A total aversion to cats. I see cats as disgusting, rotten, evil creatures. [ignis-alc][es2] My two cats have run away. I'm delighted – I couldn't stand them being around. I was seeing them as disgusting, dirty creatures. [ignis-alc][es2] Disgust and aversion to my cats. Decided to dispose of one of them. Put him over the wall of a nunnery a few miles away. [ignis-alc][es2] A similar feeling is to be found in the opiates.

There are a great number of dreams and delusions about death. Dreams of dead bodies. [cann-i][a1] Nightmares; dreams of corpses. [gink-b][vml3] Dream about death; that we had created in our world a place and the word that comes to mind is the Snew, and when people die if they have AIDS or if it is a child or whatever, they are taken to this place and it is like a paradise and a lot of greenery and a lot of warmth and sun and on this particular part of the world there are all these little areas where you could take your person who you love and the family will nurse that person and care for that person and there is not any kind of technology or drugs or anything like that, only love and flowers and stuff like that; and every family takes responsibility for that person in this area called the Snew and the person dies peacefully. [agath-a][nl2] Dream of working in an old people's home caring for the old and dying. [plac][Biggs+] Dreams about dead persons. [conv-d][a1] Dreams of dead people. [phos][a1] I dreamt that I was volunteering in a nursing home. I was told that my duty was to be with the dying patients. [vacuum][es-vac]

There are dreams in which the dreamer is dying. Dream I realized I was going to die in two days, and was doing a last minute preparation. I was not upset, and was doing last minute jobs to clean things up. [coca-c][sk4] Dreams of dying. [dream-p][sdj1] Dream I was dying, extremely ill. [vacuum][es-vac] Or of being dead. Dreams of being dead. [buteo-j][sej6]

Dreams of the death of relatives. Dream that her parents were dead. [castm][a1] The father had phantasies; seemed to see his dead sister in heaven. [agar][a1] Dreams of dead relatives. [tax-br][oss1]

Particularly of the father. Dream that she would kill her father; she tried to cry out, but could not, on account of which she was very oppressed; a kind a nightmare. [castm][a1] Dream that father died – very upsetting. [hydrog][srj2] Meditation – was standing on edge of earth, space before me, wondered how the earth is called flat when it looks round, but felt at peace with space before me and green earth next to me. Thought I'd return home, and someone would tell me my dad had died. [lsd][nl-lsd]

Dreams of the death of friends. Dream: They decided to get in and back it out of a tight parking space, so myself and another person would get in in just a minute. The driver backed out quickly (60mph) and struck another car, they both blew-up in flames, their souls exited the burning car and were ascending to heaven, and demons were busy truing to pick them off on the way. I felt stunned and relieved. I couldn't believe this just happened. [carbn-dox][knl3] Dreamed he saw a recently deceased friend hanging dead by his legs before his eyes for hours. [coca][a1] I'm at home – I'm walking – a balloon is swaying above me, then the air comes out. I tell myself that its soul has gone away. I thought a friend had died and it was true. I watched her being prepared for her funeral. [galla-q-r][nl2] Dream: All closest friends were dying in auto accidents. They were dying in groups. One accident had killed four people. When heard, not shocked – thought, that is interesting, that's the way we are going to leave the planet. [lac-del][hrn2] Dream: Death of a friend. [lac-h][sk4]

And dreams of ghosts. Dreams of the appearance of a ghost. [conv-d][a1]

Sleep is in many ways a smaller version of death My sleep felt deep as I'm at a great distance from a waking state. [galeoc-c-h][gms1] and a number of remedies have the symptom of waking with a start. Dreams of falling from a frightful height, with agitated waking. [anan][a1] Wakes with a start. [conv-d][a1] Woke in terror, sat up in a jolt. [falco-pe][nl2] Feel as if I've been somewhere else and coming back into my body is a shock. [hydrog][srj2] Jerked eyes open with real panic feeling, as if was going to get run over. Like falling off a mountain when you do this jerk. [lac-del][hrn2] Aggravated in the morning on waking. [neon][srj5] Woke up with a jerk as if I was falling off the last step of a staircase. [polys][sk4] Wakes with a start during the night. [tell][jl1] Or a fear of going to sleep. Afraid of going to sleep, because of possible dreams. [heroin][sdj-h]

This is sometimes described as the soul returning to the body with a shock. This dissociation may also be responsible for a dream state the Cannabis patient may experience in which he feels as if he is falling into a dark abyss, into empty space. We might explain it like this: As the etheric body re-enters the physical, this falling sensation occurs and is concluded by a sudden shock as the two bodies coalesce. An expression of this idea is seen in some proving symptoms: 'On regaining consciousness, violent shocks pass through his brain. [cann-i][vh1] Suddenly woke shocked into body as come from a dream. Had gone to sleep at 11:30 p.m. and then woke up, whacking back into my body, suddenly very wide awake. [haliae-lc][srj5]

Finally there is a corollary between the coming into this world and the leaving of it. Birth symbolism is important in the Miasm. *(See Motherhood & Pregnancy VIII-3)* Sometimes there is a coming together of the symbolism. Dreamed a dying man was suckling my breast and I was sexually excited by that. [sal-fr][sle1] The forked shape of the plant, with a white berry in the middle, is a reminder of the ancient forked cross, which represented material incarnation. In the stable in Bethlehem, the shepherds and Joseph held a forked staff as a sign of new life and of the new year [Herbe de la Croix]. [visc][vml3] According to an old legend the Cross was made from its wood, on account of which it was degraded to be a parasite. [visc][vml3] The magic wand with which Persephone opened the gates of the underworld was probably a mistletoe. [visc][vml3] The cocoon can be a symbol for this process of death and rebirth. At the pupa-cocoon stage, Limenitis bredowii builds a silk house around itself and hangs there quietly, until its body disintegrates and magically transforms into that of the complete, adult butterfly. [limen-b-c][hrn2] I see the image of a butterfly come over me. [rhus-g][tmo3] Dream: I walk into a bamboo shed where they kept the silkworm cocoons. I used to wonder about the magnificent transformation of a slimy worm into a beautiful butterfly. Suddenly I am in a black cocoon. I push and push and push until I break it and get out of the cocoon. I shot out like a man being shot out of a cannon. It was a great relief. It is like the process that a butterfly goes through to become a silkworm. [rhus-g][tmo3]

Kali, the destroyer goddess of Hindu mythology is also a mother creator. The sense of this female destructive power was felt in many remedies but particularly in the Shark. Vision of a dark haired woman with dripping black teeth. The dark women with the dripping grin is the dark side of myself. The dark side of the soul. [galeoc-c-h][gms1]

The sense of mother death who welcomes us back into her embrace is one that is neglected in our society and some remedies remind us of this. Mater gunuit – Mater recepit (The mother bore me, the mother took me back) was inscribed on Roman tombstones. [galeoc-c-h][gms1]

References

a1 ALLEN T. F., Encyclopedia of Pure Materia Medica
a2 ALLEN T. F., Hand Book of Materia Medica and Homoeopathic Therapeutics
al2 ALLEN H. C., The Materia Medica of Some Important Nosodes
bdg1 BEDAYN G., Corvus Corax: A proving of raven's blood
bdx1 BOND A., The Homoeopathic Proving of Tungsten
Biggs+ BIGGS K. + GWILLAM L., Placenta Humanum Welsh
br1 BOERICKE W., Pocket Manual of Homeopathic Materia Medica
c1 CLARKE J. H., Dictionary of Practical Materia Medica
es-vac EISING N., Vacuum: The Proving
es2 EISING N., Ignis Alcoholis, Succinum Provings
evans EVANS M., Meditative Provings
fkw1 FINK W., A Proving of Larus Argentatus
fr1 FARRINGTON E. A., Clinical Materia Medica
ggd1 GRANDGEORGE., The Spirit of Homeioathic Remedies
gms1 GRIMES M., Tiger Shark, A Homœopathic Proving
h1 HAHNEMANN S., Materia Medica Pura
hl9 HALE E. M., Special Symptomatology of the New Remedies
hmd1 HAMOND D., Ecstasy (MDMA) Proving
hmd2 HAMOND D., Berlin Wall Proving
hr1 HERING C., Guiding Symptoms of our Materia Medica
hrn2 HERRICK N., Animal Mind, Human Voices : Provings of Eight New Animal Remedies
htj1 HOUGHTON J., The Homœopathic Proving of Lac Humanum
jl1 JULIAN O. A., Materia Medica of New Homeopathic Remedies
k2 KENT J. T., Lectures on Homeopathic Materia Medica
knl2 KLEIN L., Helodrilus Caliginosus : Information and Synopsis of a New Proving
knl3 KLEIN L., Carbon Dioxide
knl6 KLEIN L., Coriander Proving
ll1 LILIENTHAL S., Homoeopathic Therapeutics
lrp1 LEROUX P., Lac Caninum : Remedy of Ailments From Children Sexual Abuse
lsy dm LASSAUW Y., DAM K., A Proving of Lac Caprinum
kmp4 MURPHY R., Homeopathic Remedy Guide

mrr3 MORRISON R., Burg Haamstede, Sept. 1988
nl-latex NORLAND M., Proving of Rubber, Latex from a Condom
nl-lsd NORLAND M., Proving of LSD-25
nl2 NORLAND M., Collected Provings
oss1 OLSEN S., Trees and Plants that Heal
ptk2 PHATAK S. R., Materia Medica of Homeopathic Medicines
rbp2 ROBBINS P,. Phascolarctos Cinereus, Australian Koala
rcb4 RICHARDSON-BOEDLER C., The Psychological / Constitutional Essences of the Bach Flowers Remedies
rsi1 ROSSETTI L., Lepidoptera saturniidae
rwt1 ROWE T., Carnegia Gigantea a proving of Saguaro Cactus
rwt2 ROWE T., Heloderma Suspectum Proving
rwt3 ROWE T., Urolophus Halleri a proving of Round Stingray
saunders SAUNDERS N., E for Ecstasy
sde2 SCHADDE A., Proving of Ozone
sdj-h SNOWDON J., Proving of Heroin
sdj1 SNOWDON J., Proving of Dreaming Potency
se70 SCHROYENS F., Synthesis
sej-birds SHORE J., Birds Seminar
sej6 SHORE J., Proving Buteo Jamaicensis
sej7 SHORE J., Proving Ara Macao
sk4 SANKARAN R., Provings : Similia Similibus Curentur
sk7 SANKARAN R., The Soul of Remedies
sle-swan STIRLING P., Proving of Bewick's Swan
sle1 STIRLING P., Proving of Crack Willow
sp1 STEPHENSON J., A Materia Medica And Repertory
srj2 SHERR J., Proving of Hydrogen
srj3 SHERR J., Homeopathic Proving of Chocolate
srj5 SHERR J., Dynamic Provings Vol 1
srj7 SHERR J., Homeopathic Proving of Plutonium Nitricum
stew+ STEWART + SONZ S., Musca Domestica a Proving
stj2 SCHOLTEN J., Homoeopathy and the Elements
tl2 TYLER M. L., Pointers to the Common Remedies
tmo3 TUMMINELLO P., Rhus Glabra
vh1 VITHOULKAS G., Materia Medica Viva
vml2 VERMEULEN F., Synoptic Materia Medica 1
vml3 VERMEULEN F., Synoptic Materia Medica 2
vml4 VERMEULEN F., Concordant Materia Medica
wza1 WIRTZ A., A Caring Capricious Creature, Lac Felinum

Remedies

Abbrev.	Full name	Common name
adam	Adams	Diamond
agar	Agaricus muscarius	Fly Agaric
agath-a	Agathis Australis	Kauri
agn	Agnus castus	Chaste berry
aids	AIDS	AIDS Nososde
ambr	Ambra grisea	Ambergris
anac	Anacardium orientale	Marking nut
anan	Anantherum muricatum	Vetiver, Cuscus grass
androc	Androctonus amoreuxii hebraeus	Scorpion
ang	Angustura vera	Angastura
anh	Anhalonium lewinii	Mescal buttons
ara-maca	Ara macao	Scarlet Macaw
ars	Arsenicum album	White oxide of arsenic
berlin-w	Berlin Wall	Concrete from the Berlin Wall
buteo-j	Buteo Jamaicensis	Red Tailed Hawk
cact	Cactus grandiflorus	Night-blooming Cereus.
cann-i	Cannabis indica	Marijuanna, Hashish
carbn-dox	Carbon dioxide	Carbonic Acid
carneg-g	Carnegia gigantea	Giant Saguaro, Arizona Giant Cactus
castm	Castoreum canadense	Canadian Beaver.
cath-a	Cathartes aura	Turkey Vulture
cere-b	Cereus bonplandii	The Good Plant
choc	Chocolatum	Belgian Chocolate
coca	Coca	
coca-c	Coca cola	
cocain	Cocaine	
colum-p	Columba palumbus	Dove
conv-a	Convolvulus arvensis	Bindweed
conv-d	Convolvulus duartinus	Morning Glory
conv-s	Convolvulus stans	Ipomoea stans, Bindweed
corian-s	Coriandrum sativum	Coriander
corv-cor	Corvus corax	North American Raven
cur	Curare	
cygn-b	Cygnus bewickii	Bewick's Swan
cygn-c	Cygnus cygnus	Whooper Swan
dream-p	Dreaming Potency	An Ubulawa from South Africa
falco-pe	Falco peregrinus disciplinatus	Trained Peregrine Falcon
galeoc-c-h	Galeocerdo cuvier hepar	Tiger Shark Liver

galla-q-r	Galla quercina ruber	Knopper OAK Galls
germ-met	Germanium metallicum	Mettalic Germanium
gink-b	Ginkgo biloba	
haliae-lc	Haliaeetus leucocephalus	Bald Eagle
helodr-cal	Helodrilus caliginosus	Earthworm, Common Field Worm
helo-h	Heloderma horridum	Gila Monster
helo-s	Heloderma suspectum	Gila Monster
heroin	Diamorphine	Heroin
hir	Hirudo medicinalis	Medical Leech
hydrog	Hydrogenium	Hydrogen
ignis-alc	Ignis alcoholis	Fire
ipom-p	Ipomoea purpurea	Morning Glory
irid-met	Iridium metallicum	Metallic Iridium
jug-r	Juglans regia	Walnut
lac-c	Lac caninum	Bitch's Milk
lac-cp	Lac caprinum	Goat's Milk
lac-del	Lac delphinum	Milk of the Bottlenose Dolphin
lac-e	Lac equinum	Mare's Milk
lac-f	Lac felinum	Cat's Milk
lac-h	Lac humanum	Mother's Milk
lac-leo	Lac leoninum	Lioness's Milk
lac-loxod-a	Lac loxodonta africana	African Elephant's Milk
lac-lup	Lac lupinum	Wolf's Milk
lars-arg	Larus argentatus	Seagull
latex	Latex	Rubber from a Condom
lepd-s	Lepidoptera saturniidae	Taturana, Lagarta Moth
limen-b-c	Limenitis bredowii californica	California Sister Butterfly
lsd	Lysergic acid diethylamide 25	Acid
lumbr-t	Lumbricus terrestris	Earthworm
maias-l	Maiasaura lapidea	Fossilized Bone of a Maiasaura Dinosaur
mdma	MDMA	Ecstasy
meph	Mephitis putorius	Skunk
mosch	Moschus	Musk Deer
musca-d	Musca domestica	House Fly
neon	Neon	
nux-m	Nux moschata	Nutmeg
oncor-t	Oncorynchus tsawytscha	Salmon
opun-v	Opuntia vulgaris	Prickly Pear
osm	Osmium metallicum	Metallic Osmium
oxyg	Oxygenium	Oxygen
ozone	Ozone	Ozone, Nascent Oxygen
phasco-ci	Phascolarctos cinereus	Australian Koala

phos	Phosphorus	
pip-m	Piper methysticum	Kava Kava
plac	Placenta humanum	Human Placenta
plat	Platina metaalicum	Mettalic Platinum
plut-n	Plutonium nitricum	Plutonium Nitrate
polys	Polystyrenum	Polystyrene
positr	Positronium	Antimatter
propl	Propolis	Bee Glue
ptel	Ptelea trifoliata	Wafer Ash, Hop Tree
pyrus	Pyrus americana	Mountain Ash
querc-r	Quercus robur	Oak, Red Oak
rhus-g	Rhus glabra	Smooth Sumach
rhus-t	Rhus toxicodendron	Poison Ivy, Poison Oak
sal-fr	Salix fragilis	Crack Willow
sanguis-s	Sanguis soricis	Blood of the Rat
sel	Selenium metallicum	Metallic Selenium
seq-s	Sequoia sempervirens	Giant Redwood
syph	Syphylinum	Syphilis Nosode
tax	Taxus baccata	Common Yew
tax-br	Taxus brevifolia	Pacific Coast Yew
tell	Tellurium metallicum	Metallic Tellurium
tung-met	Tungstenium metallicum	Wolfram, Metallic Tungsten
urol-h	Urolophus halleri	Round Stingray
vacuum	Vacuum	
visc	Viscum album	Mistletoe
xan	Xantoxylum fraxineum	Prickly Ash

Index